MAP2

MAP REF	PROJECTS	INSTALLED CAPACITY M.W.	AVERAGE ANNUAL OUTPUT M.U.
1	LOCH LOYAL	7	27
2	MALDIE BURN — KYLESKU	12	41
3	KIRKAIG RIVER	12	42
4	LOCHS FADA-FIONN-MAREE	35	127
5	LOCH A' BHRAOIN	13	50
6	LOCHS GLASS-MORIE I	32	83
7	TORRIDON — 3 CATCHMENTS	33	88
8	SNIZORT — BRACADALE—SKYE	4	14
9	RIVERS LING AND ELCHAIG	70	200
10	CALEDONIAN CANAL	7.8	50
11	MONADHLIATH I & II 6 MOUNTAIN CATCHMENTS	150	495
12	NEVIS	25	83
13	LOCHS OSSIAN-TREIG EARBA-LAGGAN	33	95
14	MORVERN — (GLEN DHU)	4	16
15	LAIDON — LOCH	5	12.5
16	KENMORE — GRANDTULLY—R.TAY	18	80
17	RIVERS ORCHY-ETIVE	95	170
18	SOUTH AWE I INCL LOCH LEAGANN	23	50
	MEGAWATTS	578.8	
	MILLION UNITS		1723.5

KEY

MAP	TABLE NO. IN		MEGAWATTS	MILLION UNITS
1	TABLE II(i)H(a) H.E.B. GRAMPIAN CO.	SCHEMES APPROVED AND COMPLETED	737 / 82	1962 / 284
	TABLE II(i)H(b)	PROJECTS APPROVED BUT NOT YET COMPLETE	628	1118
2	TABLE II(ii)H(a)	UNDER PROMOTION — NOT YET APPROVED	25	83
	II(ii)H(b) TABLE II(iii)H(a) & (b)	UNDER SURVEY OR CONSIDERATION	554	1641
3	ADDITIONAL PROJECTS	CONSIDERED ECONOMIC	348	1076
		MEANTIME CONSIDERED UNECONOMIC	575	1774

DEVELOPED OR PARTLY DEVELOPED BY BRITISH ALUMINIUM CO. (FOYERS. KINLOCHLEVEN. LOCHABER)

NOTE: THERE ARE FACTORS OTHER THAN ECONOMICS TO BE CONSIDERED BEFORE A SCHEME IS PROMOTED

Source: NSHEB, Evidence for Mackenzie Committee, Sundry Paper 7, HEB M5 (dated August 1961)

THE HYDRO

THE HYDRO

A study of the Development of the Major Hydro-Electric Schemes undertaken by the North of Scotland Hydro-Electric Board

PETER L PAYNE

ABERDEEN UNIVERSITY PRESS

First published 1988
Aberdeen University Press
A member of the Pergamon Group

British Library Cataloguing in Publication Data

Payne, Peter L. (Peter Lester), *1929–*
    The hydro.
    1. Scotland. Electricity supply. Generation
by water power
    I. Title
    621.31′2134′09411

ISBN 0 08 036584 1

PRINTED IN GREAT BRITAIN
THE UNIVERSITY PRESS
ABERDEEN

Foreword

by the Chairman of the North of Scotland Hydro-Electric Board
MR MICHAEL JOUGHIN CBE

Professor P L Payne was free to tell the story of hydro development in the North of Scotland exactly as he saw it. His objectively written book must be fascinating to engineers, members of the electricity industry and all those interested in the regeneration of a once dwindling economy in the Highlands and islands of Scotland.

It is as much a social history as an engineering one and the picture he paints of massive developments with thousands of workers labouring long hours in remote areas, often in bitter winter conditions, grips from the first page to the last.

This struggle of man over nature to tame the powerful natural water resources of the Highlands culminated in man and nature working together. It gave us electric power and very often enhanced scenery.

The post-war era was an exciting one. Professor Payne captures some of the excitement of that struggle in his very readable book which forms a lasting tribute to the engineering pioneers and men who transformed Tom Johnston's dream into reality and created the Hydro Board as we know it today.

Contents

Contents

List of Illustrations

List of Figures

List of Tables

Someone no doubt some day will submit to the public a complete chronicle of the teething troubles of the Hydro Board—a Board which is by statute not only a generator of electricity, but is a distributor of it over 74 per cent of the land area of Scotland; and, which is more than that: it is a Board enjoined to promote and encourage the economic and social welfare of the Highlands. When that forecasted chronicle is compiled it will be found that a public-spirited group of men had interpreted their duties on wide canvases.

Thomas Johnston, *Memories*

Acknowledgements

One of the most pleasurable tasks of the author of a study such as this is to thank all those who have helped to bring it to fruition. I have incurred many debts since 1984 when I accepted the invitation of the North of Scotland Hydro-Electric Board to write a history of the Board's major hydro schemes. I would like to emphasise that the focus of the book is indicated by its sub-title. This was never intended to be a comprehensive business history of the Board: it was always recognised that I should concentrate my researches upon the development of its major hydro-electric schemes. This was the sole restriction placed upon me. I was given completely free access to the Board's magnificent archives, and the Steering Committee appointed by the Board to assist my endeavours interpreted their remit in the most positive manner: its members tendered general advice and guidance, suggested sources, and provided innumerable constructive comments on early drafts. Certainly, they imposed no constraints: this study has greatly benefited from their help, not the least important aspect of which was the clarification of certain technical matters, the understanding and significance of which might otherwise have eluded me.

My greatest debt then has been to the members of the Steering Committee: Mr J E M Watts, Secretary to the Board, Mr A T L Murray, the Board's Chief Engineer, and Mr Frank G Johnson, the Board's Chief Civil Engineer. I would like to express my gratitude to them. Other members of the Board's staff were no less helpful and enthusiastic. I would particularly like to thank Mr M Stewart Wyllie, who has willingly shouldered many of the administrative burdens that this study has entailed, Mr I M Manson, Mr Ian Hughes Smith, Mr R McCoull and Mr Gordon Wallace.

For a year I enjoyed the invaluable assistance of Mr Duncan Ross, without whose help in the early stages of my research I would never have been able to complete this study. With a minimum of guidance—initially neither of us knew anything of the technical, economic and political complexities of the generation, transmission and distribution of hydro-electricity—he eased my investigation of the Board's voluminous archives beyond my most optimistic hopes. Cheerful, conscientious and meticulous, I could not have had a more congenial, hard-working and sensible research assistant.

Many persons assisted my inquiries into specific aspects of the Board's activities and some loaned me additional manuscript and published data. Among them I must mention the Earl of Airlie, Mr C L C Allan, Mr Peter L Aitken, Mr D M Balfour, Mr J Black, Dr John Berry, Dr Martin Chick, Mr Leslie H Dickerson, Mrs Marjorie K Finlayson, Mr J D Fraser, Mr Thomas M Lawrie, Mr Hamish Mackinven, Dr Calum A MacLeod, Mr I A Duncan Millar, Mr J K Moffat, Mr W Simpson, the late Mr Hugh W Simpson, Mr James Stevenson and Mr R M R Sturrock.

The entire manuscript was read not only by the members of the Steering Committee but by Mr Peter L Aitken, Mr Leslie H Dickerson, Mr Colin MacLean, Mr I A Duncan Millar and Mr K R Vernon, the Board's Deputy Chairman and Chief Executive. Their detailed comments were of great value and I am grateful for the many improvements and additions that they suggested.

In addition to the voluminous records housed at the Board's head office in Edinburgh, other manuscript and published materials were consulted. I began my inquiries with the inestimable advantage of the prior existence of Professor Leslie Hannah's definitive studies of the British electricity supply industry: *Electricity before Nationalisation* and *Engineers, Managers and Politicians*. Without these two books at my elbow, my own work would have taken much longer and been much poorer. But I owe Professor Hannah more than the debt incurred by the simple availability of his penetrating analyses. He kindly permitted me to read the Scottish section of the 'rough draft' of his second volume—a section which proved to be considerably fuller than the account that finally appeared as Chapters 12 and 21 in *Engineers, Managers and Politicians*. More than that, I was able to consult the papers prepared by Professor Hannah's research assistant, Miss Stephanie Zarach, for the section on Scotland. Although these materials were made available to me by the Electricity Council, Miss Zarach was extremely helpful in facilitating my inquiries. Such rare generosity must be recorded.

At the Electricity Council, I received considerable assistance from Mr R G Hancock. I would like to thank him and Professor Theo Barker of the London School of Economics for numerous kindnesses in the early stages of my research. Many relevant published sources were available at the Library of the University of Aberdeen, but on the infrequent occasions when the Queen Mother Library could not produce needed items immediately, they were obtained for me through the inter-library loan scheme. I must express my thanks to the staff of the Queen Mother Library. The assistance of Ms Jennifer A Beavan and Mrs Barbara J Ross-Hadley is particularly appreciated. I would also like to thank the staff of the West Search Room of the Scottish Record Office and Mr Correlli Barnett, Keeper of the Archives, Churchill College, Cambridge.

For transforming my manuscript into a typescript, and subsequently producing the many drafts occasioned by corrections, amendments and additions, I must express my gratitude to Mrs Norma Sim; no one could have been more conscientious, dedicated and enthusiastic. For the care and attention devoted to the subsequent process by which the final typescript was married to the illustrations, figures and tables and made into this book, I am particularly indebted to Mr Colin MacLean and Miss Marjorie Leith of the Aberdeen University Press. Several of the figures were prepared by Kenbarry Associates of Kinross, of whom Mr Ken Whitcombe was extremely helpful.

For granting permission to reproduce illustrations, the author would like to thank the following firms and institutions:

BRITISH ALCAN HIGHLAND SMELTERS LTD.: Figures 1 and 3.
THE INSTITUTION OF CIVIL ENGINEERS: Figures 2, 8, 10, 11, 21, 23, 25, 26, 27, 30, 31, 37, 40, 41, 46, 47, 48, 49 and 52.
MORGAN-GRAMPIAN (PUBLISHERS) LTD. (*The Engineer*): Figures 4, 5, 6, 9, 14, 20, 33, 36, 38 and 39.
Engineering: Figure 12.
English Electric Journal: Figure 13.
INTERNATIONAL TEXT BOOK CO. LTD. (Leonard Hill Books): Figures 17, 18, 32, 56, 57 and 58.
REED BUSINESS PUBLISHING LTD. (*Water Power*): Figures 28, 52, 53 and 54.
THE INSTITUTION OF ELECTRICAL ENGINEERS: Figures 44, 45, 63 and 65.

Peter L Payne
University of Aberdeen
June 1988

CHAPTER 1

Introduction: Questions of Choice

Many of those who tramp the hills of Scotland, often in the mists or pouring rain, surely entertain the thought that there must be further scope for harnessing the free-falling, turbulent Highland waters for the production of electricity. The belief has long existed that water-power represents a natural source of energy which is capable of development at a cost far below that of steam or other alternatives. Scotland has been seen to be 'pouring her natural wealth into the sea'. The spectacle of water 'running to waste' has 'been held to be conclusive evidence that its utilisation must result in the production of cheap power'. This idea, sedulously canvassed in the past, has occasionally given rise to a popular clamour for the development of water power, the public having been seduced by the prospect of apparently getting something for nothing.[1]

What is the reality? Just what is involved? Although one of the objects of this book is to provide answers to these questions, no attempt will be made *fully* to investigate the relevant highly complex technical issues. This is not a technical thesis but a history: a history of hydro-electric developments in Scotland since the closing years of the nineteenth century. Nevertheless, it will become apparent that every decision by the industry's engineers and managers involved difficult questions of choice, and that the options confronting the decision-makers were usually constrained by economic factors. Let one point be emphasised immediately: the overriding problems were not technical but economic. Since the beginning of this century it has been technically possible to solve—with varying degrees of success—all the major relevant civil, mechanical and electrical engineering questions. Sir Alexander Gibb recalled in 1942 that 'he had seen a good many hydro-electric schemes which had been brought into being by calling in electrical engineers alone'. The inevitable result was that 'many failures had occurred, and much money had been spent which need never have been spent'.[2]

As Sir Alexander Gibb was a civil engineer, this remark may have been professionally partisan, but it does indicate the necessity of considering the technical feasibility of a scheme in an economic context. The basic question to be determined is whether the power to be produced by a projected hydro scheme can be provided more cheaply by some other means. If the supply of electricity is to be fed into an existing transmission and distribution network, the obvious alternative—the one that most closely approximates to British conditions—is generation at a new power station driven by steam. Only if the output of the proposed hydro-electric scheme can be produced and made available to the consumer at or below the contemporary cost of thermal power can the scheme be economically justified. Alternatively, if there is no existing network of transmission and distribution, the cost of the hydro-electricity delivered to the consumer (which would in this case have also to meet the capital and operating costs of creating a distribution system) must be no more than that which a new or existing thermal undertaking could supply the same consumer *after* building extensions to its existing network.

Even this simplifies a difficult comparative calculation, but it will be clear that unless a projected hydro scheme meets certain economic criteria it should not be implemented. But even if the economic prospects appear favourable, a hydro-electric scheme cannot be put into effect unless its promoters secure Parliamentary approval. Every hydro scheme involves interference with property rights, and without the sanction of the legislature it will be stillborn whatever its economic merits.

It is the interplay between technical, economic and political factors that constitutes the essence of this study. At the same time, it presents a record and an assessment of just what was achieved by the industry's entrepreneurs, engineers and managers. Believing that some knowledge of the technical and economic problems confronting them might be useful to the uninitiated reader, a simplified and partial guide to such questions has been provided in Appendix 1.

Although this study is dominated by the North of Scotland Hydro-Electric Board, whose policies in the first two decades of its existence excited such vigorous contemporary debate, a comprehensive record of hydro-electric developments in Scotland demands that attention be given to earlier attempts to exploit Scotland's water power potential. Let us therefore begin by examining the work of the Hydro Board's predecessors.

CHAPTER 2

Hydro-Electricity in Scotland before 1943

1   Pioneering Ventures in Public Supply

Inspired by local demonstrations of the remarkable luminescence of electric arc lamps,
Scotland's first hydro-electric plant for public supply—and the second in Britain—was
installed at Greenock, Renfrewshire, in 1885.[1] Avowedly a pilot scheme, intended by
the Police Board both to forestall private developers and to educate the public in the
use and advantages of electric lighting, this early experiment was terminated after only
two years of operation. This was too brief a period to permit a proper assessment of
the scheme's long-term economic viability. Perhaps the Police Board, who had invested
heavily in the local gas works, had little incentive conclusively to demonstrate the
advantages of electricity. Only one thing is clear: the generating plant—consisting of
Anglo-American Brush dynamoes driven by ropes from a Gunther 40 h.p. turbine
installed at the Water Trust premises in Prospecthill—and the novel system of distribution cables appear to have been an unqualified success.[2] There was no failure in the
equipment: in its first test in Scotland, hydro-electricity had proved to be technically
feasible.

What is perhaps remarkable is that the next successful exploitation of the hydro-
electric power resources of Scotland was by the monks of St Benedict's Abbey at Fort
Augustus. In 1890 they constructed an 18 kW water turbine on one of the streams
draining Inchnacardoch Forest to supply the abbey and the 800 inhabitants of the village
of Fort Augustus.[3] Six years later, the Fort William Electric Light Company Ltd installed
two 60 kW turbines at Blarmachfoldach to produce electricity for the 3,000 inhabitants
of the town[4] and, in 1890, the Marquess of Ailsa engaged the services of William
Robertson Copeland to investigate the possibility of utilising the waters of Loch Doon
as a catchment area for a hydro-electric power station at Dalfarson, near Ayr. This
ambitious project, which Copeland estimated was capable of producing over two
million watts, was apparently abandoned for reasons that were to become all too familiar
in the next forty years: the scheme involved the loss of the waters above Loch Doon as
a spawning ground for salmon, the submergence of Loch Doon Castle, situated on an
island on the south side of the loch, and the problem of disposing of the large quantity
of electrical power which would have been generated.[5]

Other, smaller, contemporary schemes stemmed from aristocractic initiatives. An 80
kW power station at Ravens on Ben Wyvis, designed to supply over 5,000 people in
Dingwall and Strathpeffer, was successfully developed in 1903, the idea of, and financed

by, Colonel E W Blunt-MacKenzie, the husband of the Countess of Cromarty; and a similar scheme, devised by the Duke of Atholl, resulted in the creation of a 130 kW power station on the Banrie Burn in Perthshire to provide electricity for Blair Castle and the 1,580 people in the village of Blair Atholl in 1910.[6] By 1914 several similar private electricty generating and supply schemes had been projected and developed. They were successful enough to have continued to remain in existence until after the Second World War, but they were uniformly small and weakly financed, and their growth was constrained both by the inability to transmit electricity beyond the small and scattered communities that they had been designed to serve and, it may be conjectured, by a lack of demand for electrical power which required for its utilisation the installation of light fittings and equipment beyond the purchasing capacity—or even the desire—of the rural community.[7]

2   *The British Aluminium Company Schemes*[8]

Convincingly to demonstrate the great potentialities of hydro-electricity required a scheme whose sise and scale would not be inhibited by such constraints. The scheme came as a consequence of the voracious demands for power of a new industry, aluminium, whose appetite for electrical energy far exceeded that of the early pioneering ventures in public supply.

Aluminium was first recognised as a chemical in the first decade of the nineteenth century. It appears initially to have been isolated by Frederick Wohler in 1827, and the first specimen to be produced in Great Britain was exhibited by Faraday at the Royal Institution in 1855, when the price of the metal was £20 a pound (approx. £50,000 a ton). Competition between various small-scale manufacturers, utilising improved chemical methods, brought the cost of production down to £2,000 a ton by the mid-1880s, when the world's annual output has been estimated at rather less than 40 tons. But already dynamos had begun to be introduced into metallurgical practice, and the first economically practicable electrolytic method of reducing alumina was patented by E H and A H Cowles in 1885. This was worked both in America, at Lockport, New York, and in England, at Milton, Staffordshire. Being based on thermally generated electricity—of which vast quantities were required—the production of aluminium remained too costly for widespread use. Nevertheless, its price of 4 shillings a pound (somewhat less than £450 a ton), made aluminium reduced with sodium obsolete. Even the relatively efficient Alliance Aluminium Co. who used this chemical method at their plants in London, Hebburn and Wallsend had been unable to lower their selling price below £1,200 a ton by 1890. But the Cowles process itself was soon to be superseded by that devised independently by P T L Heroult in France and C M Hall in America in 1886-1887. Production under the Heroult patents began in Switzerland in 1888, and by 1894 the price of aluminium had been reduced to about £180 a ton. No other method was capable of competing with the Heroult-Hall process.

The British rights to the Heroult process—together with those of the method of extracting alumina from bauxite devised by Dr K J Bayer between 1887 and 1892—were acquired by the British Aluminium Company, Ltd., when that company was formed in 1894 with Lord Kelvin as scientific advisor. Since about 24,000 kWh of electricity was required to produce one ton of aluminium, it was imperative to employ the cheapest possible source of power. Immediately, the possible use of hydro-electricity suggested itself. If such power could be used at source, and the appropriate physical conditions were available to permit the generation of the required output without elaborate and expensive civil engineering works, hydro-electricity could be significantly cheaper than electricity produced by thermal generation. A suitable site was found at the Falls of Foyers on the east coast of Loch Ness. With considerable prescience, the 8,000 acre estate of Lower Foyers was purchased, together with other water-power rights from neighbouring proprietors. This both obviated the necessity of obtaining Parliamentary powers for the exploitation of the water-power potential of the Stra-therrick catchment area of some 100 square miles, and also enabled the company successfully to overcome public opposition to the possible destruction of local amenities, particularly interference with the gorge formed by the River Foyers and the almost perpendicular Lower Falls, a well-known beauty spot which constituted a major feature in the itinerary of MacBrayne's pleasure steamers which plied between Fort William and Inverness during the summer months.[9]

Development began in 1895. A concrete and masonry dam and an earth embankment were erected at the southwestern end of Loch Garth, raising the level of that loch by 20 feet and joining it with Loch Farraline to form a storage resevoir of 4.5 miles in length. This was given the name Loch Mhor. From the dam the water flowed in the original river-bed to a point immediately above the Upper Falls of Foyers where it was led into a tunnel, a half a mile in length, cut through solid rock. From the end of the tunnel the water passed through a pressure pipeline to the generating station. The first pipes, 30 inches in diameter, were made of cast iron and were buried in trenches of sandy soil. The head was 350 feet, and although doubts were entertained concerning the ability of the cast iron pipes to withstand high water pressures, they apparently functioned well and required little or no attention. Five Girard turbines and Oerlikon direct current generators with vertical shafts were installed, with two smaller auxilary sets. With an initial capacity of 3,750 kW this power was more than adequate to meet the available demand for aluminium, production of which began in June 1896. Even the small initial output of the Foyers works, beginning at the rate of about 200 tons per annum, could not readily be disposed of, and more than half the available power was employed in the production of calcium carbide[10] and in experiments in the production of ferro-silicon, carborundum, magnesium, cerium, and even precious stones.

In 1896 world production of aluminium was only 2,000 tons, but falling costs—culmulative minor improvements of the Heroult process had increased the efficiency of the Foyers plant by over 25 per cent by 1900—coupled with rising demand, as more and more uses were found for the metal, gradually boosted sales so that the company's accumulated stock of aluminium, which had reached over 700 tons by 1903, could be run down. The year 1904 represented a turning point in the fortunes of British Aluminium Co. World demand for aluminium had almost doubled since 1900 and, for the first time, the company was able to discontinue the production of calcium carbide and to devote the whole of the available power at Foyers to the electrolytic reduction process. The outlook was so promising[11] that the company was able to contemplate the exploitation of the additional water rights acquired when the Foyers estate had been purchased a decade earlier and which had received Parliamentary sanction by the Loch Leven Water Power Act in 1901. Because the time was not yet propitious , no action was taken under the power granted by this Act, but in 1904 a further Loch Leven Water Power Act was obtained which permitted some variation from the original plans and an extension of the time for their completion.

Under these Acts, a statutory company, the Loch Leven Water and Electric Power Company, was set up, with capital largely contributed by the British Aluminium Company,[12] and work began on harnessing the water power of the Western section of the Blackwater chain of Lochs stretching from Rannoch Moor to the neighbourhood of Kinlochleven. The potential of the site was carefully exploited. Damming the River Blackwater would create an eight-mile long reservoir into which would flow much of the run off of a catchment area of sixty square miles. By leading this water to a power station at Kinlochleven, situated at the head of Loch Leven, it was intended to generate the electricity required for a large alumina reduction plant and a factory to produce the carbon electrodes which played a vital rôle in the process of electrolysis. The entire project took over four years to complete; a lengthy gestation period during which the company's finances were so sorely strained that it was necessary to reconstruct the firm's capital in 1910.

By contemporary standards the scale of the undertaking was enormous.[13] The Blackwater Dam—a gravity dam—was 86 feet high and over a half a mile in length. The breadth of its base was 62 feet. The storage reservoir thus created was capable of holding 24,000 million gallons of water. This water was conveyed over three and a half miles by a closed conduit constructed of reinforced concrete, into which were diverted the waters of a number of side-streams. From the conduit the water entered the head of a pipeline consisting of six parallel steel pipes, each 39 inches in diameter,[14] to plunge over 935 feet to the eleven Pelton turbines and three auxiliary sets installed in the power houses built on the banks of the River Leven below (see Fig. 1). The total capacity of the machines at Kinlochleven was 25,725 kW, but because of the high load factor which was eventually to be achieved—approaching 80 per cent—their annual output, 160 million kWh, was far to exceed that of any previous British hydro scheme. Initially, however, only a small proportion of the available power was required. In 1909, when the Kinlochleven scheme was completed, Britain's *total* output of aluminium was about 2,500 tons, or less than a third of the designed maximum capacity of the Kinlochleven reduction plant alone.

This great enterprise was, it has been said, the last major creation of the traditional navvy,[15] whose activities in the construction of canals and, later, railways have left an indelible mark on the British countryside. Between two and three thousand men were employed at Kinlochleven, and the nature of their work and of their lives appears to have been indistinguishable from that of their eighteenth and nineteenth century forebears. Patrick MacGill's novel, *Children of the Dead End*,[16] based on the author's own experiences as a navvy at Kinlochleven, could just as easily have depicted the construction of the Woodhead Tunnel in 1845 or the cutting of the Caledonian Canal in 1805.[17] The appalling—almost suicidal—working conditions; the sheer exhaustion of excavating and shifting endless tons of earth and broken stones; the dangers of blasting through rock;

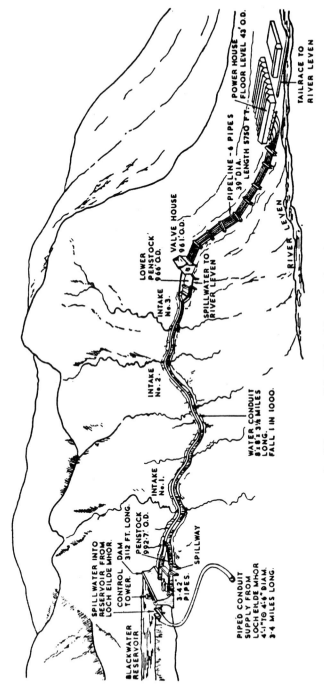

BLACKWATER RESERVOIR

SPILLWATER INTO RESERVOIR FROM LOCH EILDE MHOR.

CONTROL DAM 3112 FT. LONG.

PENSTOCK 992·7' O.D.

PIPED CONDUIT SUPPLY FROM LOCH EILDE MHOR 4·1"TO 4·6" DIAM. 3·4 MILES LONG.

3·42' PIPES.

SPILLWAY

INTAKE No.1.

INTAKE No.2.

WATER CONDUIT 8'·0" x 3½ MILES LONG. FALL 1 IN 1000.

INTAKE No.3.

LOWER PENSTOCK 966' O.D.

VALVE HOUSE 961' O.D.

SPILLWATER TO RIVER LEVEN

RIVER LEVEN

PIPELINE - 4 PIPES 39' DIA. LENGTH 5750 FT.

POWER HOUSE FLOOR LEVEL 43' O.D.

TAILRACE TO RIVER LEVEN

FIGURE 1   Diagram of the Kinlochleven hydro–electric project

the claustrophobia inseparable from tunnelling; the constant rain; the evil makeshift accommodation consisting of wooden shacks covered with tarred canvas furnished with tiers of wooden bunks round the walls; the endless gambling, drinking and fighting; the passive acceptance of ghastly and often lethal accidents, sometimes occasioned by a pick striking a charge that had failed to explode: all this is unforgettably described by MacGill. Not the least interesting feature of his book is the men's indifference to the object of their labours:

> We spoke of waterworks, but only the contractors knew what the work was intended for. We did not know, and we did not care .... There were so many tons of earth to be lifted and thrown somewhere else; we lifted them and threw them somewhere else: so many cubic yards of iron-hard rocks to be blasted and carried away; we blasted and carried them away, but never asked questions and never knew what results we were labouring to bring about. We turned the Highlands into a cinder-heap, and were as wise at the beginning as at the end of the task. Only when we completed the job, and returned to [Glasgow], did we learn from the newspapers that we had been employed on the construction of the biggest aluminium factory in the Kingdom. All that we knew was that we had gutted whole moutains and hills in the operation.

And of one who had died in the process, MacGill wrote a short song, the first verse of which ended

> Bury him deep in the red, red muck, and pile the clay on his breast,
>   For all that he needs for his years of toil are years of unbroken rest.[18]

The cost of the Kinlochleven project in human, environmental and financial terms had been great. The British Aluminium Company all but collapsed as it 'consumed its capital at a great rate',[19] and even the reconstruction of 1910 seemed likely only to postpone what to some appeared to be the inevitable liquidation. The demand for aluminium was simply insufficient to utilise Kinlochleven's generating and productive capacity. The war of 1914-18 changed all this. Aluminium was found to be superior to other materials for numerous applications and essential in those requiring strength combined with minimum possible weight. From being too generously endowed with capacity, the British Aluminium Company was confronted with enhanced demands that required further expansion. The storage capacity of the Blackwater Reservoir proved inadequate for the task. To increase the available water power, the company commissioned Balfour Beatty to build an aqueduct five miles long to bring water from Loch Eilde Mhor into the reservoir, thereby increasing the total catchment area of the Kinlochleven scheme to 66 square miles. The work, carried out under conditions of considerable difficulty, was finished within two years and involved a capital expenditure of £55,000 and the employment of 1,200 German prisoners of war and 500 British troops 'of a low medical category'.[20]

It was not enough. Military requirements had not only created an enormous additional demand for aluminium, but by familiarising engineers with the use of the material— which only two decades before had been classified a semi-precious metal—had resulted in a much greater appreciation of its potentialities. The British Aluminium Company

expected a major increase in industrial demand. How could this be satisfied? W Murray
Morrison, the company's General Manager, believed that the answer was to extend the
existing works at Kinlochleven, where a second power house would be supplied with
water from the catchment areas of Lochs Treig and Laggan.[21] To this end a Provisional
Order was promoted in Parliament in 1918, but so much antagonism was aroused that
it was decided to abandon the project. The opposition seized upon two major issues:
the diversion of water from one river basin, that of the Lochy, to another, the Leven;
and Inverness County Council's desire to use the waters of Loch Treig for industrial
development in the Fort William area and not at Kinlochleven, which was in Argyllshire.

The British Aluminium Company persevered. A new scheme was prepared which
retained certain features of the old. The same waters were to be used but they would
be conveyed to the head of Loch Linnhe for use in a power station and reduction works
at Fort William. A bill embodying these proposals was successfully promoted in 1920
and duly became the Lochaber Water Power Act, under the terms of which the Lochaber
Power Company was established. The Act permitted the company to utilise the water
of a catchment area of over 303 square miles having an annual rainfall which varied
from 41 inches in the east to over 160 inches on the slopes of Ben Nevis.[22] The run-off
was to be collected in two principal reservoirs, Lochs Laggan and Treig, joined by a
tunnel $2\frac{3}{4}$ miles long and 15 feet in diameter.[23] The natural catchment-areas of Lochs
Laggan and Treig were to be supplemented by the diversion of the upper waters of the
River Spey into Loch Laggan by means of a dam 900 feet long and 30 feet high
constructed two miles above Laggan Bridge. But perhaps the most remarkable part of
the scheme was the construction of a pressure tunnel, 15 miles in length, driven through
solid rock under the Ben Nevis group of mountains from Loch Treig to the head of a
steel pipe-line that dropped nearly 600 feet to the power station situated just over half
a mile away at Fort William (see Fig. 2).

Such was the magnitude of this vast undertaking that its construction was to be
carried out in three stages.[24] The first comprised all the works to the west of Loch Treig,
the second those between Loch Treig and Laggan, and the third stage involved the
diversion of the flood waters of the River Spey. Even the first stage took five years to
complete, and so uncertain were the economic prospects following the collapse of the
brief post-war boom that work did not begin until 1924, and then not until the company
had been given a Government guarantee under the Trade Facilities Act for the issue of
£2.5m Debenture Stock.

The most interesting of the engineering features of the first stage was the driving of
the pressure tunnel. Four vertical shafts were sunk and seven horizontal adits constructed
at approximately 2,000 yard intervals along the route of the tunnel, and the tunnellers
drove from the bottom of the shafts or the end of the adits in both directions, working
simultaneously on twenty-two separate faces. There was a further face at the western
end of the tunnel from which the pipe-line to the power station was to emerge. Except
for their entrances, the shafts and adits and the tunnel itself were driven in solid rock.
The tunnel, roughly horseshoe in section having a mean equivalent diameter of a little
over 15 feet, was lined with concrete to reduce friction.[25] Eleven of the streams that
flowed down the skirts of Ben Nevis were trapped by intake dams—several of them
of substantial proportions[26]—and diverted into the tunnel itself by means of diversion-

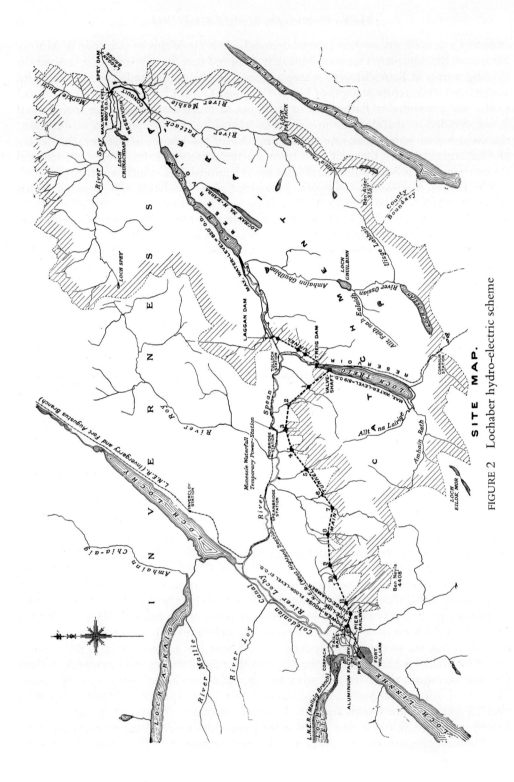

SITE MAP.

FIGURE 2   Lochaber hydro-electric scheme

channels, conduits and shafts. Three of the vertical shafts required for the construction of the tunnel were so utilised and these were supplemented by eight additional shafts. No water was to be allowed to go to waste: these streams contributed approximately 16 per cent of the water reaching the power station (see Fig. 3).

Driving the main tunnel, which began in the early summer of 1926, necessitated an immense amount of preliminary work. A temporary hydro-electric station equipped with three Francis turbines was designed and erected by the principal contractors, Balfour Beatty & Co., on the River Spean at Monessie to provide power for lighting, for the motors of pumps, stone crushers and concrete mixers, and for the air-compressors for rock-drills. A 200 feet long pier of reinforced concrete was built into Loch Linnhe at the mouth of the River Lochy to receive the mass of constructional materials required and, after extension, for the reception of ocean-going vessels carrying bauxite. A network of 3 feet gauge railway lines was laid from the end of the pier to a base camp adjacent to the West Highland section of the London and North-eastern Railway and thence to Loch Treig, a distance of nearly 21 miles.[27] This light railway served each of the adit and shaft sites and involved the construction of no less than 88 trestle bridges (built of local timber) and two with steel central spans to carry the train across the streams flowing down the sides of Ben Nevis. At each of the work sites, camps were built with sleeping huts, mess and recreation-rooms, drying sheds for clothes, stores and canteens. A small camp hospital was provided half way between Loch Treig and Fort William, and a hospital for infectious diseases erected near the base camp.

Vast numbers of men were employed: over 3,000 at the peak of activity. Early on the scene were those engaged on railway construction. Working from both the base camp and Loch Treig end simultaneously, each team was divided into three gangs. The first levelled the ground, the second laid the track and third lifted and ballasted it. Working in almost continuous rain, constantly hampered by drainage problems and, when rock cuttings were necessary before the installation of air-compressors, forced to use hand jumpers to drill the holes into which explosives were inserted, these men worked solely with pick and shovel. In advance of the railway navvies, small armies of joiners were engaged in building the wooden bridges to carry the line over the swift-flowing streams. To accelerate the work and therefore qualify for the bonus offered to Balfour Beatty for the swift completion of the railway, it was said that any man who could wield an axe and a hammer was pressed into service as a joiner. And when the main work and the tunnel began, there was an acute shortage of experienced rock drillers. Balfour Beatty had to train their own. Initially, liquid oxygen (LOX) was used as an explosive to drive the tunnel but, although it was perhaps the safest of all methods, its use was complicated, the men did not like it, and it was soon abandoned.[28] Thereafter, gelignite was employed: it was brought to the adits by special trains!

Accidents were frequent. There were several fatalities and, for all the transformation in living conditions since Kinlochleven, there was more than a whiff of the old times. Patrick Howat—whose intensively researched study of the *Lochaber Narrow Gauge Railway* clearly evokes the way of life at the construction site—retells the story of an illicit still told to him by one of the railway workers:

> At Shaft 1 ... they had a still. The Customs and Excise men were up twice looking for it but the way it was, down in the burn you always got a sort of a mist, you would pass along

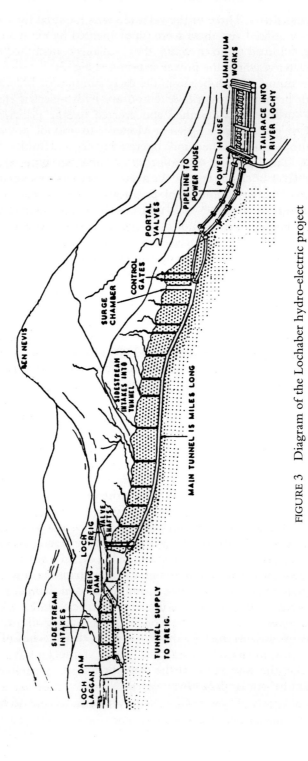

FIGURE 3   Diagram of the Lochaber hydro-electric project

and pay no attention to it. It was a real still: they were using barley and everything. I remember one day ... Mr [later Sir Andrew] MacTaggart [Chief of the Balfour Beatty's civil engineering department] came up from Base; he knew about the still and the men being drunk. ... The driver that was bringing him up the railway ... called in at Shaft 2 on the way up. Nobody knew he was coming at all but the timekeeper at 2 phoned that MacTaggart was on his way ... You never saw such a scramble! The foreman was getting everybody into the cage and down the tunnel before MacTaggart arrived. There wasn't a man to be seen—they were all down the tunnel. Some of them they had to lift into the cage to get them down and out of sight.[29]

For five years the work went on. By the end of 1929 the power station had been built and equipped with five 6,800 kW generators. These were set in a deep rock excavation so that the turbines, being as near to sea level as possible, could obtain the maximum head of water available. The factory itself, separated from the power house only by a party wall, was designed on a scale sufficient to serve the entire scheme when all three stages had been completed. In December 1929 the first aluminium was tapped from the furnaces, water power for the turbines being obtained from the side streams alone. Only the last dramatic operation of the first stage remained to be accomplished. The main tunnel had been pushed to within 20 feet of the bottom of Loch Treig. It was then necessary to break through into the Loch at a point over one hundred feet below its surface to tap the waters of the storage reservoir. After exhaustive tests by Nobel's to determine the most suitable explosive and detonating system, this was achieved by blasting out the remaining plug of rock. The charge of 1.5 tons of specially prepared gelatine was fired successfully on 3 January 1930. 'There was no great disturbance of the water in the Loch', William Halcrow laconically recorded, 'the spent gases came to the surface over an area of about 80 yards square, and the height of the waves was estimated at 3 to 4 feet. Subsequent surveys showed that approximately 3,000 cubic yards of rock had been removed'.[30] As was intended, much of it had fallen clear of the opening and that which had been shot backwards into the tunnel was easily removed by a drag scraper. It was the first time that such a hazardous procedure had been attempted in Britain. Within a month the power-station was brought into regular service.

So far the scheme had cost about £3 million and, in the discussion of its first stage at a meeting of the Institution of Civil Engineers in November 1930, W Murray Morrison—the Director of the British Aluminium Co. who had conceived and pushed through the entire undertaking—was forced to defend its economic rationality. He refused to disclose precise figures of the capital cost per unit of power available or per unit generated, arguing that it would be ridiculous for him to do so at a time when the capital cost per unit 'was out of all proportion to what it would be when the scheme was completed'. He would say only that 'approximately two-thirds of the capital expenditure had already been incurred, and only one-third of the power that would be attained when the whole scheme was completed was [currently] available'[31]. It was imperative to begin the second stage, but to do so had already necessitated a further appeal to Parliament for an extension of the time for completion and for several variations in the original plan. The company obtained their Supplementary Act in July 1930 and work began early in the following year.

Stage Two involved extending Loch Laggan by building a massive concrete gravity dam 700 feet long and 130 feet high across the River Spean $4\frac{1}{2}$ miles below the Loch; enlarging Loch Treig—the principal reservoir—by the construction of a 400 feet rock-filled dam across the River Treig about a quarter of a mile from the northern end of the Loch; and connecting the two lochs by a tunnel $2\frac{3}{4}$ miles long and 15 feet in diameter.[32] Once again, as in the main tunnel to Fort William, there were to be side intakes into the Laggan-Treig tunnel, three in number. Although the water level of Loch Laggan was not raised—to have done so would have submerged valuable property and necessitated many costly road diversions—that of Loch Treig was raised by 35 feet. This increased the total storage depth to 124 feet and involved raising the level of the West Highland line of the London and North-eastern Railway, which skirted the loch, for a distance of about $1\frac{1}{2}$ miles. About 1,000 men were employed in the second stage of the Lochaber scheme. Those working on the Laggan dam were accommodated at Roughburn camp, adjacent to the site of the dam, and those on the Treig dam and on the tunnel at Fersit, roughly half way between the two lochs.

Less dramatic than the first stage, the second more than doubled the catchment area of the Lochaber scheme and, by raising the level of Loch Treig, increased the head of water available.[33] The civil engineering was completed in 1934, a period of slack demand for aluminium. It was three years before three additional pipes were laid from the end of the main tunnel to the Fort William power station to exploit the additional available water power. The 69 inch diameter steel pipes were delivered in 30 feet lengths and welded together *in situ*, the first time this type of construction had been employed in this country. In turn, five more 7,000 kW Pelton turbines were installed in the power station, extensions were made to the adjoining aluminium factory, the productive capacity of which was raised to some 20,000 tons per annum, and a carbon factory was added to the growing Fort William complex.

Not until 1938 did this massive investment—the cost of which was approximately £5m—begin to contribute to the output of the British Aluminium Company, quite fortuitously coming on stream at a time of steeply rising demands associated with rapid rearmament. It was the needs of war that accelerated the completion of the project. Stage three—Parliamentary permission for which had been granted by yet another Act in 1938—involved impounding the headwaters of the River Spey by a dam 943 feet long and 57 feet high near Laggan Bridge, 37 miles from Fort William, and diverting them into Loch Crunacham, where the water flowed through a two-mile tunnel into Loch Laggan. The Spey Tunnel, built by the 1st Tunnelling Company of the Canadian Army and supervised by Balfour Beatty, was completed in 1941 and the remaining civil engineering works in 1943,[34] by which time two further turbines had been installed at the power station.

This great enterprise, conceived by W Murray Morrison during the First World War, had taken a quarter of a century and the Second World War to bring to a successful conclusion. With a catchment area of nearly 350 square miles—nearly half of which had been purchased by the British Aluminium Company[35]—high average rainfall, a head of about 800 feet, and an exceptionally high load factor (approximately 60 per cent), the annual output of the Lochaber far exceeded that of any other British hydro-electric scheme. Indeed, in 1930 William Halcrow believed it would be 'the largest single water-power station that can be constructed in Scotland'.[36] And if W Murray Morrison had been reluctant to discuss the cost of the electric power produced in 1930,[37] when capital expenditure per kilowatt of installed capacity appears to have been about £80, an exceptionally high figure for the period, the subsequent extensions—which permitted the full use of those parts of the scheme, such as the Fort William-Loch Treig Tunnel, built on a scale appropriate for the planned maximum capacity—reduced the figure to £50. But even this, as Paton and Guthrie Brown later observed, is no basis for a final economic judgement on the Lochaber project. 'What counts ultimately is cost per unit of power produced';[38] and here Lochaber, with its high load-factor, showed to great advantage, certainly in the context of other actual or potential British hydro or thermal schemes.[39]

3   The Public Supply Schemes

While the British Aluminium Company's Lochaber scheme was under construction, the Grampian Electricity Supply Co. began to exploit the water power resources of the adjacent catchment area of Loch Ericht. The potential of Loch Ericht had long been recognised. Its use had been envisaged in the Highland Water Power Bill of 1899, an industrial project which failed to gain Parliamentary sanction. Although the Loch Ericht Water and Electricity Power Act *was* passed in 1912, in explicitly refusing the promoting company permission to alter 'the natural level of the water', Clause 15 of the Act effectively destroyed its economic rationale, since reservoir storage was essential for its success.[40] In 1919 an ambitious scheme by Dundee Corporation involving Loch Ericht, Loch Rannoch and Loch Tummel likewise came to nothing, partially because of the strong opposition of those who believed that it would 'take away the whole of the power [to the City of Dundee] without giving right of participation to those who inhabit the valley'.[41]

The Grampian Electricity Supply Bill avoided these earlier pitfalls and undoubtedly benefited from the momentum given to hydro-electric development in the Scottish Highlands by the Snell Committee, whose interim reports had been published in 1919 and 1920.[42] The bill passed in 1922 because proper observance had been paid to the Committee's 'fundamental principles', including the comprehensive treatment of a single catchment area and the reservation of part of the available power for use by the local population within the watershed, and because the promoters were men of undoubted probity and local standing. They included the Duke of Atholl and John William Beaumont Pease, the Chairman of Lloyds Bank.[43] The Act authorised the use of waters of Loch Ericht, Loch Rannoch and Loch Tummel and the diversion into Loch Ericht of waters from the adjacent watersheds of Loch Seilich and Loch Garry, a total catchment area of some 418 square miles. The power this generated would be distributed throughout the counties of Perth, Kinross and Forfar, and parts of Inverness-shire, Argyllshire and Stirlingshire, an area of over 5,000 square miles. It was also intended to provide bulk supplies to the areas served by the Scottish Central Electric Power Company and the Fife Electric Power Co.[44]

The authorised capital of the Company at its inception was £1.75m. This sum proved very difficult to raise, and the Grampian Co. turned to George Balfour for technical and financial assistance. George Balfour, a Scot by ancestry, was born in Portsmouth in 1872, the son of a skilled millwright from Dundee working in the Portsmouth dockyard. Educated at Plymouth Technical Institute, at 16 he took up a five-year apprenticeship in mechanical engineering with the Blackness Foundry in Dundee, a firm with which the family had connections. While an apprentice, he attended evening classes at University College, Dundee, where he added mathematics to his practical engineering skills. He qualified as a journeyman fitter in August 1893 and became involved in numerous projects from the construction and management of tramways to electrical supply undertakings in Scotland. It is said that as assistant engineer to Edinburgh Corporation he inaugurated the lights in Princes Street. Queen Victoria may have imagined that she was doing so when she pressed a brass gadget in a beautiful booth but, receiving a signal, George Balfour down below pulled the switch.[45]

In 1902 Balfour went to London to become commercial engineer of the British branch of a prominent New York firm of mechanical and electrical engineers, J G White & Co. He was responsible for obtaining orders for numerous tramways and electric utilities, which brought him appointments to their boards as White's representative. Indeed, he became managing director of the Arbroath Electric Light and Power Co., the Scottish Central Power Co., and the Fife Tramways, Light and Power Co. In 1907, determined to establish his own firm, Balfour resigned from White's and, in the following year, he persuaded his former colleague, J G White's secretary, Andrew Beatty, to join him in forming the firm of Balfour Beatty. Registered as a private company in 1909 with a capital of £50,000, subscribed by themselves and few friends, Balfour Beatty were initially interested only in financial and technical management, but within a few months they had been awarded a contract worth over £140,000 for the construction of the Dunfermline tramway. This contract was the first of many. The firm were later greatly to expand the civil engineering and constructional side of their activities under the direction of Andrew MacTaggart, who had first been engaged to superintend the Loch Eilde Mhor extension to the Kinlochleven scheme during the war.

But such works involved very heavy capital expenditure and George Balfour soon recognised that the financial difficulties of potential customers threatened to retard the remarkably rapid expansion of his thriving firm. ' "I have always felt", he said, "that there was a great demand for an organisation with ample capital resources, capable of dealing with the developments of large public and other works at a time when such undertakings could not look for or obtain assistance from bankers, due to the fact that they had not reached a stage when they could submit proposals which would justify any banker granting credit facilities".'[46] He determined to create such an organisation: a company which would give him improved access to finance which would be used to fund large-scale projects until they were either completed and earning money or were sufficiently far advanced for capital issues to be made. Thus, in October 1922, a new company, Power Securities Corporation Ltd., was formed with an issued capital of £1 million, half in 7 per cent preference and a half in ordinary shares. £100,000 of the £1 ordinary shares and all the £1 preference shares were sold to the public, but the remaining ordinary shares were issued to the directors of Balfour Beatty and to three major manufacturing firms with which Balfour had became associated: Armstrong,

Whitworth, Babcock and Wilcox, and British Thomson-Houston. George Balfour was chairman of the new corporation, and Andrew Beatty and William Shearer, a Scot who had read law at Edinburgh University and had been the first secretary to Balfour Beatty, were joint managing directors. For £220,000 Power Securities acquired the ordinary share capital of Balfour Beatty, as well as interests in various utility companies for which they had acted either as engineers or managers.

Thus, when George Balfour was approached by the directors of the Grampian Electricity Supply Co. for financial assistance at the end of 1922—a period of deep depression—he had the means to help. Indeed, Power Securities was expressly formed for such a purpose. Power Securities purchased a controlling interest in the Grampian Co. which was soon transferred to the Scottish Power Co. Ltd., the Scottish arm of Balfour's new enterprise, and Balfour Beatty became engineers and managers of Grampian, as they already were of the other electrical undertakings of the Scottish Power Group. Not that work began immediately. Balfour realised more clearly than the promoters of the Grampian Act that the huge and sparsely populated area over which they had acquired the right to distribute electricity could never profitably be developed unless some part of the hydro-electricity capable of being generated by the waters of Loch Ericht and Loch Tummel was exported to the industrial areas of Central Scotland. This explains the overwhelming economic importance of the arrangements to provide bulk supplies to the Scottish Central Electric Power Co. and the Fife Electric Power Co., both of which had been acquired by the Scottish Power Group. But not only had the newly-created Central Electricity Board decided that the Grampian area was too unpromising a consuming area to warrant the extension of the national grid to this part of Scotland but, by nominating Townhill and Bonnybridge as selected stations, the Board effectively wrecked the Grampian Company's intention to sell electricity to the Scottish Central and Fife Power Companies. It was not until June 1927, when the Central Electricity Board agreed to take a bulk supply of electricity on favourable terms from the Grampian Co. by means of a link with the national grid at Abernethy, that Balfour was prepared to exercise the powers granted to the Grampian Company five years earlier.[47]

It has already been observed that one reason why the Grampian Company had been able to put through its bill in 1922 was that the company's proposals envisaged the comprehensive development of its entire catchment area. How this was to be achieved within the constraints imposed by the Act was later explained by A S Valentine and E M Bergstrom to members of the Institution of Electrical Engineers.[48] The authors, members of the staff of Balfour Beatty responsible for the hydro-electric side of the undertaking, emphasised that as the amount of power capable of being developed in any individual catchment area is dependent upon the amount of storage available in relation to the yearly distribution of the run-off, the natural configuration of the Loch Ericht area provided exceptional storage facilities. While the Grampian Act permitted the Company to vary the level of Loch Ericht between Ordnance datums 1128 and 1205 and to raise the level of the loch by 52 feet, no artificial variation in the level of Loch Laidon was permitted, and at Loch Rannoch storage was only available btween the levels of 664 and 672 feet. This was 'totally inadequate to compensate completely for the water flow from this catchment area for power purposes'. To overcome this potentially crippling restriction, it was proposed to operate the two power stations that the overall plan demanded in parallel, and to distribute the output according to the different conditions of flow in the two catchment areas constituting the entire watershed. Had the catchment areas of Loch Ericht and Loch Rannoch been exploited separately, or had they been only partially developed without proper consideration being given to the optimum power possibilities of the whole watershed, it would have been impossible to have developed the available water resources in the most rational or economic manner (see Fig. 4).

An analysis of the many relevant factors resulted in a conviction that the scheme should be planned in such a way that in times of flood a power station on the River Tummel should take the base load and that storage would be effected at Loch Ericht, but that during periods of low water, a power station utilising the water of Loch Ericht would take the base load and that Loch Rannoch would serve as the storage reservoir. By following this basic principle, it was believed that the maximum power that could economically be developed would be available for commercial use. The consequence was that the works in connection with the Loch Rannoch power station, which used the Ericht water, were designed for an ultimate capacity of 48,000 kW, and those for Tummel Bridge, downstream from Loch Rannoch, were designed for an installed capacity of 34,000 kW.

Construction began in 1928. The Grampian scheme was the first big hydro-electric power project in the Highlands designed for public supply and not, like the British Aluminium Company's schemes, for a specific industrial purpose. It was to be completed in two stages. The major elements in the first stage, known as the Ericht Development, involved extending Loch Ericht and raising its water level by building a concrete gravity dam, over 1,400 feet long, at the southern end of the Loch; driving a tunnel, of horseshoe section equivalent to 12.33 feet diameter, for nearly 3 miles through solid rock;[49] and building a steel pipeline to convey the water from its exit from the tunnel down to a generating station situated at the western end of Loch Rannoch (see Fig. 5). Various minor works, designed to divert the waters of a number of streams (including the River Truim and Allt Ghlas) into Loch Ericht, were also carried out. This first stage was completed in November 1930. The Rannoch power station—equipped initially with two vertically arranged Francis turbines designed for the conditions under which they would operate at the completion of the scheme—was linked to the national grid at Abernethy, a distance of 58 miles, by a 132 kV transmission line carried on 97 feet high steel pylons. When the line was brought into operation it was claimed to be the first of that voltage to be erected in the United Kingdom. In addition to bringing a bulk supply of 12,000 kW to the Central Electricity Board, the Rannoch station took over the supply for most of the Grampian Company's area of distribution, and the Arbroath steam plant was shut down.

In 1930 the bulk supply agreement between the Grampian Company and the Central Electricity Board was extended to provide for the delivery of 24,000 kW. This doubled the Company's assured market, encouraged them to provide supplies in the sparsely populated parts of their authorised area, and gave them an added incentive to embark on the second stage of their development plan. This—the Tummel Development (see Fig. 6)—was begun in the Spring of 1931.[50] The works were designed to exploit the

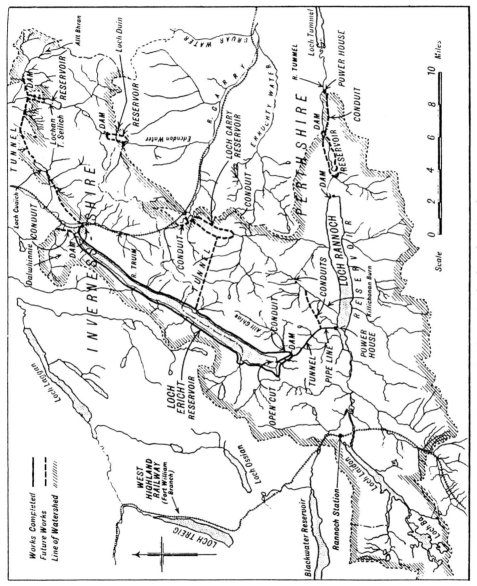

FIGURE 4 Grampian hydro-electric scheme

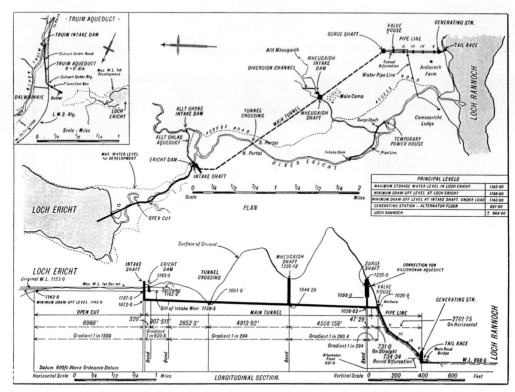

FIGURE 5   Diagram and profile of the first stage of the Grampian scheme: the Ericht Development

fall between the normal water level of Loch Rannoch and the River Tummel at Tummel Bridge. Again, William Halcrow was the consulting civil engineer and Balfour Beatty the engineers and contractors. The scheme involved the construction of a control weir close to the outlet of the River Tummel from Loch Rannoch; the deepening of the river channel to an intake dam at Dunalastair, four miles down-stream; and the cutting of an open aqueduct from the reservoir created by this dam for a distance of three miles on the south side of the river valley to a concrete forebay structure. From this building— which may be likened to a miniature dam—two steel pipes were constructed to carry the water to a power station situated on the banks of the river below.

This scheme, which made use of an available head of about 170 feet, possessed a number of ingenious features and provided a fish ladder of eighteen pools at the Dunalastair intake dam. The Tummel power station—equipped with two generating sets, the turbines being of the horizontal Francis type—began to supply current in November 1933. Not the least of the difficulties successfully overcome by the contractors was the carriage of heavy electrical equipment from the nearest railway station, at Struan, to Tummel Bridge, eleven miles distant. The road from the station was completely unsuited for heavy traffic. Its foundations were weak, and fifteen small bridges

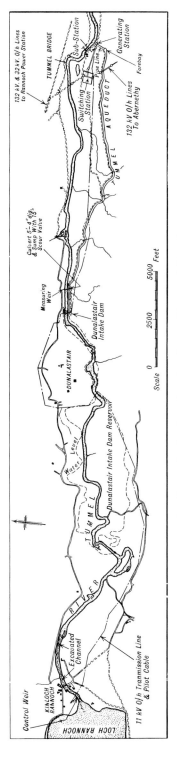

FIGURE 6   Grampian hydro-electric scheme: Tummel Development

and a large number of culverts had to be strengthened. For five miles the road had an average gradient of 1 in 15, and during the winter months was made impassable by snow and ice. Over this road the whole of the material had to be hauled by motor lorries and trailers. The heaviest load of all, the 75 ton transformers, were brought to the site on special trailers, carried on seven axles, and hauled by three 15 ton traction engines. To get these and other massive pieces of electrical equipment, such as the turbine cases and rotors, to the power station necessitated the construction of a 60 feet steel bridge across the River Tummel: the bridge built by General Wade in 1730 could not take the strain. Further improvements in the housing of the labour force were provided by Balfour Beatty. The main camp at Tummel Bridge, which could accommodate 500 labourers, consisted of twelve timber huts, each of them electrically heated; a licensed canteen; a recreation hall, in which weekly film shows—'talkies' at that— were given, and which boasted billiard rooms and a library; and a sports ground. A qualified medical orderly was always on hand. It was a far cry from the horrors of Kinlochleven.

Meanwhile, the authorised capital of the Grampian Company had been increased to £4 million and the area of supply granted by the 1922 Act had been extended. Further powers were conferred on the Company throughout the 1930s. By 1936, the capacity of Loch Ericht had been enlarged by the building of a dam at the northern end of the loch, the heightening of the original loch at the southern end, and the construction of a five-miles tunnel from Loch Garry (which was also dammed at its northern end) to divert its water from the River Garry into Loch Ericht. The supply of water to Loch Ericht was further enhanced in 1940 by a system of tunnels and aquaducts which captured the headwaters of the River Trome (the Allt Bhran) and the waters draining into Loch Seilich and Loch Cuaich. The major tunnel, between Loch Seilich and Loch Cuaich, was four and a half miles long and 9 feet in diameter. Its construction involved the removal of 100,000 tons of rock.[51] These developments, completed in the first year of the war, meant that the waters of 379 square miles of the Company's total catchment area of 418 square miles had been brought under control.

By the end of 1940 the area served by the Grampian Company had grown to 10,000 square miles, with a total population of about 414,000: it was the largest electrical distribution area in Britain. About 20 per cent of the premises had been connected. In addition to 106 million kWh supplied to the Central Electricity Board in 1940, bulk supplies were being sold to six associated companies within the Scottish Power Group and to four local authority undertakings. Outside the City of Aberdeen, practically the whole public supply of Northern Scotland was being produced directly or indirectly by the Grampian Co., who had constructed nearly 1,500 miles of 132,000 and 33,000 volt transmission lines and numerous 11,000 volt lines, in addition to distribution networks. The total capital expenditure incurred by the Company had been £6 million on which the average return over the decade ending in 1940 was but 3.8 per cent. Reporting two years later, the judgement of the Cooper Committee on the Grampian Company was characteristically objective and fair:

> The evidence before us leaves no room for doubt that the decision taken by the [Electricity] Commissioners and the [Central Electricity] Board in 1931 to leave the development of

the Northern Area to the Grampian Company ... has been justified by the results which have been achieved ..., and in view of the criticism which has so frequently been directed against the Grampian Company in the course of their Parliamentary promotions, we feel bound to record ... that they have proved themselves under conditions of unusual difficulty to be competent planners of electrical development and capable suppliers[52].

It was a fitting verdict.

In addition to the remarkable skills of the engineers and contractors and the sheer hard work and dogged persistence of the well-managed labour force, the Grampian scheme had demonstrated that Highland water power could be exploited to serve the public in general: that hydro-electricity could be transmitted to consumers at considerable distances from power stations in remote, sparsely populated areas. It has to be admitted that by 1940 perhaps only one of five premises within the Company's area of distribution had been connected and that the economic viability of the Grampian scheme depended heavily on bulk sales to the Central Electricity Board, but the Company had shown the feasibility of a carefully designed system in which two power stations working in parallel and feeding into a transmission grid could each operate economically at a load factor much lower than those which characterised the British Aluminium Company's schemes. There is no question that the demonstration effect of the success of the Grampian scheme was profound. 'New prospects were opened up for the development of the water-power resources of the Highlands'.[53]

It is unlikely that a similarly invigorating effect was produced by the early years of the Ross-shire Electricity Supply Co. This company succeeded the venture instigated by Colonel E W Blunt-MacKenzie for the supply of power to the market town of Dingwall and the boarding houses of Strathpeffer.[54] Within two years of its establishment in 1926 which was assisted by a loan of £20,000 at 5 per cent interest under the Trades Facilities Act, the Ross-shire Co. was in severe difficulty. Although a dam had been built across the River Conon to utilise the waters of Loch Luichart, which fed two 500 kW sets in a power station situated at the foot of the falls some 120 feet below the reservoir, the company encountered problems reminiscent of those which had plagued the Strathpeffer and Dingwall Electricity Supply Co. Of these, the local newspaper, *The North Star*, had commented:

> ... it may be of interest to the public to know that many times while they were sound asleep in bed the staff, and sometimes the Proprietor, were on the hillside in very stormy weather endeavouring to keep the supply in being ...[55]

The consequence was that the Ross-shire Electric Supply Co. asked the Scottish Power Co. for managerial and financial assistance in 1928. Three years later complete ownership and control had passed to Balfour's company when Scottish Power acquired all the issued share capital and repaid the loan given under the Trade Facilities Act. The capacity of the Loch Luichart power station was then increased, the system extended, and by 1938 an area of about 340 square miles adjacent to that of the northern extremities of the Grampian area was being supplied.[56]

Meanwhile, two important hydro-electric schemes had been constructed south of the

Highland line: the Falls of Clyde and Galloway Schemes. The genesis of each of them pre-dates the War of 1914–18. The first to be completed was that of the Clyde Valley Electric Power Co. which exploited the power of the Falls of Clyde. Suggested in 1909 by Sir Charles Ross, the original project lapsed as no adequate outlet could be found for the power that it was capable of generating.[57] The Clyde Valley Co. pushed ahead with thermal stations at Yoker, Clyde's Mill and Motherwell until, by the end of the First World War, it had become the largest generator and distributor of electricity in Scotland. To undertake the post-war reorganisation that this growing system demanded, the Clyde Valley Company appointed G T Goslin of Glasgow Corporation Electricity Department their General Manager. He, in turn, appointed Edward MacColl, who had built up a remarkable reputation with the Corporation's Tramways, to be his chief technical engineer. Within a few years, MacColl had devised a range of equipment for the control of high pressure transmission lines, electrical generators and transformers, and had so mastered the problems of thermal generating stations that he was able to achieve a significant reduction in fuel costs. A man so receptive to new ideas was bound to support a renewed initiative—by the Power and Traction Finance Co.—to harness the Falls of Clyde. The promotors (a consortium of Sir William Arrol, John Brown, Cammell Laird, English Electric and the Prudential Insurance Co.[58]) were confronted with two major difficulties: 'Storage against periods of drought and an area wherein to sell the electricity.'[59] Since the Clyde Valley Company were the 'authorised undertakers' for the area surrounding the Falls, the Power and Traction Co. had no alternative but to approach the Company.

Having investigated the average flow of the River Clyde and gone into the legal complexities of water rights and the preservation of amenities, MacColl strongly supported the scheme. He decided that no storage was necessary. With a very large catchment area of over 400 square miles providing the assurance of reasonably continuous water supplies, the Falls of Clyde were capable of development by a run-of-river scheme. All that was required was the diversion of the waters of the Clyde by means of regulating weirs equipped with automatic flood gates to two stations, three miles apart, at Bonnington and Stonebyres. In 1924 the Lanarkshire Hydro-Electric Power Co. was promoted as a subsidiary of the Clyde Valley Co. The scheme was completed within three years, the stations being specifically designed to work in conjunction with the Clyde Valley's thermal stations. The lay-outs of the two stations were similar; the natural fall of the river being utilised by the diversion of the flow through tunnels, 2,300 feet long and 10 feet in diameter at Bonnington and 1,550 feet long and 11 feet diameter at Stonebyres, the effective heads being 174 feet and 91 feet respectively. In both cases single reaction turbines in vertical settings were originally employed. The installed capacity at Bonnington was 9,840 kW and that at Stonebyres 5,680 kW. The aggregate available power was therefore over 15,500 kW. Dependent as they are on only a partially regulated flow and with variations in the quantity of water available from week to week, or even from day to day, run-of-river schemes are usually characterised by low load factors. In fact, Bonnington and Stonebyres, serving the densely populated and highly industrialised area of West Central Scotland as part of a mixed thermal/hydro system, achieved a percentage load factor approaching 60.[60]

The Falls of Clyde scheme, completed in 1926, was noteworthy for several reasons.

It marked the emergence of Edward MacColl as a pioneer in the use of hydro-electric power for public supply in Scotland; 'MacColl's Folly', the coal lobby called it. And it showed that hydro-electric schemes need not offend against scenic beauty. Not only were the two power stations 'well proportioned in concrete, forming a white mass against the green valley that is positively pleasing', but the scheme provided ample allowances of compensation water to preserve the attractions of the famous falls.[61] Lastly, at a capital cost of £422,000 the average cost per kW installed was the lowest of all the pre-war hydro-electric schemes.[62]

Three years after the completion of the Falls of Clyde scheme, the Galloway Water Power Company was incorporated.[63] The area this company sought to exploit was apparently so unfavourable for development that it had been ignored by the Water Power Resources Committee: 'the country ... does not provide the high, steep declivities which automatically attract the hydro-electric engineer on the look-out for promising sites; nor are there in the immediate neighbourhood large markets for power to guarantee a sufficient and steady demand'.[64] Nevertheless, Loch Doon had long been considered a possible catchment area for a hydro-electric scheme.[65] it was the subject of a scheme by the Ayrshire Joint Electricity Authority which was given official approval by Parliament, the Electricity Commissioners and the Secretary of State for Scotland in the early 1920s, but nothing came of it. The verdict of Kilmarnock's Electrical Engineer on the scheme is significant: 'Hydro-electric stations in this country can only compete with steam stations, first, when the price of fuel is excessively high; second, when freight charges are high; third, when the power generated can be utilised at a very high load factor. None of these conditions exist in the county of Ayr.'[66] The apparent impasse was to be overcome by the sheer determination and expertise of Colonel William McLellan and the transformation wrought in electricity supply by the creation of national grid, the first section of which to be approved by the Central Electricity Board was that for Central Scotland in 1927.

In 1923 William McLellan, Charles Merz's partner since 1899 in perhaps the most influential firm of British consulting electrical engineers, after discussing the possibilities of hydro-development for south-west Scotland with two fellow residents of Kirkcudbrightshire, Wellwood Maxwell and Scott Elliott, approached James Williamson, the chief engineer of the civil engineering firm of Sir Alexander Gibb & Partners, to re-investigate the potential of the area.[67] McLellan and Williamson, in collaboration with J Guthrie Brown, a senior engineer with Gibbs, found that although the hydro-electric potential was much greater than had been anticipated, the construction of a base-load plant could not be built without immense storage reservoirs, the cost of which would render any scheme to harness the potential economically impactical. Furthermore, since the south-west of Scotland was sparsely populated and agricultural in character, the local potential demand for electric power was far too limited.

When this crippling constraint was removed in 1927, McLellan resurrected his proposals. The construction of the grid would make the Galloway scheme not only viable but, because nearly all the generating stations 'selected' by the Central Electricity Board under the Electricity (Supply) Act of the preceeding year would be coal-fired stations constructed for base-load operation, almost essential. The Galloway scheme—suitably amended by Sir Alexander Gibb & Partners—could be employed to cope with the very peak loads which constitute the supply engineer's biggest nightmare.[68] Thus, in the spring of 1928, Merz and McLellan and Sir Alexander Gibb & Partners successfully approached the Power and Traction Finance Co. to obtain both finance and their support in the promotion of a bill to develop Galloway's water power resources.

Enormous preliminary difficulties remained.[69] The powers already granted to the Ayrshire Joint Electricity Co to utilise the waters of Loch Doon had to be acquired; the opposition of powerful fishing interests had to be overcome and the considerable number of landowners and tenants whose interests would be affected, won over. Unexpected technical difficulties were encountered in amending the original plants to permit peak-load operation; even the Central Electricity Board entertained doubts about the financial viability of the scheme. The decision to 'Buy British' added tens of thousands of pounds to the costs; British suppliers demanded particularly high prices for water turbine parts. And, when the bill came before Parliament, it encountered fierce opposition from the Mining Association of Great Britain. The bill was piloted through the two Houses with consummate skill, and many objections were deflected either by delicate negotiations (often conducted by William McLellan) behind the scenes or by the insertion of clauses to meet the sometimes unreasonable demands of the objectors. Among the clauses embodied in the bill was one which was to influence all subsequent hydro-electric developments in Great Britain:

> In the construction of the works all reasonable regard shall be paid to the preservation, as well for the public as for private owners, of the beauty of the scenery of the districts in which the said works are situated. For the purpose of securing the observance of the foregoing provisions and of aiding the Company it shall be lawful for the Secretary of State, after consultation with the Company, to appoint a Committee. The Committee may make to the Company such recommendations as they may think reasonable and proper for the preservation of the beauty of the scenery.[70]

The bill was given the Royal Assent in May 1929, and not the least of the factors which produced this outcome was the prospect that the implementation of the scheme would involve the employment of some 4,000 men, all of whom would be drawn from trades—including coal-mining—that were suffering from severe unemployment.

Even then construction did not begin for two years. Despite having been given all the necessary powers, the Galloway Water Power Company, incoporated immediately after the passage of the Act, could not contemplate building operations until the Central Electricity Board, to whom they expected to sell about 90 per cent of their output, expressed their unambiguous intention to buy; until, in fact, the Galloway power stations had been designated 'selected' stations. This was not forthcoming until January 1931. Meanwhile, the Company set about establishing its administration under Thomas Lawrie, who was appointed permanent secretary at the end of 1930; raising the necessary finance, expected to attain a figure of about £3 million; and grappling with the numerous environmental issues which were anticipated, perhaps the most complicated of which were the preservation of the Dee and the Doon as salmon fishing rivers and the conservation of Loch Doon Castle.

Work finally began in 1931. Certain novel features characterised the scheme. To make maximum use of the comparatively slow descent of the water from its highest point, Loch Doon, to sea level (a fall of just over 700 feet in a distance of some forty miles), it was decided to employ what is known as cascade development. That is, the water from the highest reservoir, Loch Doon (itself created by closing its natural outlet to the Firth of Clyde by a dam and, with the aid of a tunnel, diverting its water eastward into the valley of the Galloway Dee), augmented by that from various tributaries, is passed through four power stations one after another before it reaches the sea, near Kirkcudbright. A fifth power station, Glenlee, uses water from a separate reservoir, Clatteringshaws Loch, created by constructing a dam across the Blackwater of Dee and flooding the adjacent marshland. This water, after passing through a tunnel of nearly 19,000 feet, is fed to the turbines at Glenlee, whence it passes into the River Ken to join the main river and thus contributes to the head utilised by the final power station at Tongland (see Fig. 7).

Nine dams were necessitated by this ingeneous scheme. They were designed by James Williamson of Sir Alexander Gibb and Partners.[71] Several were of a composite design. These consisted of slender concrete arches but because 'the sides of the valleys were not steep enough to provide natural abutments, artificial abutments were built in the form of a mass concrete gravity dam against which the arch dam section could thrust. The amount of concrete required for this composite design was much less than if gravity dams had been used throughout'.[72] Even then, the expenditure on dam construction was much higher than had been estimated because the underlying rock formations turned out to be worse than had been revealed by the extensive trial borings which preceded the work.[73] Several large tunnels, aquaducts and pipe lines were also constructed. The excavation of the largest tunnel, that which connects Clatteringshaws reservoir with the power station at Glenlee, was every bit as difficult as had been anticipated, but the badly fissured sandstone through which it was driven proved to be sufficiently hard as to be virtually self-supporting.

An interesting feature of all the civil engineering work was the extensive use made of 'models to determine the most satisfactory form of those hydraulic structures for which it was felt that ordinary engineering experience offered an insufficient guide'. During the early stages the experimental work was carried out mainly in the laboratories of University College, London, but later larger scale models than could be built in the laboratory were constructed on the site itself.[74] Of the many problems investigated with the use of models were those relating to the design of fish passes and the effects of rapidly changing water pressures on descending smolts. Indeed, so much attention was paid to such matters that one independent consultant was to write, 'Looking through the early files of correspondence on this scheme, one might almost have been led to believe that it was a scheme for the preservation and improvement of the salmon fisheries on the River Dee'.[75] Certainly, the preservation of fishing was taken very seriously. The advice of numerous experts, including that of W L Calderwood, formerly Inspector of Salmon Fisheries in Scotland, was taken. George Hill explains that

The pass at Tongland, though not the highest in the scheme, was of particular importance because this dam was at a point of the river below which no spawning could take place. Therefore the future of the Kirkcudbrightshire Dee as a salmon river depended entirely

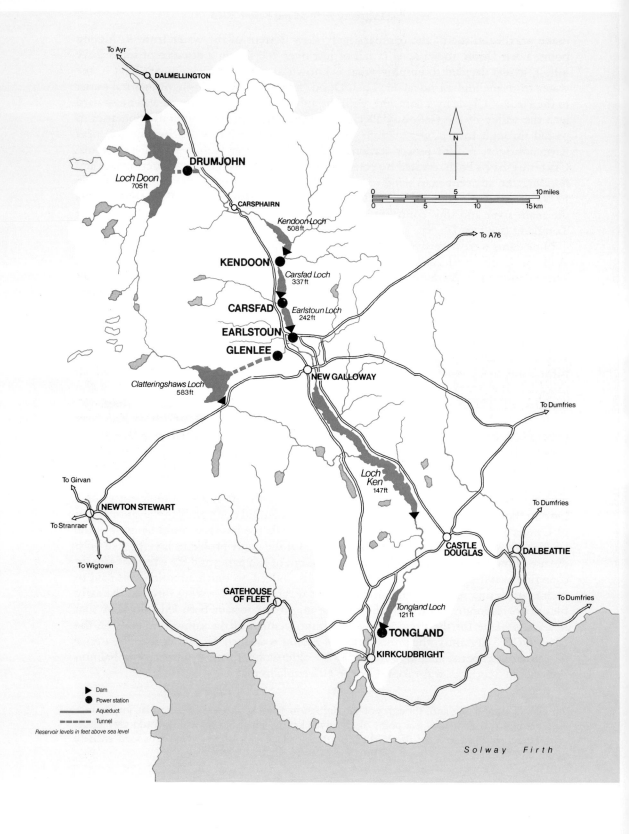

To Ayr

DALMELLINGTON

Loch Doon
705 ft

DRUMJOHN

CARSPHAIRN

Kendoon Loch
508 ft

KENDOON

Carsfad Loch
337 ft

CARSFAD

Earlstoun Loch
242 ft

EARLSTOUN

GLENLEE

Clatteringshaws Loch
583 ft

NEW GALLOWAY

To A76

N

0   5   10 miles
0   5   10   15 km

To Dumfries

Loch Ken
147 ft

To Girvan

NEWTON STEWART

To Stranraer

To Wigtown

To Dumfries

CASTLE DOUGLAS

DALBEATTIE

To Dumfries

GATEHOUSE OF FLEET

Tongland Loch
121 ft

TONGLAND

KIRKCUDBRIGHT

▶ Dam
● Power station
─── Aqueduct
- - - Tunnel
Reservoir levels in feet above sea level

Solway   Firth

upon the success of the Tongland ladder. To alleviate some of the problems a working model was constructed which allowed the engineers and fishery experts to determine the best construction of orifice, baffles, pool size, gradient and flow to reduce turbulence and present the salmon with an attractive entrance to the ladder.[76]

Such experiments resulted in recommendations which were incorporated in the final design. It was all very expensive!

The entire scheme, which cost about £3 million, or £29 per Kilowatt of installed capacity, went into operation in October 1936. It was the largest integrated hydro-electric development in the United Kingdom. Within a few hours of the switching into service of the number two machine at Carsfad on 27th October, the Central Electricity Board asked for and obtained the full available output for all five stations which, with the available water supply, amounted to 99,000 kW.[77] While some of the output was used locally, the bulk of it was, as expected, exported through the Grid to the industrial areas of Central Scotland and North West England. The Central Electricity Board had planned to take 195 million units annually from the Galloway Co., but so pleased was the Board with the development that in 1938 280 million units were taken.[78] It was a remarkable achievement.

4   The Abortive Schemes

The Galloway Water Power Act of 1929 was the last hydro development to be passed in the inter-war period. In retrospect, it is perhaps easier to explain the rejection of six subsequent schemes than to understand why that for Galloway was approved. George Hill's explanation is highly plausible.[79] His meticulous study makes it clear that the success of the promoters of the Galloway scheme was due to a unique combination of persistence, diplomatic skills and luck. The timing of the measure proved to be of critical importance. It is apparent that Lord Meston, the director of Power and Traction who appeared before the Lords Committee to give evidence on behalf of the promoters, was correct in arguing that 'The broad objects of the scheme are to make electricity generally more available throughout the country and to effect economies in fuel by concentrating the generation of electricity in fewer and more efficient stations', for in so doing he was seen to be advocating the very policy recommended in all the contemporary studies concerning electricity supply, particularly that of the influential Weir Report of 1925 which culminated in the 1926 Act.

Lord Meston was also able to emphasise the promoters' concern for the welfare of the environment. This, he could rightly claim, was no mere platitude but had been demonstrated by the responsible attitudes taken by the Power and Traction Group towards the design and construction of the Falls of Clyde scheme, and by the amenities clause in the Galloway bill itself. Then there were the employment-creating opportunities implicit in the scheme. It was inconceivable that the tunnelling, which bulked

facing page
FIGURE 7   The Galloway Scheme

so large in the civil engineering works, would not take numerous miners off the dole. Similarly, the Group's commitment to 'Buy British' must have disarmed additional potential opposition. While Lord Meston's advocacy was winning the approval of the Upper House, William McLellan was orchestrating the attempt to secure the support of a majority, drawn from all parties, in the Commons, often by introducing new clauses or amending existing ones to give priority to the local unemployed or to those who would lose their jobs when old, inefficient steam-powered stations were forced to close down as a result of the proposed schemes.

While the bill was being eased through Parliament, aggrieved interests outside were being placated by judicious concessions. But all these delicate negotiations would probably have been to no avail had the coal lobby launched their expected onslaught on the bill. That this failed to materialise was due, Hill believes, 'to the fact that [at this juncture] there was apparently nothing of substance to be concerned about'. It is necessary to consider contemporary conditions:

> Although a national grid system was under construction, it was still in an embryonic state, with overwhelming wayleave problems and environmental opposition. Thus until the early 1930s electricity supply was carried out in a very parochial manner. In this situation unified, nationwide opposition to a proposed supply scheme would be without precedent. The hydrographic conditions necessary to sustain large-scale generation in this country exist mainly in the North of Scotland which was not included in the early grid plans.[80]

With the coming of the grid, these conditions were irrevocably altered. The coal lobby, now thoroughly alive to the threat of hydro power, intensified its opposition to any further ventures. Co-ordinated with that engendered by the bitter antagonism of the landed and sporting interests, this powerful combination thwarted all six of the Scottish hydro-electric bills promoted between 1929 and 1942. But alongside this readily explicable hostility, based as it was on selfish self-interest, there was something more. In the almost endless debates which resulted in the suffocation of all the schemes— whether they were motivated, like the British Aluminium Company's project, solely for private profit, or like Galloway at least partially inspired by the provision of public benefit—it is apparent that many of the Scottish peoples' own representatives in Parliament betrayed a curious ambivalence towards the hydro bills put before them. Although the projected schemes would provide employment and other advantages to their urban constituents, they could not rid themselves of a deep suspicion that the promoters of the bills, animated by private enterprise, might exploit the Highlands even more ruthlessly than the landlords. As Norrie Fraser put it:

> To the people of Scotland, now concentrated in the Clyde Forth area, amid the debris and dolour of mining and industrial development, climbing their grim cliff dwellings in the Scottish tenement, and having sacrificed the starry firmament on high for the spluttering street lamp, the Highlands of Scotland were a symbol of that inviolable beauty on which the dirty grasp of the industrialist must not fasten.[81]

This feeling was revealed most strongly, particularly by Tom Johnston, in the debates on the succession of bills whose principal purpose was to harness the power of the waters of Loch Quoich and the adjoining Lochs in a catchment area to the west of Fort Augustus. The West Highland scheme was first disallowed after prolonged investigation by a Select Committee in 1929 and, after rebirth as the Caledonian Power scheme promoted by the British Oxygen Company and designed specifically for the production of calcium carbide at Corpach, was thrice rejected on the second reading in the House of Commons.[82] The first of the Caledonian Power bills was defeated in 1936 by a vote of 199 to 63, with 22 Scottish members for and 16 against;[83] the second in 1937 by a vote of 188 to 140, with 47 Scottish members for and 11 against;[84] and the third was lost by a vote of 227 to 141.[85] On this occasion, 43 Scottish members supported the bill and 18 rejected it.

The main thrust of the arguments in favour of each of these ill-starred measures was that the Highlands constituted a distressed area and that only industrial development would stem the inexorable external migration which, to use an uncharacteristically inept metaphor by Tom Johnston, threatened to turn the place into 'a desert'.[86] Again and again, this argument was repeated, with growing desperation. It was recognised that the tourist trade was important, and that this depended on the preservation 'of the amenities of the beautiful Highlands of Scotland', but as Malcolm MacMillan, the Member for the Western Isles, observed, 'if you ask the people of Kinlochleven, Lochaber, Galloway and the rest whether they would rather depend upon the future prospects of the tourist trade or obtain a steady wage and regular employment [from industry] the answer every time will be for industrialism'. The case was put even more powerfully by Frederick Macquisten, KC, Conservative member for Argyll and the 'chairman of a company which makes carbide on the other side of the world':

> I beseech hon. Members for the sake of the Highlands to give this industry a chance. Let us get some employment for our people. A power station is not an unsightly thing. [Nor does the industry] disfigure the landscape … there is no smoke or smell because the anthracite is not burnt but is blended with the lime … If I thought that the undertaking would destroy the beauties of the Highlands from the tourist point of view I should not support it, but you cannot expect the people of Inverness to live for ever on the Loch Ness monster. You must find work for the people …[87]

The trouble was that members for other constituencies wanted the same thing. The Welsh felt that a carbide factory should be located at the source of the anthracite in South Wales and the electricity generated in thermal stations, despite Macquisten's assertion that water power was essential. 'No one outside an engineering mental hospital (or under a dictatorship in Germany)' he said, 'would dream of making carbide with electricity generated from coal. It cannot be done.' The members for the English and Welsh mining regions thought otherwise. They formed a strange alliance with other English MPs influenced by their well-known attachment to Scotland's romantic beauty, no matter if they never visited the place except to shoot everything in sight! And when they sneered at the figures presented by Robert Boothby during the 1938 debate, that between 3,000 and 5,000 workers would be employed for a period of from three to five years in carrying out the scheme and between 300 and 500 would be employed permanently at the factory at Corpach, he acknowledged that 'to anyone from a congested industrial district they are very small, but when it is remembered that there are only 15 crofts in the whole area which we are discussing, employment for 300 to 500 people is a considerable thing'.[88]

Compared with this line of argument, carbide production, whatever its strategic importance, came a poor second. Not that the members were left in ignorance of the importance of this raw material. This was emphasised in each one of the three debates. In 1936 Brigadier-General Sir William Alexander, maintained—with a wealth of illustration—how vital it was in case of war, 'and goodness knows, there are enough rumours of war around today'. And he quoted from the report of the Nitrogen Products Committee of 1921 that 'There are blocks of undeveloped water power in Scotland of a sufficient size for the operation of a large factory'. He was vigorously supported by the Marquess of Clydesdale who affirmed that 'Approximately 90 per cent of the aeroplanes manufactured for the Royal Air Force require oxy-acetylene welding. In a case of emergency, if the importation of carbide were stopped, possibly 90 per cent of the manufacture of aeroplanes in this country would be brought to a standstill.'[89] It remained for the Secretary of State for Scotland, Walter Elliot, to tell the House in the following year of the vast quantities of carbide being made in Germany and Italy:

> It is interesting to see that the biggest factory in the world, with an output of 70,000 tons and a ... capacity of 200,000 tons, has been situated in Venice. The amenities of Venice are well known to hon. Members, either by experience or through song and story, and I do not think it can be said that the amenities of North Italy and Venice are entirely without relevance to those ... who run the tourist traffic in that country.[90]

And in 1938, as the war got closer, Sir Thomas Inskip reiterated the arguments and begged the House to pass the bill: 'We are the only important nation in Europe which does not at the present time manufacture calcium carbide for itself. Italy does it, Russia does it, Japan does it and Germany does it'.[91]

It was to no avail. Boothby's biting wit and eloquence; the measured appeals of those to whom the production of carbide was of cardinal significance; the passionate pleas of those who saw in the Caldonian Power Bill a means of arresting, even reversing, generations of outward migration from the Highlands: all were overruled. They were outvoted by a majority some of whom sought to protect or promote their own interests, whether these were the welfare of the colliery districts or the right to use the Highlands as a game reserve, and some of whom, like Tom Johnston (reversing in the 1938 debate his earlier position), believed that it was wrong 'to hand over to a private corporation, for purposes of gain, the great national resources of our country'.[92] These groups constituted the core of the opposition to the Caledonian Power Bills. They were supported by a penumbra of more specialised objectors. For example, the Member for Inverness, Sir Murdoch Macdonald, was concerned that the scheme would involve the diversion of water 'from its natural course down to the sea though the River Ness and shoot it out through a tunnel on the west coast'.[93] Mr Ralph Assheton, member for the Rushcliffe division of Nottinghamshire, disingenuously raised the spectre of armies of Irish navvies pouring into the Highlands, adding that South Wales needed help more than the Highlands.[94] And Captain Ramsey, the indefatigable spokesman for the coal lobby, suggested that a carbide factory at the extreme end of a long stretch of water could easily be found and bombed, whereas such a building would be less vulnerable in an industrial area, either because it would be less conspicuous or because it would be better defended.[95]

It was the same with the other two schemes that failed to secure the sanction of Parliament. In 1929 the Grampian Electricity Supply Co. introduced a bill to extend their area of supply and to develop the waters of Lochs Affric, Mullardoch, and Monar, and generally the area from which water is finally discharged into the Beauly Firth. Although there was no opposition from either the landlords on the fishing interests, and vigorous support from many of the towns it was proposed to supply (some of which were without either electricity or gas) and from the Electricity Commissioners and the Central Electricity Board, the bill was rejected by a Select Committee of the House of Lords. What killed the measure was the evidence of A M MacEwan who argued that the city of Inverness would receive no benefit and that the natural beauty of the area of Loch Affric and hence the tourist trade would be irrevocably harmed.[96] He was supported by J S Highfield, on behalf of the Mining Association, who produced figures to show that the electricity required in the area could be as economically produced by steam stations as by water power, and that if the scheme were adopted a number of miners would be thrown out of work. Great play was made with the fact that no large private consumers were wanting to take a supply, although, as *Engineering* observed, it 'is well known [that] demand in the electrical industry, as other branches of commerce, follows and does not precede the availability of the product'.[97]

When in 1941 the Grampian Company put forward another bill to develop Glen Affric, it too was rejected. Having been recommended to Parliament after an exhaustive inquiry held under the Private Legislation Procedure (Scotland) Act, the confirmation bill was turned down by the Commons in September.[98] All the usual arguments both for and against were reiterated but on this occasion the emphasis was somewhat different from what had gone before. The general flavour of the debate was accurately mirrored in the wording of the amendment moved by Edward Keeling, the member for Twickenham, with which the debate was inaugurated. Instead of the usual formula 'That the Bill be read a Second time upon this day three months', thereby effectively shutting out the measure for the session, Keeling moved that

> this House, while giving the greatest weight to the decision of the Commission which held an inquiry in Scotland, declines to read a Second time a Bill confirming a scheme which is contentious, disturbs national unity, cannot be carried out during the war and may not be suitable or beneficial in the unpredictable conditions prevailing after the war.[99]

Anticipating the criticism that the Grampian bill 'ought to be left to Scottish Members to deal with', Keeling argued that 'it is certain that English people are as much interested in the Highlands—they go there quite a lot—and ... are as much entitled to debate this matter as Scottish members would be to debate a Bill which affected Westminster Abbey or St James's Park. Moreover, there has been so much bitterness in Scotland, both in the Press and elsewhere, about the scheme that perhaps only Sassenachs can view it calmly and dispassionately'.

Keeling then condemned the measure on the grounds that 'the interests of the Highlands ought to prevail over the interests of the Grampian Electricity Supply Co.', and that the bill would simply reinforce the tendency for electricity generated in Scotland to be sold in the Lowlands and coastal districts or even in England by being sent to the grid. He emphasised that 'not one of the promoters' witnesses gave any evidence of any industry being induced to go to the Highlands', and attacked the findings of the plebiscite which indicated that the local population was almost unanimously in favour of the bill by stating that as tenants of Highland Estates, a subsidiary of the Scottish Power Co., they would 'hardly ... have answered ... in a way unfavourable to their own landlords'. But his main point—one repeatedly taken up during the course of the debate—was that 'to grant further hydro-electric powers over a wide area to a private interest will ... embarrass if not stultify the post-war planning of the Highlands'. He ended his speech with 'a few words on the question of amenities', by contrasting the existing 'wooded shores, heather-clad hillsides, rocky gorges, tumbling waterfalls' with what would take their place: 'huge white dams ... wide stretches of rotting vegetation and slimy mud ... and here and there the blackened skeletons of trees ... projecting above the ooze'. It was, he declared, futile to look to the amenity clauses for protection, for they could be overridden if they threatened to imperil the financial success of the scheme. 'Never in the history of private bills have so many words pretended so much and achieved so little'.[100]

In vain did the bill's supporters emphasise that the reason for seeking the powers granted by the Bill was that its passage would permit construction to begin 'at the very earliest practicable moment after the war is over'; that the Grampian Company's supply of electricity would soon fall short of the demand; and that the scheme involved the complete development of the Affric-Cannick catchment area. Once again, they were unable to convince a majority to back the scheme. Those who voted against the bill did so because of the amenities issue; because they had been won over, yet again, by the intense lobbying of the colliery interests and, because of a feeling—most clearly expressed by Philip Noel-Baker—that the 'derelict conditions of many ...coalfields ... and industrial areas' required more immediate assistance than 'remote country districts' whose future proposerity depended on the holiday industry more than on hydro-electricity. There is, however, little doubt that many were influenced by Tom Johnston's promise that the Government intended to lay a comprehensive plan before the House for the co-ordination of the nation's hydro-electric resources. He asked the Members:

> Ought we to proceed with a Measure which cannot, in the near or in any visible future, be operated but which, if passed, would, to some extent, confer most valuable natural resources and assets upon a private corporation and would tie the hands of the Government of the day when the whole question of regionalisation and ownership of hydro-electricity comes to be considered? If we confer these powers now, we mortgage the future. We mortgage the water forces of two glens and do so for nothing. We are doing it in advance of any possible operational necessity.[101]

Although few doubted Tom Johnston's *personal* determination to evolve a proper plan for the Highlands, some members were openly cynical of the Government's intentions. As David Robertson, the Member for Streatham, observed: 'All I heard from the right hon. Gentleman the Secretary of State for Scotland is that at some time the Government, or somebody, will talk about doing something. Ever since I was a boy I have listened to people talking about doing things for the Highlands.' So far, he said, the only person who has actually achieved anything was the Member for Hampstead, Mr George Balfour, who is 'not a good talker, but is a very good doer'.[102] For all that, it could not be denied that private companies would be unlikely to undertake 'the less economic or doubtfully economic schemes'. It remained for the labour member for the Sedgefield division of Durham, John Leslie, to give expression to what decades of bitter controversy seemed to have made inevitable. 'If the water-power resources of the Highlands are ever to be developed in the interests of the nation, ... the State will have to tackle [the] job'.[103] So it proved.

CHAPTER 3

The Genesis of the North of Scotland Hydro-Electric Board

1 Tom Johnston's 'Council of State'

When, in the debate on the second Glen Affric scheme, the Secretary of State for Scotland, Tom Johnston, surveyed the arguments for and against the measure, he took pains to emphasise that many of those who had supported the bill at the inquiry in Edinburgh or were doing so in House, were moved by a genuine belief that although the scheme could not be put into effect in wartime, it was important to be ready to begin construction immediately on the cessation of hostilities. He implied that not a few of those holding this view were motivated by an overwhelming desire to do *something* for the Highlands, whether the instrument were to be a private corporation or some government agency, and that they feared that if they failed to take the opportunity presented by the initiative of the Grampian Electricity Supply Company in 1941, they would not get another chance for many years. The Secretary of State wanted to allay such anxieties. 'There is no necessity to assume that Parliament will delay a decision upon the future of hydro-electricity until after the war', he said, enigmatically. Pressed by the member for East Fife, Mr Henderson Stewart, to be more forthcoming, he became instead increasingly evasive: 'I hope the hon. Gentleman will not seek to push me further than I have gone'. To many members of the House, this simply was 'not good enough ... there are people ready to go ahead now, and ... we should give them the powers and let them make their plans, so that they can be put into operation immediately the time is ripe'.

Tom Johnston would not be drawn. It was all very mysterious, and the mystery was made even more impenetrable by the fact that the original inquiry into the Grampian scheme had been held *in camera* because it was feared that 'questions of considerable gravity and importance to the national security might be raised'.[1] Was this concern for secrecy simply to avoid the disclosure of the possible 'location of proposed and existing generating stations and transmission lines', or was there, as some have since suggested, a more sinister explanation? Was the government contemplating the exploitation of Highland water resources for the production of heavy water as an essential component of an atomic bomb?[2] It is highly improbable, if for no other reason than that the *existing* generating power of the British Aluminium Companies installations at Kinlochleven and Lochaber could have been utilised for such a vital purpose. A more plausible interpretation of Tom Johnston's reticence is that he alone knew that he had accepted

36

PLATE 1   Tom Johnston

office under certain conditions, one of which promised[3] to be instrumental in overcoming the impediments to the systematic development of Highland water power.

In February 1941, when the Prime Minister had 'hypnotised' Johnston into accepting the post of Secretary of State for Scotland in his reconstructed cabinet, Churchill had agreed to permit Johnston to set up a Council of State, composed of all the living ex-Secretaries for Scotland, irrespective of Party. The Prime Minister said that he would look sympathetically upon any issue about which they were agreed.[4] By the Autumn of the same year Johnston had persuaded Lord Alness, the one surviving Secretary for Scotland, and Sir Archibald Sinclair, Walter Elliot, Sir John Colville, and Ernest Brown, all former Secretaries of State, to serve on the Council.[5] At its inaugural meeting, held on 29 September 1941, it was agreed that the Council would 'consider Scotland's post-war problems, set up enquiries as necessary (deciding their priority) and survey the results'.[6] The very first subject Johnston asked the Council to consider was 'the further development of hydro-electricity in Scotland .... The Second Reading Debate on the Glen Affric Bill,' he said, 'had [revealed] strong pressure for a comprehensive review of the whole subject.' Anticipating a favourable response to this request, Johnston had already tentatively approached Lord Cooper, the Lord Justice Clerk, to act as Chairman of this inquiry. Sir Andrew Duncan, President of the Board of Trade, had offered to provide technical assistance. The Minutes do not reveal the Council's reaction to the Secretary of State's anticipation of their agreement. It is clear that Lord Alness 'doubted the propriety of the Lord Justice Clerk enquiring into so contentious a subject', but his hesitations were overcome by the euphoria of the moment and the desire to exploit the prevailing national spirit of co-operation to achieve something for Scotland.[7]

2   The Cooper Committee and its Report

Within a few weeks, the committee had been appointed. In addition to Lord Cooper, it included Neil Beaton, the Chairman of the Scottish Co-operative Wholesale Society and the son of a Sutherland shepherd; John A Cameron, of the Land Court; Lord Weir, the Scottish industrialist who had been Chairman of the Committee on the Supply of Electrical Energy in 1926, and James Williamson, the chief civil engineer to Sir Alexander Gibb & Partners during the construction of the Galloway scheme. Weir was initially reluctant to join the committee, claiming that membership might distract him from his many other wartime commitments. He was at this time Director-General of Explosives at the Ministry of Supply and Deputy Chairman of the Supply Council. It is clear that he not only believed that consideration of the future of Scottish water power at this stage of the war constituted an unwelcome diversion of his energies from more pressing matters, but that the hydro-electricity could make only a marginal contribution to Britain's energy needs. It was some time before he succumbed to Johnston's entreaties and was persuaded to participate.[8] The Committee was officially appointed on 27 October 1941. Its remit was:

> To consider (a) the practicability and desirability of further developments in the use of water power in Scotland for the generation of electricity, and (b) by what type of authority or body such developments, if any, should be undertaken, and under what conditions,

having due regard to the general interests of the local population and to considerations of amenity, and to report.[9]

Meanwhile, Lord Cooper had already begun his investigations. His initial impressions were far from encouraging. Writing to Tom Johnston in September, he recalled that 'the entire field of hydro-electric development was exhaustively explored' by the Snell Committee between 1918 and 1921 who had 'examined 55 witnesses and spent nearly £10,000'. He continued,

> with the exception of Glen Affric and the West Highland schemes (which have both been rejected by Parliament), practically every scheme of any size which the [Snell] Committee investigated has already been carried out by the Grampian Co., the British Aluminium Co., the Galloway Co. or the Clyde Valley Co. Broadly speaking, all that is left is a large number of small and isolated schemes the commercial feasibility of which is in doubt.

Nor did Lord Cooper think that there was any point in re-surveying the water power resources of Scotland. The Committee 'now to be set up could hardly do otherwise than simply accept the results of the [Snell] investigations ... it would not be feasible to examine the question afresh in wartime, nor [has] anything new emerged since 1921 which would justify [such a course]', certainly not the 'amateurish chapter in the Report of the Hilleary ... Committee.'[10] Nevertheless, it was as the result of his very careful examination of the Hilleary Report[11] that Lord Cooper decided that something could and should be done, a conviction that was strengthened during the course of the inquiry conducted by the Committee over which he presided.

Rarely can such a Committee have performed its task more energetically or to such purpose. In addition to an exhaustive historical investigation, based largely on the reports and records of previous Parliamentary Committees and Commissions, technical evidence and advice was provided by Sir Cyril Hurcomb and other members of the Electricity Commission, and the Chairman, Sir Archibald Page, and senior officials of the Central Electricity Board, including the Board's Scottish manager, Edward McColl. All the major government departments in Scotland were consulted, and evidence was taken from many representatives of local government. The powerful Fishery interests in Scotland responded enthusiastically to the invitation to state their case. Lord Meston and Tom Lawrie represented the Galloway Power Company and Ian Murray and Mr Gargill, the Grampian Electricity Supply Company. The electro-chemical and electro-metallurgical industries were represented by Murray Morrison, British Aluminium Co., J L Hardie, the British Oxygen Co., and Holbrook Gaskall, ICI. The foremost civil engineering consultants on hydro-development gave evidence. These included Sir Alexander Gibb, W T Halcrow, and R W Mountain, of Kennedy & Donkin. Among the various bodies concerned with Highland development, environmental issues and electrical policy from whom evidence was taken were the Scottish Development Council, the Association for the Preservation of Rural Scotland, the Highland Development League and the Saltire Society; and detailed technical questions were addressed by such people as Captain W N McLean, the Director of River Flow Records. The Committee itself was peripatetic, meeting to confer or to take evidence in Edinburgh, Glasgow,

London and Inverness, and inspecting a number of districts in the Highlands. And during the course of the inquiry the Committee was deluged by advice, information and not a little abuse in the editorial pages of the national and local press.

The Committee's Report was published on 15 December 1942. It was, as Tom Johnston later told the House of Commons, 'by common consent, a masterly production and a model of terse, constructive and courageous draftsmanship.'[12] On this occasion, the usual Parliamentary courtesies did not exaggerate. In truth, the Cooper Report is a remarkable document: clear and unambiguous, systematic, analytical and realistic. It begins with an historical survey which emphasises that 'most of the difficulties of the present situation, in so far as they are not inherent in the physical characteristics of Northern Scotland, have their roots in the history of the last twenty years'. This 'revealed a number of disquieting features':

> All major issues of policy, both national and local, have tended to become completely submerged in the conflict of contending sectional interests. Local opinion has vacillated widely from time to time and has been, and is, acutely divided both on general principles and on the merits of individual proposals; and some of the views and policy which have been locally advanced have been neither self-consistent nor technically practicable. The opposition of land-owning and sporting interests seems to have been pressed further than was justifiable for the protection of their interests and in some cases to have been taken more seriously than was intended; and in several instances strenuous opposition has been offered by the Mining Association with the object of preventing hydro–electric development so as to maintain or increase the demand for coal ... In the result the whole subject has become involved in an atmosphere of grievance, suspicion, prejudice and embittered controversy.

The consequence was that as the Highlands sunk into deepening depression, valuable water power resources ran to waste. While private enterprise had been either prohibited or discouraged, the State itself refused even to frame a plan or programme for the development of these resources: 'the only policy which can be deduced from the action ... of a succession of Parliaments and of governments is that they will neither develop the resources themselves nor allow anyone else to do so.'[13]

In reviewing the electrical development which had been carried out in Northern Scotland, the Report explained that, although in 1931 the Electricity Commissions had prepared a scheme for the Highlands, it was not carried out because 'it was only the [area] to the South and East of the Caledonian Canal which held any reasonable prospect of ... being commercially sound', and the supply of this area had been left to the Grampian Co. to deal with. Being anxious to remove any misconceptions concerning the wisdom of this decision, Lord Cooper and his colleagues went out of their way to substantiate their assertion that, far from exploiting the area 'for the profit of the shareholders of the Scottish Power Co.', the Grampian Company had made but a modest return on a very large investment and that complaints 'as to the alleged improper delay in giving suppliers in remoter sections of the area' betrayed ignorance of what *had* been done and 'a failure to appreciate the inherent difficulties of supply' in very sparsely populated rural areas. 'There are large tracts of the Grampian territory [in the region of the Cairngorms] in which the provision of a supply is, and must remain, quite impracticable, the demand being far too small and too sporadic to bear the cost of transmission and distribution.'

What had so far been achieved had been made possible by the contract with the Central Electricity Board—which had 'enabled the Grampian Company to take advantage of the existence of the grid in the Central Scotland District'—and the financial backing of the Scottish Power Co. Ltd:

> far from the Northern Area having been exploited ... the plain fact is that the development which has so far taken place has to a considerable extent enjoyed the benefit of hidden subsidies from the Central Electricity Board contract and from the resources of the Scottish Power Co. .... The repeated objections which have been taken to this contract ... and the frequent criticisms which are still made against 'using the Highlands as the power house for the Lowlands' completely overlook the elementary fact that it is impracticable to build up gradually over a period of years a general public supply system in a thinly populated rural area unless from the first a market can be found for a substantial proportion of the power which, when initially provided, is necessarily far in excess of the initial or immediately prospective public demand.[14]

As the Inquiry proceeded, it became clear to the Committee that it was essential 'to provide a substantial new source of power in the extreme north of the Grampian territory .... in the vicinity of Inverness and Easter Ross ... a substantial load is rapidly building up, and unless provision is soon made for meeting it not only will this area be starved but the entire development will be jeopardised'. Even to consider the construction of a large steam station in a district so remote from coal and so rich in water power, was regarded as a major planning error. It was believed that *only* hydro development was appropriate. This argument was supported by careful analyses of the comparative costs of steam and hydro-electric generation; the general question of the future of water-power as a method of generating electricity; the nature and extent of the local potential resources; and the utilisation of the power capable of development. It was fully accepted that 'the local demand, especially if confined to the hill country, could not within any predictable period absorb more than an insignificant fraction of the total [undeveloped water resources]', but the suggestion 'that it would be better to leave the resources undeveloped rather than to allow the power to be exported to the south or even to be used locally in large-scale electro-chemical and electro-metallurgical industries', was firmly rejected. To have decided otherwise was 'tantamount to the acceptance of a policy of despair with regard to the whole problem of the future of the Highlands.'

How then were the water power resources to be exploited? The Committee had received numerous 'practical suggestions' which envisaged the creation of small or medium-sized schemes of not more than 2,000 kW capacity. These had been carefully examined and found wanting. They would 'at best afford a very partial and unsatisfactory solution and would yield in solid advantage to the Highlands and the country at large a very meagre return for the heavy and largely unremunerative expenditure which would have to be incurred.' The Committee believed that there was no realistic alternative to the creation of 'a new public service corporation called the North Scotland Hydro-Electric Board' which would 'be responsible for initiating and undertaking the development of all further generation of electricity in the Northern Area for public supply, and its transmission and supply in bulk to the existing undertakers. It should further be responsible for generation, transmission and distribution in all areas outside the limits of existing undertakers.' In framing its development programme 'the Board should have three primary objectives':

(a) to attract to the Highlands through the offer of cheap and abundant power a share in the vital and expanding electro-chemical and electro-metallurgical industries;
(b) to develop such futher power as may be required for the consumers of existing undertakers or for consumers in its own distribution area, the surplus being exported to the grid; and
(c) to develop on an experimental and demonstrational basis isolated schemes in isolated districts.[15]

In order to achieve these objectives, the Committee made a series of additional recommendations and, 'at the risk of exceeding [its] remit', numerous suggestions for their successful implementation. Indeed, a sequential programme was suggested.

Certain issues were regarded as being of such importance that they were re-emphasised. To the Committee there was 'no feasible alternative to the establishment of an *ad hoc* public corporation' working to a systematic plan which would co-ordinate the generation, transmission and distribution of electricity 'in an area covering in whole or in part the districts of twelve county councils and over fifty burghs .... local government boundaries will be entirely irrelevant'. The task confronting the Board would call for the same type of highly specialised and technically skilled qualifications which are found in the Central Electricity Board. But if the Central Electricity Board was to be the model for the new organisation, the Committee emphatically rejected the idea of entrusting its scheme to the Central Electricity Board itself:

> ... the problems of the Northern Area call for a different policy and outlook from that of the Act of 1926, and we do not consider that it would be desirable to saddle the same body with the duty of carrying these different policies into effect. The vital necessity of treating hydro-electric development as an integral part of the wider plans for the regeneration of the Highlands seems to us to require a separate executive authority, acting in close collaboration with the Commissioners and the Central Electricity Board but free to develop their plans with full regard to Northern conditions and interests.[16]

After considering the perennial problems of the fishery interests; the necessity of ensuring that the Board should not be held up to ransom by unreasonable demands for compensation occasioned by the acquisition of land for the construction of works and wayleaves; and making strong recommendations that rating anomalies prejudicial to hydro-development be rectified, the Committee concluded its Report by addressing the highly controversial subject of Amenities. They had 'no doubt that the complaints which have been made and the fears which are entertained on the score of injury to amenity have been seriously exaggerated', and this finding was illustrated by several specific examples. Furthermore,

In the majority of cases the underdeveloped water resources of the Highlands are situated in the loneliest and most inaccessible parts of the British Isles. We venture to doubt whether many of them have been visited once in a lifetime by one person in a thousand of the population of the United Kingdom. To take an example which has been much discussed, in the whole of Glen Affric (over 12 miles in length) there are only 7 houses with an aggregate permanent population of 23 persons, consisting of 5 deer-stalkers and 2 gardeners and their respective households .... What is true of Glen Affric is true to a much greater extent of most of the resources of the farther West and North. The only persons who have seen many of them in their natural state and who would be able to praise or to deplore the changes which would be affected by their development would be a handful of deer-stalkers, salmon anglers, ghillies and gamekeepers, and the adventurous spirits who have traversed the mountain districts on foot.[17]

For all that, the Committee recognised that concern for amenities was both sincere and significant. Thus, on the precedents of past schemes, it was believed that 'all legitimate interests will be amply safeguarded if provision is made for the appointment of an Amenity Committee', and the imposition upon the new Board of a general obligation to have all reasonable regard to the preservation of the scenic beauties of the districts within which they were to operate. With a characteristic flourish, the Report ended:

If it is desired to preserve the natural features of the Highlands unchanged in all time coming for the benefit of those holiday-makers who wish to contemplate them in their natural state during the comparatively brief season imposed by climatic conditions, then the logical outcome of such an aesthetic policy would be to convert the greater part of the area into a national park and to sterilise it in perpetuity, providing a few 'reservations' in which the dwindling remnants of the native population could for a time continue to reside until they eventually became extinct.

But if, as we hope and believe, the policy to which this report is a small contribution is to give the Highlands and the Highlanders a future as well as a past and to provide opportunity in the Highlands for initiative, independence and industry, then we consider a few localised interferences with natural beauties would be an insignificant price to pay for the solid benefits which would be realised.[18]

3   The Reception of the Report of the Cooper Committee

Even *before* the publication of the Report of the Cooper Committee, Tom Johnston was busy attempting to ensure its favourable reception. Addressing representatives of the Association of County Councils and the Convention of Royal Burghs in November 1942, he outlined the main recommendations of the Report and fully explained the roles of the Amenity and Fishery Committees.[19] '*It is now or never for the Highlands*', he told them, and made it plain that if opposition came from persons interested in amenities and salmon fishing or from any other sources, it would be very difficult to put through any Bill to give effect to the recommendations. While to the Land President's Committee [on Post-War Reconstruction?], he wrote:

I believe that the best, and indeed the only, chance of solving this problem of hydro-electric developments in the Highlands which for long has been a matter of acute controversy is to take advantage of the substantial degree of national unity which now exists to pass the legislation to establish the machinery recommended by the Cooper Committee.[20]

Building on this good will, Johnston talked to people representing all shades of political opinion and every interest in order 'to make the Bill not only workable, but acceptable to the community.' With skill and good humour he attempted to disarm his most formidable antagonists, not least those Scottish peers whom he had, earlier in his career, lampooned in a series of scurrilous articles in *Forward*, by discussing with them all the points of the forthcoming Bill and explaining how its implementation would lead to the regeneration of the Highlands.[21]

Meanwhile, the civil servants in the Scottish Office, who shared Johnston's belief that the Highlands had long been unduly neglected, were seeking out both the source and precise nature of the potential opposition to the forthcoming measure in order to brief the Secretary of State and to prepare counter-arguments. At the end of October 1942, for example, Mr A J Aglen of the Scottish Home Department in London wrote to his colleague Mr D Milne at St Andrew's House, Edinburgh, that he had attended a meeting of the Electricity Commission at which

> Mr Halcrow was insistent ... that given a proper hearing it would have been possible to justify the Caledonian Scheme before the war to all fair minded persons. The proposals were, however, not given a hearing before a [Select] Committee and the promoters accordingly did not have the opportunity of demonstrating that legitimate objections had been met. He mentioned in passing that Inverness Town Council had employed three separate consulting engineers on three separate occasions in order to get a report against the scheme, but that none of the engineers had submitted an unfavourable report. He also alleged that the Town Council's real objection was not to the reduction in, and regulation of, the flow of the River Ness, but to the fact that the proposed carbide works were not to be situated in or near the Burgh.

Although Halcrow believed that attacks would come from Lord Belper, 'who has a shooting lodge at Glen Quoich', and from Mr Goodbody and Dr Barrow, of the *Inverness Courier*, 'real opposition would be from the Coal Owners' Association who are very powerfully represented in Parliament.'[22]

This could have been predicted. What was particularly disappointing was that the measured arguments and amenity proposals of the Cooper Report appeared to have failed to assuage the doubts of those who feared for the beauty of the Highlands, the purity of the crofters' life-style, and the sanctity of grouse and salmon. Members of the Cooper Committee were vilified in the press. One of them was told in a letter to the *New Statesman* that he should be taken to the shores of Loch Laggan where his nose should be held under the slime until he thought again. But what particularly upset Tom Johnston was that his 'old paper the *Forward* seemed to find hospitality ... for some sad, indeed inexcusable, attempts at sabotaging [the proposals] ... Great landowners and sporting *gentrice* who lived in London or the Riviera most part of the year, and saw amenity in the Highlands only along the barrel of a sporting rifle, joined hands with a half-baked Celticism which objected to selling any water power to the southern counties of Scotland, even at a profit.' Nevertheless, Johnston believed his preliminary work had placed the Bill 'outside partisan politics'. By the time that it was presented to the Commons, he had secured the support of 'the leading personalities in all parties, eight Cabinet Ministers, as its sponsors', including Sir Kingsley Wood, the Chancellor of the Exchequer.[23]

4   The Bill in Parliament

Tom Johnston moved the Second reading of the Hydro-Electric Development (Scotland) Bill in the House of Commons in February 1943.[24] He presented the measure as a 'partial remedy' for the illness that afflicted the Highlands. It was more than simply a means whereby the 'great latent hydropower' of the region could be harnessed. Its object was nothing less than bringing to an end that outward migratory flow by which 'the population was rapidly bleeding to death'. He told the Commons that he thought 'that industries, whether owned nationally, co-operatively or privately, will be, and ought to be, attracted to locations inside the North of Scotland area as a result of this Measure.' Of course, the ordinary consumers would have priority, but when their demands had been met, and those of the authorised undertakers and 'the hoped for and expected large power users', the surplus would go to the grid. It would be sold to the Central Electricity Board, and the profit arising would 'be used for reducing distribution costs and distribution schemes in the more remote areas [and] ''in the carrying out of ... measures for the economic development and social improvement of the North of Scotland district [Subsection 3 of Section two]'' '. This was the famous social clause which gave formal recognition to the fact that the North of Scotland Hydro-Electric Board was envisaged not simply as an organisation to provide electricity but as an instrument for the rehabilitation of Northern Scotland.

The Board itself was to consist of five members, four of whom, including the chairman and deputy chairman, who was to be the chief executive officer, were to be appointed by the Secretary of State for Scotland and the Minister of Fuel and Power acting jointly. The fifth member of the Board was to be nominated by the Central Electricity Board. Their first task was to prepare a general scheme or survey of the water power resources which it proposed to *examine* with a view to their possible uses for the purpose of generating electricity. This 'development scheme' was to be submitted to the Electricity Commissioners for their approval on technical grounds and then to the Secretary of State for confirmation.

Once approved, specific projects were to be selected from the overall development scheme and made the subject of 'constructional schemes'. These would set out in detail the nature and precise location of the various civil engineering works—for example, dams, aqueducts, tunnels, pipes and power stations—required for the exploitation of individual catchment areas, of which there might be, the Cooper Committee had estimated, as many as seventy. These too would first go to the Electricity Commissioners for technical examination. Each constructional scheme would then be made public and every opportunity afforded to the lodging of objections with the Secretary of State who would, at this stage, also consider whether the recommendations of the Amenity and Fisheries Committees concerning the scheme had been properly taken into account in its formulation. If the objections by the public proved to be more than simply frivolous, the Secretary of State was under an obligation to hold a public meeting. Only then was he permitted to confirm or to refuse to give his approval to the scheme. Should he find that the objections were of little or no substance, or that the benefits expected to be derived from the scheme were such that the public interest warranted overriding the objections, he could still confirm it, with or without amendment. After all this, every constructional scheme had to be laid before Parliament and if either House, within forty days, objected, the scheme was to be annulled.

Not without reason did Lord Alness, who was later to introduce the measure in the Lords, emphasise that he could not 'imagine a more exhaustive set of checks and safeguards' than those embodied in the Bill.[25] The controls imposed on the actions of the North of Scotland Hydro-Electricity Board were far more stringent and inhibiting than those envisaged by the Cooper Committee, who had sought to protect the Board from obstruction and sabotage by existing vested interests. Indeed, Lord Cooper was extremely concerned that the qualifications and safeguards would emasculate the Board, and was only convinced of their necessity by the arguments of Lord Weir.[26] The civil servants in the Scottish Office too were anxious to minimise the potential opposition. In drafting the Bill they were always conscious of the fate of the numerous abortive measures presented to Parliament in the 1930s.[27] It is not known what Tom Johnston felt about the political necessity of restraining the Board's powers but, if he did find the need for checks and Parliamentary safeguards frustrating, he made a virtue of necessity. 'Parliament, in my view, must be supreme', he told the Commons.

This assertion was not universally accepted. In contradiction to the member for the Pollok division of Glasgow, Commander Galbraith, who felt that the amount of control 'left to the House ... [is] far too slight' and that the authority given to the Secretary of State in making appointments to the Board was too great, several Scottish members sympathised with the arguments of Henderson Stewart, the Liberal National member for East Fife. Stewart was horrified at 'the pre-historic timidity' of the Bill:

> This new body is charged with one of the most hopeful tasks ever committed in peace-time to a body of Scotsmen, a task requiring drive, enthusiasm and dauntless enterprise. Yet see how this wretched Board is encumbered. Fifty-eight times in the course of the Bill it is instructed to refer its decisions to Government Departments, either in London or in Edinburgh, and in 32 of these cases permission and approval must be sought here in London before anything practical can be done .... Unless the Bill is altered the Highlands will certainly experience ... repeated, excessive and exasperating delays .... I have never seen such a bureaucracy-ridden Measure as this [in twenty years] .... This Bill is a veritable El Alamein of obstacles.

After several pointed thrusts at both pettifogging civil servants and jealous local authorities, whom he assumed had forced Johnston to compromise the clear recommendation of the Cooper Committee, he characterised the measure as a 'hotch-potch of Scottish Nationalism and English Socialism'. If it was enacted in its present form, he believed that the Act would positively encourage 'the conflicting interests of land-owners, coal companies, deer-stalkers and amenity enthusiasts on the one hand, and the Board, chemical industries, local authorities and the public on the other hand' to fight out every construction scheme with the same 'ruthless energy' as had been displayed on previous occasions. 'When I contemplate the prospect of 70 such miserable Debates in the House', he told the House with feeling, 'I am frightened at what I see ahead of me .... If we are not going to trust the Board to do the job for which it is being created, we have no right to set up a Board at all.' And he moved the Amendement that

> this House, recognising the vital part to be played by hydro-electric power in the regen-eration of the Highlands and the development of Scottish life and industry, which it regards as a major object of national policy, welcomes the proposal to establish a public service corporation in the North of Scotland for the generation and distribution of electricity from water power; but declines to give a Second Reading to the Bill which so circumscribes the powers and duties of the Corporation by bureaucratic controls and needless references to Parliament on details of its work that it robs the Corporation of freedom and initiative in the conception and prosecution of the undertaking (for the financial solvency of which it will be responsible) and will cause repeated delays in the performance of its tasks and unjustifiable postponement of the betterment of Scottish conditions.[28]

The Amendment was seconded by Stewart's fellow National Liberal, Sir Henry Fildes, the member for Dumfries.

Mr Malcolm MacMillan, the member for the Western Isles, would have none of this. With all its weaknesses, the Bill promised to do something to arrest the outflow of people from the Highlands and Islands. Like Tom Johnston, he illustrated his powerful speech with migration statistics covering every part of Northern Scotland. He attacked those who based their opposition to the Bill not on its fundamental principles but on details of administration; those who used the amenities issues 'to obstruct measures of this kind' either because of a 'sentimental Celtic twilightism' or because they were the unwitting tools of the landlords; and those who would postpone every decision 'until the war is over and normal conditions return'. And he appealed to the House to join with the supporters of the Bill to push it through. Among those supporters, he claimed, were the Scottish Office and even the Treasury:

> We may offer a prayer of thanks, very whole-heartedly, that on this occasion—how he did it I do not know—the Secretary of State got £30,000,000 to guarantee the development of the scheme.[29]

With these sentiments, the majority agreed, though there were some members who warned the enthusiasts that they should not imagine that the passage of this single measure would turn the Highlands into a Garden of Eden. Mr Pethick-Lawrence, member for Edinburgh East, reminded the House that the Cooper Report had said that 'it could not be guaranteed that everyone in Scotland, however far away from sources of supply, would obtain electricity',[30] and Commander Galbraith, with considerable prescience, expressed 'very considerable doubts as to whether the introduction of electricity into the Highlands [would] succeed in restoring them to prosperity or even succeed in attracting new industries from the better economically situated Southern areas, or that it [could] actually provide any great measure of employment.'[31]

Whatever misgivings were entertained of the measure, and there were many cogent criticisms in detail, it was patently believed that the Bill represented a unique opportunity 'to confer advantages not only on the Highlands but on the country as a whole'. The Lord Advocate having promised to amend the bill at the Committee stage so as to take account of many of the objections raised in the debate, Mr Henderson Stewart withdrew his Amendment, and the Bill was read a second time without a division.

It was the same in the other House where the Bill was introduced with remarkable lucidity by the ageing Lord Alness. In the Lords, the enthusiasm for the measure was even less restrained than in the Commons. One after the other, the peers praised Tom Johnston and expressed their support for the principles underlying the measure. Even those, like the Earl of Listowel, who thought that 'what will be achieved will probably be less than some enthusiasts believe' were prepared to accept that it would 'certainly do more than some of its gloomy critics would allow'. And even if it took many years to attract and establish the appropriate light industries, and to carry the distribution network to the isolated districts of the Highlands, as time passed 'an increasing number of farmers, crofters, lumberjacks and fishermen [would] enjoy for the first time the blessings of electricity in the home and [would] be able to face as never before the long darkness of the winter months.'[32]

Viscount Samuel, in a speech which predicted with remarkable accuracy 'the immense increase in international travel which is likely to follow in post-war years', expressed grave anxieties concerning the scenic beauties of the Highlands. He did not think that the Amenities Committee had been given sufficient power to prevent the desecration of the area, an argument that received support from Lord Hamilton of Dalzell who, as one-time chairman of the Galloway Amenity Committee, was able to speak from his own experience. 'I found at once that the powers of an Amenity Committee were so limited as to be almost futile', he informed the House, and he explained that the ruins of Doon Castle would have been submerged had it not been for the intervention, not of the Amenity Committee but of the Commission for the Preservation of Ancient Monuments. And he pointed, too, to what he regarded as the ruination of the Falls of Clyde in his own native county of Lanark. But such expressions of doubt were over-whelmed by goodwill towards the measure. Indeed some peers were disappointed that the Bill did not go far enough. Their spokesman was the Earl of Airlie who 'had hopes of something on a more far-reaching scale than this Bill':

> We had a greater expectation of power all over the countryside .... there are many things besides the production of electric power for industry. There is power for agriculture, forestry, fishery, tourist traffic, cheap transport, and many other things. These are all bound up with the prosperity of the country, and I have a feeling that two of them—cheap power and cheap transport—should be supplied by means of a flat rate.[33]

Lord Airlie emphasised the need for haste: 'People will not continue to be content with the conditions in the rural parts today'. And he argued that since it was implicit in private enterprise that the existing undertakings could not be expected to provide a comprehensive system of generation and distribution of cheap electricity in anticipation of demand, the State would have to do it. It was, as Lord Airlie himself acknowledged, a strange and unexpected intervention coming as it did from the Conservative side of the House, and it was not forgotten by Tom Johnston.

There was a final flourish by Lord Lovat. He appealed for the constructional work to be undertaken by the men of the Highland Division when they came home and not by Irish navvies, particularly not 'Glasgow imported Irish [navvies]', and told the House that to him power stations—which had been described by Lord Listowel earlier in the debate as being not altogether unattractive structures—had all 'the morbid attractions of the bearded lady of the circus'. But, as Lord Alness observed in his summing up, the Government had 'no reason to complain of the reception which [the] Bill ... received in [the Lords]'. Having promised that each and every proposal that had been made would be carefully considered before the Committee stage, he moved the second reading and, once again, the Bill was passed without a division. The debates had exhibited a greater amount of unanimity and goodwill than had been accorded to any major Scottish measure than anyone in either House could remember.[34] The passage of the bill through Parliament, everyone agreed, was a personal triumph for Tom Johnston.

CHAPTER 4

The Difficult Years of Infancy: The Board under Lord Airlie, 1943-1945

1 *The Creation of the Board*

The Hydro-Electric Development (Scotland) Act was passed in August 1943,[1] and the first members of the Board were appointed in the following month. In accordance with the Constitution, laid down in the First Schedule to the Act, the chairman, the deputy chairman and two other members were appointed by the Secretary of State for Scotland and the Minister of Fuel and Power acting jointly, and the fifth member was nominated by the Central Electricity Board from among its own members. Only the deputy chairman, who was to be the Board's chief executive, was required to devote his entire time to the duties of his office.

It must be assumed that Tom Johnston had a major influence on these initial appointments.[2] Certainly, those taking office had already revealed sympathy with the objects of the Board. Lord Airlie, the first chairman, had criticised the Bill that had brought the Board into being only because he felt that it did not go 'far enough'.[3] He had gone on to express the belief that only the State could achieve the wider objectives implicit in the Bill. Such a statement from a major Scottish landowner, an Old Etonian, Deputy Governor of the British Linen Bank, director of Barclays Bank and the twelfth holder of the Earldom, must have surprised many of his fellow Scottish peers, and even he felt obliged to preface his remarks by the disarming phrase 'strange though it may seem'. The more reactionary of his social circle were doubtless equally incensed by his tribute to Tom Johnston, 'not only [for] his work in regard to the [Hydro-Electric Development] Bill but [for] the work he has done throughout Scotland .... no one has got a move on more quickly in a short time than he has'.[4] To Lord Airlie it was a privilege to have been offered the chairmanship of the Board;[5] for Tom Johnston to have secured his acceptance was an act of great political sagacity.

For his deputy, Lord Airlie had A E MacColl. This appointment too was inspired. MacColl had considerable experience of hydro development. In the 'twenties he had been chief technical engineer to the Clyde Valley Company when the Falls of Clyde run-of-river scheme had been planned and instigated.[6] In 1927 he had been appointed Engineer of the Central Scotland District of the Central Electricity Board.[7] As such he was responsible for the creation of the first regional grid system in Britain. The Clyde Valley Electrical Power Company and Glasgow Corporation—by both of which organisations MacColl had previously been employed—owned supply systems which

50

were not interconnected although both employed a frequency of 25 cycles per second, whereas 50 cycles was standard in the rest of Scotland. One of the most important objectives of the Central Electricity Board was to standardise the frequency at 50 cycles throughout Great Britain. This would permit all generating stations to be interlinked in a national grid. MacColl's initial responsibility as District Engineer for Central Scotland was to organise the change of frequency in his area. This was accomplished so successfully that the methods adopted were later applied almost uniformly throughout the country.

MacColl was appointed Manager for Scotland in 1931. In addition to his work on the change of frequency, between 1929 and 1932 he was involved in the construction of the 132 kW grid lines and substations. In this task he worked closely and harmoniously with the staff of Kennedy & Donkin, the consulting engineers appointed by the Central Electricity Board to supervise grid construction and plant erection. His own staff meanwhile were principally engaged in acquiring wayleaves for the overhead lines and sites for the substations, a duty which frequently involved MacColl in delicate and complicated negotiations.

The commissioning of the grid lines and substations necessitated extensive testing and much ingenious improvisation, at which MacColl was peculiarly adept. The first section of the grid in Great Britain to be run commercially at 132,000 volts was that between Bonnybridge and Dalmarnock. This took place in May 1929. A year later, in April 1930, the Minister of Transport, Mr Herbert Morrison, officially inaugurated the Central Scotland scheme, and in November the 132 kW line between Rannoch Power Station and Central Scotland became operative. In the following three years the grid was extended to the South of Scotland, and the fact that the administrative and maintenance costs of the Scottish section of the grid were the lowest in the country was credited either to MacColl's own technical ability or to that of his staff, whose work in successfully overcoming manifold problems owed much to his interest and encouragement.

In the early years of his career with the Central Electricity Board, MacColl had been responsible for the negotiations with the Grampian Electricity Supply Co. which resulted in the purchase of bulk hydro-electricity for the grid. His interest in the development of water power was renewed when the western section of the South Scotland scheme was linked with the Galloway scheme. In 1936 while engaged on working out the detail of a scheme for the development of Loch Sloy, a small loch about 800 feet above Loch Lomond, he conceived the idea of going beyond his remit and proposing, not an orthodox scheme utilising Sloy's natural relatively small catchment area, but a massive pumped storage scheme. This would have drawn power from the grid to pump water from Loch Lomond, which would have served as the lower reservoir, up to Loch Sloy during the night. This water, supplemented by the run-off in Loch Sloy's catchment area, would then flow through generators installed in a power station on the shore of Loch Lomond during the hours of maximum daytime demand. This was a remarkably bold conception. The original design envisaged the use of eight turbine-alternator-pump units each of 45,000 kW capacity, the intention being to use this 'reversible hydraulic station' as MacColl called it, to supply the short peak load of the Central Electricity Board's grid system in Central Scotland. With a total installed capacity of 360,000 kW, it would have dwarfed all existing Scottish schemes.

It was too big a step forward. The Board's Technical Development Committee visited the site in 1937, further surveys of Loch Sloy's catchment were instigated, and the original plan was modified. The 'second edition of the scheme' called for a large extension of Loch Sloy's catchment area by means of dams and aqueducts. This would have increased by five-fold the amount of power available from rainfall and have permitted a reduction in the number of pumps in the power station from eight to four. But this modification also failed to satisfy the Board. MacColl was told to abandon the scheme, ostensibly because it was expected to be uneconomic.[9]

The survey of the water power resources of Scotland prepared by MacColl in collaboration with J Henderson and James Williamson for the Hilleary Committee received a similar rebuff. When the original report, complete with pages of detailed statistics, figures and maps, was submitted to the Central Electricity Board, it was rejected immediately.[10] With Henderson he had estimated the available water power in the Highlands, and with Williamson, a co-ordinated system of generation and transmission which would enable surplus electricity to be exported to Central Scotland.[11] The version that appeared as Chapter 13 of the Hilleary Report had been rewritten and was largely bereft of statistics. In this emasculated form it was later to be described by Lord Cooper as 'amateurish'.[12]

These setbacks to his ambitious plans greatly disappointed MacColl. A man who found control from above exceeding irksome, he particularly disliked intervention from London. He may have attempted to pass this off by explaining that the people from London with whom he had to deal seemed always to be very tall and, as a short man, he instictively tended to oppose their views, but there is no doubt of his fundamental resentment of any opposition to his cherished schemes.[13]

By 1937 MacColl had spent ten years with the Central Electricity Board; a decade of feverish activity which had culminated in the completion of the grid in South Scotland. His great engineering and innovative skills had been fully employed. The organisation which he had created had become a prototype for all other areas of the Central Electricity Board and during the next five or six years he became increasingly fretful. His job, he felt, had become a matter of routine, completely unsuitable for a creative engineer. This partially explains the energy with which he conjured up plans for exploiting the water power resources of the Highlands. London and the onset of war conspired to put a stop to them and condemned him to what he regarded as inactivity. He may have evolved elaborate contingency plans for implementation in emergencies but these, he felt, could equally well have been devised by an administrative engineer. He gave evidence to the Cooper Committee; his advice was sought in the framing of the consequent Bill, particularly in connection with the function of the Board. The relief and pleasure with which he must have received the invitation to become its deputy chairman and chief executive can only be imagined. At last his talents would once again be fully used.

He could now be confident that no major constraints would be imposed upon him by the other ministerially appointed members of the Board, Neil Beaton and Hugh MacKenzie, Provost of Inverness. Quite the reverse. Unlike the representative of the Central Electricity Board, Sir Duncan Watson, they had no technical knowledge,[14] and the entire Board were enthusiastic supporters both of public ownership and enterprise and Scottish self-determination.[15] Neil Beaton, chairman of the Scottish Wholesale Co-operative Society, was a close friend of Tom Johnston. He had been a member of the Cooper Committee and had offered tangible support to the attainment of the objectives of the Hydro-Electric Bill by promising that when electrical power was available the SCWS would 'plant industries in the Highlands'.[16] It must be presumed that Provost Hugh MacKenzie had either indicated a similar eagerness in his evidence to the Cooper Committee or that his appointment to the Board was dictated by political factors.

2   The Board's Staff and Advisors

For the first few months of its existence the Board's routine business was carried out by the civil servants of the Scottish Home Department. The first members of the Board's own staff did not take up their duties until January 1944, a few weeks before the Board took possession of their permanent offices at 16 Rothesay Terrace in Edinburgh. MacColl, who had considerable experience in building up new organisations, gathered a group of relatively young and committed engineers around him. As Chief Civil and Hydraulic Engineer he appointed Angus Fulton. A self-effacing but remarkable man, those who remember him testify to his intense enthusiasm, even fanaticism for hydro development. He is said to have made a contribution to the Board equalled only by 'old man MacColl' himself. Like MacColl, he was a driver of men.[17]

Not that the original senior members of the staff needed much driving: they were all caught up with the excitement of harnessing the water power of the Highlands and turning the Board into a commercial success. W Guthrie was taken on as Chief Electrical Engineer and David Fenton as Commercial Engineer. Fenton had been educated at George Watson's College, Edinburgh, and Edinburgh Univesity. His first employment was with Kennedy & Donkin, the eminent consulting engineers. He was a member of the staff of the Central Electricity Board in London from 1933 to 1938. He left the CEB a year after he had been called to the bar to become personal assistant to the General Manager of the Midland Counties Electric Supply Co., and it was from this post that MacColl recruited him for the North of Scotland Hydro-Electric Board. He was then 36 years of age.[18]

Another Scot, fully committed to the ideals of the new Board, was Thomas Lawrie. 'Much more than an electrical engineer, he believed in electricity as a great social service and he was determined to see the benefits of power taken to the remote areas in the North of Scotland'.[19] Lawrie was born in Laurencekirk, Kincardine, and was educated at Leighton Park School, Reading, and King's College, Cambridge. After engineering training in Scotland and the United States, he worked in the hydro-electric department of English Electric. He became engineer and secretary to the Power and Traction Finance Co. in 1927, and from 1930 secretary to the Galloway Water Power Co. and the Sudan Light and Power Co. After three years in the Royal Navy, he was released from the forces to become the Hydro-Board's secretary in January 1944.[20]

These four ambitious, energetic men, together with MacColl and A N Ferrier, the Chief Accountant, constituted the driving force of the Board in its infancy. It was, in the light of the magnitude of its objectives, only a small team and it was to be grossly over-worked. In retrospect, it has been argued that a more sustained attempt should have been made to recruit a number of the leading officials of the Grampian Electricity Supply Co. That this was not done initially was ascribed to Tom Johnston's detestation of private enterprise and to the reluctance of the Grampian Co. to let its senior men go.[21] Be that as it may, within a few weeks of its establishment, and even before the permanent staff took office, MacColl called five consulting engineers, all with considerable hydro-electric experience, to Edinburgh to discuss just how the Board could best fulfill its functions. These five consultants were invited to constitute the Board's Panel of Technical Advisers. They were W T Halcrow, later Sir William Halcrow, James Williamson, and J Guthrie Brown of Sir Alexander Gibb & Partners, on the civil engineering side, and J R Beard, Senior Partner of Merz & McLellan, and S B Donkin of Kennedy & Donkin, on the electrical and mechanical side.[22] If this distinguished group of consultants imagined that, having assisted in the initiation of the Board's activities, they would thereafter be consulted on an *ad hoc* basis, they were to be mistaken. The Panel of Technical Advisers was to become a permanent and indispensable part of the Board's organisation for the next fifteen years.[23]

But if the rôle of the Panel of Technical Advisers was wholeheartedly constructive, the two statutory Committees, the Amenity and Fisheries Committees, were potentially very inhibiting. Appointed by the Secretary of State within a few months of the creation of the Board, they had sufficient power if not to halt the Board's schemes at least to make their attainment both more difficult and infinitely more expensive. The objectives of the civil and electrical engineer were not likely to be congruent either with those of the environmentalists or with those of people whose duty and desire it was to look after the interests of the salmon. And there was an understandable anxiety that members of the two committees might use their position to fight a rearguard action on behalf of resident Highland lairds and absentee English estate owners who held properties solely for sporting and pleasure purposes. The criteria employed by Tom Johnston in selecting the membership of the two committees are unknown, but it must be presumed that those who were invited to serve were knowledgeable, highly respected, influential, and not unsympathetic towards the objects of the Board.[24]

Certainly, every attempt was made to secure their acquiescence in the forthcoming schemes, not least by the appointments of Mr W L Calderwood, who for over thirty years had been Inspector of Salmon Fisheries of Scotland, as Fishery Advisor to the Board, and of Dr John Berry as the Board's Biologist.[25] By retaining the services of these two eminent piscatorialists and taking their advice in the planning stages of the civil engineering works, the possibility of incurring insurmountable objections by the Fishery Committee was minimised. The same rationale dictated the creation of a Panel of Architectural Advisors consisting of Dr R Fairlie, Mr James Shearer and Mr H O Tarbolton, though it must be emphasised that their appointment was not entirely defensive: the Board genuinely wanted to make a positive contribution to the amenities and architectural heritage of the Highlands in a way which at the same time would contribute to the region's regeneration.

3   *The Development Scheme*

When the Board's Panel of Technical Advisers first met in October 1943, it soon became evident to this 'somewhat war weary group of Consultants that ... Edward MacColl intended to drive ahead at full speed and produce electricity in the North of Scotland at a much earlier date than anyone had visualised'.[26] The Board's first duty was to produce a Development Scheme showing the water resources in the area under its jurisdiction which might eventually be the subject of more detailed and operational 'constructional schemes'. Almost unbelievably the Development Scheme was completed within three months. Drawing heavily on the previous Report which, with the help of J Henderson and James Williamson, he had himself prepared for the Hilleary Committee, MacColl drew up a list of 102 possible areas for water power development. They ranged from minor projects like 'No 59:Loch nan Gillean (Plockton) and streams' with a potential annual output of 4 million units to 'No. 62:Rivers Affric, Cannich, Farrar, Glass and Beauly: 440 million units'. It was estimated that the total potential annual output—the summation of the individual schemes—was 6,274 million units, a much higher figure than had been suggested by any previous enquiry.

Every possible site, however small, had been listed and assessed. MacColl was clearly determined to avoid the possibility of being refused permission to go ahead with any scheme in later years because of a failure to include it in the 'Development Plan'. He wanted to keep every option open and there would probably never be such a favourable opportunity of 'staking a claim to a site', as it were, than in fulfilling this, the first of the Board's statutory duties.[27] The Development Plan itself is singularly uninformative. It consists simply of a list of possible projects, each one of which is numbered and 'approximately delineated' in an accompanying map. With the exception of 'approximate estimates' of the annual capacity in kilowatt hours of each of these resources, there are no figures, no cost calculations, no explanations: nothing, in fact, that could be seized upon and objected to. That the Board itself was conscious of the starkness of this important document is suggested by the inclusion of a number of end 'Notes', the first of which states that 'The Board are advised that the water power resources of their area are greater than previously estimated: they therefore consider it their duty to examine *the whole of their area* exhaustively', and the second that 'it will be understood that precise details ... of the position and size of power stations and other works do not form part of the Development Scheme: they will be included in subsequent constructional schemes'.[28]

Although the Board was giving no hostages to antagonistic members of Parliament, this did not mean that MacColl and his advisers had not drawn up the plan conscientiously. Indeed, Guthrie Brown of Alexander Gibb & Partners and the Board's Panel, was astounded by MacColl's 'detailed knowledge ... of the various areas and their value for water power development. It seemed as if he had walked over all the areas himself and assessed their potentialities ...'[29] Since no less than 22,000 square miles of country, much of it extremely wild and remote, was involved and as rainfall data was both inadequate and defective, it is improbable that at this stage more was done than to investigate the separate schemes in sufficient detail to allow the relative merits of the hundred or so distinguishable catchment areas to be assessed and compared, but it was enough. The Development Plan was approved by the Electricity Commissioners on 15 March 1944 and confirmed by the Secretary of State a week later.

4   Strangled at Birth?

The way ahead must now have seemed clear. Indeed, the first projects selected for 'constructional scheme' status in Perthshire, Dunbartonshire, Argyllshire and Inverness-shire were already being surveyed and planned in detail, and a start had been made on devising a number of distribution networks. But these manifestations of a healthy and vigorous birth were alost immediately to be jeopardised by a threat to the Board's very existence.

For some time before the war the belief had been growing, even among Conservatives, that the distribution of electricity needed to be reorganised. Whereas the generation and transmission of electricity had, since 1926, been dealt with by the Central Electricity Board on a national scale, distribution remained local and fragmented, co-ordinated only by regional groupings, joint municipal authorities or joint electricity authorities. These arrangements were increasingly perceived to be woefully inefficient. Herbert Morrison 'envisaged the establishment of a National Electricity Board, with regional boards controlling large distribution areas under the central direction of the NEB, and a National Consultative Committee on which both local authorities and consumers would be represented', and his proposals had been accepted by the Labour party in 1932.[30] The Conservatives, hesitating to go this far, persisted with unsuccessful attempts at reorganisation that would essentially leave unscathed the power of existing undertakings. Even the war failed to quell an insistent clamour for reform. The major political parties may have had different solutions but they both recognised the need for change initiated by Government action.

Thus, when the Coalition Government felt able to give some thought to post-war reconstruction, electricity supply constituted one of the problems on the agenda. It was the subject of a critical report by Sir William Jowitt in August 1942 which was sufficiently convincing to induce the War Cabinet's Reconstruction Committee to set up a Sub-committee on the Electricity Industry to consider the many positive suggestions that had emerged. This, in turn, led to the creation of another sub-committee under the chairmanship of the Minister of Fuel and Power, Major Gwilym Lloyd-George, whose remit was to put forward definite proposals that could be embodied in legislation. The Lloyd-George committee presented its report to the War Cabinet Reconstruction Committee in December 1943. This recommended that 'generation should come under the national control of a Central Generating Board modelled on the CEB and that there should be 14 regional distribution boards on the public corporation ... model, with national co-ordination being through a central authority and an Electricity Advisory Council consisting of the board chairmen, and chaired by the Minister ... [who was] to have powers to give general directions on [such] questions [as] the simplification of tariffs, the extension of electricity service to rural areas' and the extent to which investment should be tailored to other aspects of national economic policy.[31]

All this was deeply disturbing to Tom Johnston and to the senior civil servants in the

Scottish Office. These new proposals conjured up the very real possibility that the North of Scotland Hydro-Electric Board could lose its independence, even its existence, in the event of legislation on the lines recommended by Lloyd-George. Steps were immediately taken to 'reserve the position [of] the North of Scotland District both on the side of generation and on that of distribution', and Tom Johnston sent a memorandum to Lloyd-George requesting that

> the powers and duties of the [Hydro-Electricity] Board ... and the relationship of that Board to the Secretary of State for Scotland should remain unimpaired; and that any transfer of the generating or distribution functions of existing undertakings in the District necessitated by a decision to transfer undertakings elsewhere to a Central Generating Board or to Regional Distribution Boards should be to the North of Scotland Board

Reference was made to the Cooper Committee, 'upon whose Report the [Hydro-Electric Development (Scotland)] Act is based', and it was pointed out that the Cooper Committee had 'carefully considered whether the functions now vested in the Hydro-Electricity Board could be entrusted to the Central Electricity Board, but [had] rejected the idea on the grounds that Highland problems 'call for a different policy and outlook from the rest of the country''. It was emphasised that 'The Government accepted this view .... [and that] the arguments which led to this decision in 1943 have lost none of their force'.

So far as distribution was concerned,

> it seems equally undesirable ... to set up a new distributing body in the North of Scotland District. Moreover, the existing Hydro-Electric Board, which has, of course, distributing functions already outside the areas of supply of existing authorised undertakers, is comparable in status and organisation with the Regional Boards proposed by the Sub-committee and there is no apparent case for superseding it by a new Board of the same kind.

Indeed, argued Johnston, moving from defence to attack, a strong case could be made for extending the Board's area in both generation and distribution so that it covered the entire North of Scotland.[32]

Lloyd-George's response to this memorandum was diplomatic but uncompromising:

> In considering proposals for re-organising the whole of the electricity supply system of this Country, we had in mind in a general way the same kind of problem as you were handling in the Highlands; in other words we feel that the development of power for the many services that it can perform has hitherto been seriously held up by the existing system of electricity distribution. In particular the agricultural districts in the whole of Great Britain have suffered considerably from that system of distribution ....
>
> In a sense therefore I think it may be said that you have led the way and that we are following the example you set of a publicly appointed Board for controlling the distribution of electricity in a specified area. If you will look at Appendix D of my Committee's Report, you will see that the North of Scotland is suggested as Area No. 1 and that there will be 12 other similar Areas for the rest of the country.
>
> On the distribution side ... I do not think there is any fundamental difference between us, but I am afraid I cannot say the same about the generation side .... the Members of my

Committee were convinced that ... it is most desirable that all forms of generation of electricity for public use should be brought under common control. I regard it as one of my main duties, as Minister of Fuel and Power, to co-ordinate the fuel and power resources of the country. [However electricity is produced] it should be under the control of one Central Generating Board ... on the generation side, efficiency demands unification ... If you are prepared to accept this general principle, I have no doubt that we could go a long way to meet local sentiment in the North of Scotland by arranging for a special Sub-committee of the [Central Generating] Board, composed largely of representatives drawn from the locality, to deal with purely local aspects of the problem.[33]

Tom Johnston immediately composed a reply. This accepted that 'there need be no difficulty in using the Hydro-Electric Board as the distributing authority in the first of the 13 areas' suggested by Lloyd-George's Committee, but was adamant that 'there is a fundamental difference between us on the generating side'. Lloyd-George had to accept the fact that although the main function of the North of Scotland Board was to generate and distribute electricity, it *is much more than an electricity body*'. Johnston was

quite satisfied that a central generating board of the kind suggested by your Committee would not be able to command the confidence which the new Board has secured and that if it were to replace that Board on the generating side all the old controversies and difficulties would come to the surface once more.

And he warned Lloyd-George, 'any proposal to scrap or mutilate the present Board by taking away the generating power so recently conferred upon it by general agreement in Parliament would I assure you rouse a tremendous and all party protest'.[34]

Lloyd-George would not budge, but he was prepared to be conciliatory. 'I need hardly say', he wrote on 22 April, 'that I am anxious to meet your point of view as far as I possibly can ... so far as distribution is concerned, I do not think that there should be any difficulty'. But when he came to generation, he acknowledged that 'the position is ... more difficult'. And he made a number of suggestions none of which represented any real departure from his belief that 'the resources of this country should be regarded as a whole, and that, in the interests of national efficiency, there must be some adequate machinery for securing proper co-operation between every organisation in the country engaged in the generation of electricity'.[35]

Johnston was totally unconvinced by Lloyd-George's arguments and unimpressed by his apparent concessions. Indeed, the more he thought about it, the more threatening he found Lloyd-George's recommendations to be. With the assistance of his private secretary, C C Cunningham, and A G Aglen, of the Scottish Home Department in London, he drafted yet another response. 'Your proposals ... would ... drive a coach and four through the whole conception of the Act of 1943' he wrote.

... the North of Scotland Board would lose its distributing functions altogether and there would be no assurance either that the new Regional Distribution Board for the Highlands would co-operate to the same extent in the economic development of that area or would be able to obtain current at a price which would make it possible to develop distribution or supply new industries in the remote areas of the Highlands and Islands. The ... Board would also lose the general control of generation in the North of Scotland District ... and the financial advantages which it hopes to derive from that control ....

Johnston's counter-proposal, doubtless equally unacceptable to Lloyd-George, rested on the recognition that 'Parliament had already created in the North of Scotland District a Public Board comparable in type and function to the proposed Central Generating Board and Regional Distribution Board and has given it the duty of developing both generation and distribution ... with a view to the economic development and social improvement of that area'

> That being so, I think it is both reasonable and appropriate that the North of Scotland Board should be given, in respect of the North of Scotland District, the functions proposed to be given elsewhere to the Central Generating Board and the Regional Distribution Boards .... I do not think that in such an arrangement there need be any lack of co-ordination[36]

A deadlock ensued. It was to be left to the successors of the protagonists to take action during the early years of Attlee's first post-war administration. Meanwhile, the future of the Board was problematical. It is not difficult to imagine a weaker, less committed Scottish Secretary, giving up the struggle or fatally compromising the principle upon which the Board had been based. Tom Johnston had fathered the Board. It was perhaps his proudest creation. He was determined to fight for its survival.

But while Johnston, infinitely experienced in Parliamentary tactics and methods, was working behind the scenes (for all these negotiations had been conducted with utmost secrecy), MacColl, increasingly mistrustful of London and the machinations of English politicians, pushed ahead with all possible speed. To him it was imperative to begin to build, to begin to harness the water resources of the Highlands, if only to try to ensure the future of the Board. If the dams were put up, no one—not even a London-based Member of Parliament—could tear them down.

5   The First Constructional Scheme: Loch Sloy, Winter 1944-1945

It was almost inevitable that of the projects enumerated in the Development Scheme, the first to be the subject of a Constructional Scheme was Loch Sloy. It possessed numerous characteristics that might advantageously be exploited for hydro-electric development and, of considerable importance, the site had already been exhaustively investigated for that purpose. MacColl and James Williamson already had a scheme. Freed from the constraints that had previously bound him, what was more natural than that MacColl should resurrect Loch Sloy?

The loch itself was small and shallow, less than a mile of peaty water lying 780 feet above sea level in a valley to the west of Loch Lomond overshadowed by the peaks of Ben Vane (3,004 feet) and Ben Vorlich (3,092 feet). The area around Loch Sloy was a jumbled mass of rock and mountain. There were no houses and no cultivated ground in the whole of the catchment area which received a high rainfall, estimated to be 115-

120 inches in an average year. What made the site particularly favourable for the provision of water power was that the loch was capable of providing high level storage, streams that could readily be diverted to increase the reserve of water, a rocky gorge where there was a suitable site for a dam, level ground nearby on the shores of Loch Lomond, on which to erect a generating station, and—highly unusual in Scottish hydro-electric development—there was no fishery problem. Loch Lomond itself could accommodate very large inflows of water without its own level being materially affected. Furthermore, hidden from the hills above Loch Lomond only by the smoke of large factories, lay the industrial area of Clydeside constituting a major market for the power.

It was proposed to provide this power from water stored in a reservoir to be created by damming Loch Sloy and by enlarging the catchment area of the Loch to an area of 27.6 square miles by means of an elaborate series of aqueducts and stream diversions. The water was to be led by tunnel, two miles in length, through the heart of Ben Vorlich to emerge at a point about a quarter of a mile above Loch Lomond, whence it would be carried down the eastern face of the mountain by four steel pipelines to a power station at Inverglas Bay on Loch Lomond. In the power station it was proposed to install four vertical shaft Francis turbo-alternators with a total capacity of 130,000 kilowatts.

This was 'a straightforward plain hydro-electric' scheme;[38] it possessed none of the 'reversible hydraulic' features of its predecessors,[39] neither was it as big. Although the installed capacity would make it the largest of all the Scottish hydro schemes, it fell far short of the adventurous 360,000 kW pumped storage scheme of 1935. Why had MacColl apparently abandoned his original scheme?[40] Was it that the Central Electricity Board's earlier objections had convinced him of its unsuitability? Was it that the Electricity Commissioners—whose duty it was to examine the scheme before its submission to the Secretary of State—had made it known that they would not approve a mammoth pumped storage scheme? Was it that the anticipated post-war demands for electricity were expected to make the use of scarce power for night time pumping operations impractical in the immediate future? Or was it that MacColl, impatient to begin construction and conscious that his sophisticated reversible hydraulic scheme might be subject to delays that would be avoided by the adoption of a 'straightforward plain' scheme, chose the latter in the interests of haste? David Fenton has pointed to the contradictions inherent in MacColl's own character: 'He would fight like a tiger for the rights of the Board, and then for some inexplicable reason he would give away far more than seemed reasonable at the time'.[41] Fenton himself did not elaborate on this observation, but perhaps the decision on the form taken by the Sloy scheme exemplified this characteristic?

Whatever the explanation, it was a perfectly orthodox scheme which formed the centre-piece of the Board's Constructional Scheme No.1. In addition to Sloy this included two lesser projects, at Loch Morar and Kyle of Lochalsh, designed to supply the local requirements of the areas in which they were situated.[42] The cost of carrying out these three projects was estimated at £4.6 millions, of which £4.1 millions was attributable to Sloy. The reason for linking these very different projects can only be conjectured. It must be presumed that, like Sloy, the detailed planning of Morar and

Lochalsh was either completed or relatively advanced in 1944 and that, by presenting them for confirmation in the same constructional scheme, the Board intended to demonstrate their readiness to fulfil their statutory obligation to supply remote areas with current despite the fact that 'there is no prospect that they will pay their way'[43]. Politically and tactically it was of overwhelming importance that the selection of Sloy as the first large scheme was justified. *Simply* to have argued that it was, as Lord Airlie was later to say, 'a bread and butter scheme', able to produce a substantial revenue for the Board with which to finance unremunerative projects *in the future*, would have raised all the old spectres of exploiting the Highlands for the benefit of those in the Central Lowlands or, even worse, in England! To have dwelt too long on the appeals of the Central Electricity Board for power for the grid, however desirable for the public interest, would have revived all the wrath of the Scottish nationalists, for whom power from the glens should stay in the glens whether there was a demand for it or not. Sloy *had* to be coupled with two manifestly uneconomic projects in order to attain the major objective: a scheme so remunerative that it would carry some part of the burden of the lesser generating works enumerated in the Development Scheme and of the frightening costs of distribution in remote areas.

This, then, was Constructional Scheme No.1. The Amenity and Fishery Committees were consulted and approved it *in principle*;[44] in June 1944 it was welcomed by the Electricity Commissioners. Submitted to the Secretary of State for confirmation, it was then published. 'After the manner in which the Act had in 1943 been passed by agreement of both Houses', Guthrie Brown wrote later, 'it had been reasonable to hope that the days of bitter criticism of every hydro-electric scheme produced in Scotland were over. Not so however, ... the scheme produced an unexpectedly large amount of opposition'.[45] Although no objections were made to the schemes at Loch Morar and Lochalsh, Loch Sloy aroused all the old animosities. Formal objections were lodged with the Secretary of State on behalf of the County Council of Dunbarton, the Clyde Valley Regional Planning Advisory Committee, the Joint County Council of Perth and Kinross, the County Councils of Perth and Inverness, and a number of private individuals. There was no alternative but to hold an Inquiry.

This was held in Edinburgh, under the Chairmanship of Mr John Cameron, KC, at the very end of the year. It proved to be protracted and acrimonious. In making his Report at the end of the proceedings, Mr Cameron felt obliged to express his regret 'that this, the first Public Inquiry under the ... Act [of] 1943, should have taken a full six days'. And he appealed for guidance as to the constraints that should be placed upon the scope of such inquiries in the future. As he said, interpretations of 'the public interest' differed widely and he had experienced 'some difficulty in fixing fair and reasonable limits to the investigations'.[46] The vagueness inherent in the Act on this point was ruthlessly exploited by the counsel for the objectors, who seized every opportunity to emasculate the Board and inhibit its future activities.

The Board itself made mistakes born of inexperience, enthusiasm and impetuosity, and had it not been for Mr Cameron's sympathetic handling of the Inquiry, might have experienced a most demoralising setback. In submitting their Scheme, dated 13 June 1944, the Board had indicated a specific site for the proposed power station and pipe line for the Loch Sloy project, but so hurriedly had the plans and drawings been drawn up that it was only after their publication that the Board began serious investigations of the proposed site which borings revealed was quite unsuitable. Ten days before the opening of the Inquiry, the Board issued new documents containing certain 'amendments', one of which involved shifting the proposed site of the power station by half a mile! Seizing upon this remarkable alteration, Dumbarton County Council and the Clyde Valley Committee moved for an adjournment of the hearing, ostensibly to enable them to examine the implications of the change. This was refused by Mr Cameron. Although the change of site was within the very wide limits of deviation allowed to the Board and therefore legally unexceptionable, the Chairman criticised the Board for taking refuge in this technicality: 'In my view the Board should be scrupulous to avoid a situation in which it would be alleged, even colourably, that they had failed to place their projects fairly and fully before the public as enjoined by the Statute'.

Another problem arose as a direct consequence of the Board's haste. Negotiations with the Ministry of War Transport over the diversion of the Loch Lomond Trunk Road necessitated by the site of the power station were still in progress when the Scheme was published. No agreement had been reached and the possibility existed that the Ministry would refuse permission for the diversion to take place. Mr Cameron felt that it was 'unfortunate that the Board had not taken steps before putting forward a Scheme for confirmation, to assure itself that there is no room for reasonable doubt that the requirements of other Government Departments can be met.'[47]

This potentially disastrous start seriously undermined the confidence of the Board's representatives: Lord Airlie, who was to be the first witness, was severely shaken. However, the Dean of Faculty, Mr R P Morison, KC, appearing for the Board, retained his composure and in his opening speech put with remarkable clarity, the Board's case for proceeding with Construction Scheme No.1.[48] Although there may have been unfortunate errors in the original presentation of the Scheme, there were few in the evidence presented by the witnesses, all of whom were well prepared and thoroughly convincing.[49] What could not have been anticipated was Mr Hill Watson's appeal to the Cooper Report to argue that the Board had erred in not beginning their series of Constructional Schemes with a project to develop the water resources of Easter Ross in accordance with a specific paragraph in that Report. Mr Cameron, envisaging interminable disputes over the priority to be accorded to the hundred or more projects listed in the Board's Development Scheme, refused to permit this line of cross-examination: 'The permutations and combinations of the projects listed in the Board's Development Scheme are almost limitless, and disputes once entered upon would become endless'.[50]

Although the Perth and Kinross Joint County Council, and the County Councils of Perth and Inverness withdrew their opposition during the course of the Inquiry, the remaining objectors of the Loch Sloy Scheme pursued their case tenaciously. Every one of the Board's witnesses was subjected to gruelling cross-examination. Great play was made with the Central Electricity Board's inclusion of Loch Sloy in their generating programme for 1947 *in anticipation* of a successful outcome to the Inquiry, and numerous possible alternatives were canvassed, including much less 'financially extravagant' steam stations. But the principal objections put forward by Dunbarton County Council was that the waters of Loch Sloy should be reserved for the domestic and industrial needs of the county. Subsidiary pleas of lack of adequate specification of the Board's plans and intention, and of interference with the amenity of Loch Lomondside were also advanced, but, in the words of Mr Cameron, 'only as makeweights'. The objections on grounds of amenity were not pressed. They related mainly to the pipe-lines and to the power station, and were rapidly disposed of. Mr Cameron could

> see no reason why a power house *per se* should be a disfigurement of the landscape. It is not as though Loch Lomond and its banks were untouched by the hand of man: indeed in this very area the blank and undistinguished visage of the Inversnaid Hotel is a constant reminder of the needs of man and the means he has adopted to satisfy them.[51]

The fundamental issue, as stated by the County Clerk of Dunbarton, was that the Council 'must have Loch Sloy as a security for its future development of water necessities'.[52] The substantiation of this claim necessitated a detailed survey of what these needs were likely to be and the resources available to meet them. Inevitably, the evidence was highly technical. It involved estimating future demographic trends; some heroic assumptions about the post-war industrial and shipping needs of Clydeside; and a consideration of the country's 'grandiose' housing schemes. The County's plans and projections were so optimistic and so speculative that Mr Cameron believed that it would be unwise to expect their complete fulfilment. That being so, he was forced to conclude that the County of Dunbarton had more than sufficient water to meet their needs, even if Loch Sloy were denied them. He was particularly critical of the County Council's 'uncompromising attitude':

> An offer by the Board ... to permit the County Council to draw off a proportion of the stored water from the [Sloy] reservoir was firmly rejected both by the County Clerk and the County Water Engineer. For them it is all or nothing. I cannot help feeling that, had the County's case been stronger and their needs more real and pressing, this offer would not have been so summarily refused.[53]

After carefully considering the evidence and written submissions, Mr Cameron decided that the objectors had not succeeded in overturning the Board's claim that it was in the public interest that the Constructional Scheme should go ahead, and he recommended that it be confirmed by the Secretary of State. Tom Johnston willingly did so and, after lying before Parliament for forty days, the scheme became operative on the 28 March 1945.

6 The Second Constructional Scheme: Tummel Garry, 1945

(a) The Public Inquiry

If the public inquiry into Sloy was difficult and unnerving, that into the Second Constructional Scheme was infinitely worse. The Scheme itself embraced two projects: Tummel-Garry and Gairloch, the latter being a small undertaking for the development of a catchment area of 13 square miles in Ross and Cromarty, which raised no objections. The Tummel-Garry project had three principal features. The first was the impounding of the waters of the upper tributaries of the River Garry and a stream known as the

Errochty Water by means of a dam situated in Glen Errochty, the impounded water being led by a tunnel and pipe-line to a power station near the head of Loch Tummel. The second was the impounding of the waters of Loch Tummel, the River Tummel and tributary streams by means of a dam across the River Tummel situated about one and a half miles *above* the Falls of Tummel. These waters were to be conveyed by tunnel and pipeline to a power station—to be known as Clunie—situated *below* the Falls of Tummel. One consequence of this part of the scheme would be to raise the level of Loch Tummel by 17 feet and substantially lessen the flow of water over the Falls of Tummel. The third feature of the project was the erection of a dam, incorporating a power station, across the River Tummel at Pitlochry. This would create a reservoir above the dam which was intended to enable the Clunie power station to be developed as a peak load station. Without such a dam there was a very real risk that the lower reaches of the River Tummel would be damaged by the fluctuating mass of water that would otherwise have passed down the river. In other words, the Pitlochry dam would create a balancing reservoir which would even out the variations in the river beyond it. By incorporating a power station, it would, at the same time, contribute substantially to the total volume of electricity generated by the overall scheme. It did mean, of course, that that part of the Tummel immediately above Pitlochry dam would cease to be a river in the strictest sense of the word and would assume the nature of a loch whose contents were constantly being changed.

Essentially, what the Board sought to do in this large, ambitious and ingenious scheme was to take advantage of the vast storage capacity already existing in the reservoir at Loch Ericht and to exploit the potential power of the 700 million gallons of water a day passing into the River Tummel from the Grampian Power Company's Tummel Bridge tailrace on its way down to Pitlochry, water which would otherwise have run to waste so far as its generating capacity was concerned.[56] The Tummel-Garry scheme was designed for a capacity of 150,000 kW: 16,000 kW of this would be installed at the Pitlochry power station, which would operate at an annual load factor of 40 per cent; 57,000 kW at Clunie, with an annual medium load factor of 22 per cent; and 75,000 kW at Loch Tummel (later called Errochty), which was designed to be run intermittently at a low load factor of 12 per cent. Loch Tummel was essentially a peak load station intended to meet heavy daily demands for short periods. The total cost was estimated at £6,174,000, or £41 per kilowatt installed. The civil engineering works alone would absorb £5 million. Tummel-Garry was avowedly a revenue-earning undertaking, profit being made by supplying energy to the Central Electricity Board (particularly to meet peak load demands on their Central Scotland grid) and to two authorised undertakers, the Grampian Electricity Supply Company and the Corporation of Aberdeen.[57]

The effect of the determined opposition to the Loch Sloy project had greatly disturbed the Hydro-Electric Board, and grave misgivings were entertained concerning the prudence of pressing forward with Tummel-Garry at this time. It was, everyone agreed, certain to be bitterly opposed. MacColl, however, had no doubts. The power which Tummel-Garry was capable of generating was much needed, and the scheme, by being economical, would produce the revenue with which to finance the smaller, loss-making projects. Furthermore, if Tummel-Garry could be pushed through, the opposition to future constructional schemes might be reduced. 'It was a bold decision to take, but it was typical of MacColl. If there was to be a fight to enforce the principles of the 1943 Hydro-Electric Development Act, then, in his opinion, the Board should go all out and settle the issue once and for all'.[58] There must have been times during the ensuing furore when the wisdom of these tactics was seriously questioned.

The Board even failed to convince the Amenity and Fisheries Committees. When they were consulted, the Amenity Committee, by a majority of three to two, recommended that the Pitlochry reservoir and generating station be omitted from the scheme, while the Fisheries Committee was unanimous that the Board should forgo the proposed diversion of water from the upper Garry and its tributaries, except the Errochty. The Board would accept neither of these recommendations.[59] The only unambiguous support for the scheme came from the Central Electricity Board and the Electricity Commissioners, who gave it their formal approval on 7 February 1945. It was then submitted to the Secretary of State and published. There was, as anticipated, an immediate commotion. No fewer than twenty five objections were lodged with the Secretary of State and, as Tom Johnston later recalled, 'many newspapers ... opened their columnms to strings of vituperation from the letters–to–the–editors brigade; fantastic and ridiculous imaginations from beauty lovers, some of whom saw in their visions the Highlands being converted into an amalgam of a Black Country, a rubbish heap and a desolation; commercial salmon interests, anglers, and hoteliers, whose business they foretold would be ruined, all cried aloud in protest.'[60]

The formal opposition was led by the County Council of Perthshire, the local riparian owners and the inhabitants of Pitlochry, who were so antagonistic that the Board's engineers, completing their detailed surveys, were ostracised and denied accommodation at all but one of the hotels in the neighbourhood. The fact that this hotel was owned by an Irishman only reinforced the prejudices and fears of the local community. So great was the outcry that Tom Johnston deemed it expedient to appoint a *tribunal* to hold the necessary enquiry: on this occasion Mr John Cameron was supported by Sir Robert Bryce Walker, CBE, DL, JP, and Major G H M Brown Lindsay, DSO, DL, JP. The inquiry was held in Edinburgh during the closing stages of the European war. It began on 25 May 1945 and lasted ten full days. The transcript of the proceedings, which ran to 1,188 foolscap pages, records in minute and graphic detail the battle over the Tummel-Garry scheme, in the course of which was prophesied the ruin of the scenery, the anihilation of the salmon and the extinction of the tourist trade.

The Dean of Faculty, Mr R P Morison, KC, sought to deflect the most telling criticisms of the scheme in his opening address. He emphasised at the outset that 'as a non-profit-making statutory body with public rights and public duties, this Board has no concern but to promote the public interest. The Board has no sectional interests to serve. It has no selfish motives to pursue ...'.[61] But in carrying out 'the specific duty which Parliament has imposed upon it', the Board had 'got to balance its budget'. This could *only* be achieved 'by the supply of electricity to the Central Electricity Board [from] schemes which are necessarily economic and supply electricity at a profit'.[62]

In his sustained attempt to secure the Board's position from the anticipated assault, the Dean of Faculty made the point that 'in no sense are the Board obliged ... to accept the recommendations of [the Amenity and Fisheries] Committees. [They] were not appointed for the purpose of dictating to the Board what the Board had to do, they were appointed ... for the purpose of giving advice and assistance to the Secretary of State and the Board'. The Dean was particularly anxious to diminish the impact of their recommendations that certain features of the scheme br omitted. To do so, he asserted, would wreck it:

> the three stations are to a large extent interdependent. If Pitlochry were omitted Clunie would have to run up a uniformly steady load by day and a similar smaller load at night, and therefore it could not meet the peak demands during the day for electricity. The consequence of omitting Pitlochry accordingly would be that the revenue of Pitlochry would be lost and the revenue of Clunie materially reduced. The consequence of that would be the delay, and partial suspension of the development of the West Highlands and Isles ... [Similarly] it is impossible to exclude the tributaries of the Garry and the Garry itself from the scheme... the Errochty itself only taps some 22 per cent of the catchment area. The Garry and the other streams amount to 78 per cent of the available catchment area, and [therefore] it would not be at all an economic proposition to do without the Bruar, the Dail-na-Mine and the Edendon Water, and the suggestion that Errochty should be abandoned would result in the taking away of the only large power storage in the scheme.[63]

The fact was that the Board had to obtain and sell as many kilowatts as possible. Unless it was permitted to do so, it could not provide for the ordinary consumers in the Highlands, to supply whom was necessarily uneconomic. Hence the overwhelming necessity for Tummel-Garry. 'There is no other available source of power, steam or water, which could deliver the output of the Tummel-Garry scheme at a lower cost. ... It is intended too, if the project is approved to link it up with the Fannich scheme. And the Tummel-Garry scheme will thus form what might be called the backbone of the development of the whole of the Board's area'.

Of those who argued that the Board should begin with Affric and Quoich and not go to Pitlochry, the Dean was particularly scathing:

> That, of course, is the old cry, 'Go anywhere you like, but for heaven's sake don't come to us', but it is quite inappropriate that the Board should develop Affric and Quoich for the purpose of financing other economic schemes. They are too far away, the cost of transmission is far too great to bring the electricity to the Central Electricity Board grid, and in any case it seems most inappropriate that current available for the development of the Highlands in the North should be taken to the Lowlands. The proper policy ... must be ... get your economic schemes in the South where the cost of transmission to the Central Electricity Board is not great, and then you get an economic scheme with sufficient revenue to supply and finance the uneconomic schemes in the North part of the Board's area.

This was, of course, the essence of the Board's scheme. To the Dean of Faculty, the public interest demanded that it be approved, but because the opponents of Tummel-Garry had been 'so tireless in their propaganda and versatile and vocal in their objections; because every point, good, bad or indifferent, that could possibly be stated against the scheme [had] been stated with the greatest of emphasis and with endless repetition', he had no alternative but to devote considerable attention to a denial of the allegations of those who claimed that the amenities of the district would be irrevocably damaged, the tourist trade impaired, and the salmon fishings destroyed. It was a powerful statement, knowledgeable, subtle and convincing, but its impact on the tribunal must have been somewhat diminished by the Board's first witness, Lord Airlie.

Lord Airlie, Tom Johnston commented in his memoirs, possessed a sensitive nature, 'he had not been hardened to public controversy interlaced with personal malediction'.[64] For months before the Public Inquiry he had been subjected to ill-informed criticism and vicious abuse. It had got under his skin. He was nervous, and his anxiety was made all the more intense by the inability of his deputy, Edward MacColl, the Board's chief executive, to give evidence. MacColl had been ill and, following an operation, was not fit enough to go into the witness box.[65] It is apparent that Lord Airlie felt exposed and particularly vulnerable to technical questions. Certainly, he came out of his first period of cross-examination, which lasted many hours, rather badly. At times he was made to seem indecisive and ill-prepared. He fell into a number of traps set by Mr Hill-Watson, the foremost of his tormentors, who managed to create the impression that the Board *could* have gone to Affric or Quoich and that the Cooper Committee may have *expected* the Board to do so. Lord Airlie was made to look as if he was dancing to the tune of the Central Electricity Board in providing power for England at the expense of Pitlochry;[66] and his inability to conjure up the numerous statistics demanded of him and his understandable reluctance to publicise the adverse vote of the Amenity Committee, interpreted as deviousness or even dishonesty.[67] Mr Hill-Watson had a field day with the artistic impressions of the valley of the Tummel and of Pitlochry after the completion of the works. These were drawn by Frank A Wemyss, a member of the staff of Sir Alexander Gibb & Co., the principal civil engineering consultants, and displayed by the Board at the Inquiry. Lord Airlie was taunted unmercifully about them:

> Who is Frank A Wemyss?... We cannot find him. He is not a well known artist; he is not registered in any of the artists' societies so far as we can find out. Who is he? So far as you know he might not have been in Scotland at all?

Having milked this line of questioning dry, Mr Hill-Watson continued caustically:

> They [the impressions] seem to be all of them taken from the air? ... If the artist was in an aeroplane they perhaps might look something like that, but you could never see that if you are a human being on your two feet?... Are you going to erect an enormous pillar for people to stand on?

So it went on, to Lord Airlie's great discomfort. He became increasingly agitated and confused, and finally blurted out: 'Personally I do not like these things being done any more than you do; I am a lover of the countryside, but I believe this is to the advantage of the public as a whole, and therefore I am bound to support it'.[68]

It had not been a good day for either Lord Airlie or the Board. It was redeemed only by the sheer clarity of the Dean of Faculty's opening address and Lord Airlie's early statement that

> Quite frankly we think we have come to the parting of the ways, the point of decision. Do the people of this country want electricity or do they not? ... Our remit was to do what

we could ... to try and develop the generation of electricity by hydro-power ... we feel we have come to the point ... where the interest of amenity and fishing have perhaps to give way to the larger issues. That is our honest opinion[69]

By the next morning, Lord Airlie had recovered his composure. Asked if the Board was 'presenting this proposal to the Tribunal as a test case and whether the interests of amenity and fishing are to give way to the electrical interests?', he replied, 'No, I would not say [that], it is presenting this scheme because ... it is the right scheme at the right moment ... The fact that it may prove to be a test case is another matter'. Indeed, Lord Airlie was sufficiently confident to criticise the counsel for the parochial nature of their questions. 'You are promoting a scheme which will ... confer no benefit whatever on Pitlochry?', he was asked. His reply emphasised the benefit to the North of Scotland and Islands and to every woman in the countryside: 'if you offer them some of the amenities that their brothers and sisters have got in the towns you then will find that their country instincts will lead them to desire to stay where they are, but if you do not give them water, transport, housing and power, I do not think they will'.[70]

After the horrors of the opening day of the inquiry, it was a brave performance. Lord Airlie was followed into the witness box by a galaxy of technical experts. Sir John Kennedy, one of the Electricity Commissioners, emphasised that the Commissioners were 'not trying to tie up this Board in very tight leading strings' but, as the loan-sanctioning authority, the Commissioners had to satisfy themselves that the schemes put forward would show satisfactory financial results. The Tummel-Garry scheme not only met this test but promised to alleviate the critical power shortage anticipated in the near future, a point confirmed by J D Peattie, Deputy Chief Engineer to the Central Electricity Board. Peattie was followed by James Beard, senior partner of Merz and McLelland, James Williamson and Thomas Lawrie, who gave evidence in place of Edward MacColl.

Lawrie was in the witness box for the equivalent of two whole days.[71] Questioned on every aspect of Tummel-Garry, many of the points put to him were probing, repetitive and occasionally savage. Lawrie was imperturbable. A sustained attempt was made to get him to agree that Affric was a possible alternative to Tummel-Garry, but he would not budge. He steadfastly predicted, against all the odds, that the scheme would attract not repel visitors: 'I am told that the Tennessee Valley Authority have two million visitors a year'.[72] J Guthrie Brown was equally self-possessed. Revealing a complete mastery of the civil engineering works and the economics of the scheme, his answers were illustrated by a mass of statistics. He positively enthused over the minimum flows of water expected at various parts of the scheme, referring to their volume in terms of cusecs. 'What is this curious word?' asked the chairman. 'It really means cubic feet per second ... I am afraid it is the way that most engineers work in hydro electric matters'. 'You can call them 'grand Llamas' if you like, so long as I know what they mean', Mr Cameron testily responded.

Guthrie Brown was followed by members of the Royal Scottish Society of Painters in Water Colours; hotel proprietors; architects; surveyors; and, above all, piscatorialists and biologists. All testified either to the benefits expected from the scheme or to the Board's conscientious efforts to minimise any damage that might be inflicted on their various interests. The Board's Fishery Adviser, Mr W L Calderwood, and Biologist, Dr John Berry, spent hours explaining the most esoteric features of the life cycle of the salmon, the nature of their spawning beds, their food, their ability to pass through turbines without damaging themselves, and the methods used to count them. They discussed the relative merits of different types of fish passes and fish ladders; the conclusions of experiments carried out at Imperial College; and the inadequacies of the biological data available to the Fishery Committee.[73]

Not until the end of the sixth day of the Inquiry did the witnesses for the objectors have their say. They were led into battle by Provost McGlashan, the essence of whose case was that such was the relatively small proportion of the *nation's* generating output to be supplied by Tummel-Garry—0.79 of 1 per cent—that Perthshire was being asked to pay too high a price for this small addition to the national supply, especially when the Tummel area already made a substantial contribution through the Grampian Power Company.[74] He was followed by an army of fishery experts, architects, civil engineers, hoteliers, youth hostelers, preservationists and environmentalists, no less well qualified than the Board's witnesses, who predicted the imminent destruction of the amenities 'of an area which is said to be and known to be the most beautiful in Scotland'. 'Could the Board not go elsewhere?', they chorused. To Affric? To the remotest parts of the Highlands? To a steam station? After all, Tummel-Garry will only save 120,000 tons of coal. Once again, hours of evidence were devoted to the needs of the salmon: dozens of smolts would be torn apart by the Francis and Kaplan turbines; they would never climb the fish ladders, and if by some strange chance they did, they would find their spawning beds ruined. Mr. William Malloch, Chairman of the Tay Salmon Fishery Board, so vehemently contradicted Mr Calderwood and Dr Berry that he provoked the Chairman into the observation that 'It seems to be a very uncertain business being a fishery expert, is it not?'[75]

A 'sinister plot' was uncovered on the penultimate day of the proceedings. It became apparent from the evidence of the chairman of the Council of the National Trust for Scotland, Sir Iain Colquhoun, that a number of persons had gifted certain of the waterfalls of Scotland to the National Trust, expressly to prevent the 'Board getting at them for hydro-electric purposes'. This was certainly the case with the Falls of Tummel, whose previous owner, Dr George Freeland Barbour, proprietor of the estate of Bonskeid, explained that he felt 'the National Trust would be in a better position ... to ensure that the amenity would be injured as little as possible'[76]

Finally, after nine exhausting days, the eminent King's Counsels made their closing speeches. Inevitably, there was nothing new in what they said, they simply reiterated their most telling points. Mr Hill-Watson concentrated on the iniquity of the Electricity Commissioners who, in insisting that the Board develop 'bread and butter schemes' such as Sloy and Tummel-Garry, were arrogating to themselves powers which were not even contemplated in the 1943 Act. And he went into the economic basis of Tummel-Garry, showing that on an expenditure of some £7.5m the Board would make a 'profit' of only £86,000. 'Would any reasonable businessman invest such a sum for a return of a little over 1 per cent?', he asked.[77] The scheme was grotesquely uneconomic, yet its implementation would wipe out the Tay Salmon Fisheries, destroy the tourist trade and ruin the amenities of Pitlochry. It was not as if the Highlands would benefit, only 350 houses in Gairloch would receive electricity, the rest would be exported! What would the soldiers say when 'they return and find in place of the beautiful Clunie Bridge a contractor's plant in operation near Pitlochry, the river about to be flooded and the position entirely altered, the beautiful confluence of the Garry and Tummel completely destroyed; they may wonder very much who were the people responsible for the vandalism ... which has been created'[78]

If Counsel for Perth County Council and others combined vivid imagery with statistics, Mr T B Simpson, KC, for the National Trust for Scotland, was sarcastic and malicious. He poured scorn on those 'sending out little expeditionary forces to sell in remote West Highland glens the idea that they must have electric cookers', and on those who were preparing to destroy Pitlochry, in a truly Prussian manner, by erecting along their artificial loch 'a seat every fifty yards, a police notice every hundred, and a restaurant every half mile'. And he concluded by adding two lines to a well-known stanza 'written to describe 1745, but it might have been written to describe 1945':

> Cam' ye by Atholl lad with the philabeg,
> Doon by the Tummel and banks of the Garry,
> Saw ye the lads with their bonnets and white cockades,
> Leaving their land to follow Prince Cherlie
>
> Saw ye the lads with their cusecs and kilowatts
> Leaving the rivers defaced by Lord Airlie[79]

Nothing could have been more calculated to wound the Chairman of the Hydro-Electric Board. Nor could Lord Airlie have derived comfort from Mr J L Clyde, KC, representing the Association for the Preservation of Rural Scotland. Mr Clyde drew attention to the fact that 'the Association did not oppose the Loch Sloy, did not oppose the Morar scheme, and does not oppose and is not opposing the Gairloch scheme', but that they feel they *must* oppose Tummel-Garry, largely because the Board had not seriously looked for an alternative to this area of great national beauty. 'They say they are compelled to go into an area already adequately supplied with electricity and to erect works which will do nothing at all for that area but will afford a means of selling electricity immediately at a remunerative price to the Central Electricity Board'. And even that was doubtful: 'If the coal price goes down in the future, the Tummel-Garry scheme won't be remunerative. If the coal price goes up, then the profit made from Loch Sloy will increase and they will get their remuneration there'. The case for Tummel-Garry could not be sustained:

> Mention has been made of a development scheme, a development scheme which quite obviously is just a collection of the dreams of hydro-electric engineers. There is no coherent scheme or policy at all. Lord Airlie, and indeed Mr Lawrie, admitted in the course of their evidence that they had no integrated development policy. They just looked round, they saw what they regarded as a plum in the Tummel and Garry valleys, and they decided to go ahead ... Mr Lawrie admitted that there were other bread and butter schemes but he had not examined these in detail. He admitted that he had never communicated any of the other alternatives to the Central Electricity Board, and Mr Peattie on behalf of the Central Electricity Board ... said that he had not considered alternatives to the Tummel-Garry

Scheme as a means of getting electricity. No alternative was ever communicated to the Electricity Commissioners, and the Electricity commissioners came here and told you that they had never considered any alternative to the Tummel-Garry scheme. The fact is ... that alternatives have never been critically examined at all, but the greedy eyes of the Board have concentrated on this plum and they just disregarded the whole of the rest of the tree ...

And they had done so, concluded Mr Clyde, in order to meet the demands of the Central Electricity Board and to appease the Electricity Commissioners.[80] The price would be paid by Pitlochry. Mr Gordon Thomson asked the Tribunal to contemplate the Falls of Bruar 'with one-tenth part of the water trickling over them and you will then be able to imagine that substitute for natural beauty which Lord Airlie proposes to introduce to that district'.[81]

Finally, after ten days of bruising and acrimonious exchanges, the Dean of Faculty, Mr R P Morison, closed for the Hydro-Electric Board. Eschewing the 'wealth of literary allusion and lyrical rhapsody which characterised some of the speeches of [his] learned friends', he concentrated on the 'plain broad facts' which established the scheme as being in the public interest. Indeed, 'even although damage to the amenities and damage to Mr Malloch's fish are established they cannot outweigh the paramount public interests of national considerations provided by the supply of uneconomic areas and the national electricity position'. There was, he affirmed, 'no other project which can produce the same output at the same cost by the same time ...There will be change, but the charges of vandalism or desecration so freely used in the evidence and the arguments of my learned friends are gross exaggeration .... the essential beauty of hill and mountain, river and loch in this district will remain unimpaired ... there is no ground of apprehension that the tourist custom in exsistence of Pitlochry will diminish or that the livelihood of the inhabitants of Pitlochry will be impaired'. And he concluded:

> We are at the parting of the ways, but of course my learned friends have intrepreted the phrase parting of the ways in numerous ingenious fashions which were never intended by Lord Airlie ... I submit that the rejection of this scheme means a very certain delay and a partial frustration for ever of the electrical development of the Highlands, in particular the inestimable benefit of electricity for the small people, the small consumers who live in isolated areas and who receive, very properly, the first priority under the Act. That is the first national interest. The second is the grave difficulties of future supply of electricity in Central and South Scotland[82]

It was now up to the tribunal. Their report, anxiously awaited, almost completely vindicated the Board. After reviewing the evidence in detail, they concluded that 'a case of sufficient urgency has been made out to overcome the objections which have been maintained against the Constructional Scheme and that it is in the public interest ... that the scheme should be confirmed'.[83] The seriousness of the objections was not denied. Each of them was carefully examined and judged in the light of the public interest. Of agriculture, for example, the tribunal were satisfied 'that there will be no substantial interference with the balance of agriculture in the district if this scheme were confirmed, and that the total acreage of land capable of being cropped or used for pasture which will be submerged is negligible in the light of the larger issues involved'.[84]

The tribunal believed therefore that the case against the scheme rested upon an assessment of its effects upon amenities and fisheries. While accepting that some loss of beauty would result from a substantially diminished flow of water in the upper Garry above Struan, and that the Falls of Bruar, the Falls of Struan and the Falls of Tummel would also be adversely affected, losses such as these would be 'a small price to pay' for a project 'which will bring the amenities of life where few existed before' and inject new energy into the straths and glens of the Highlands'.[85] Nor would the possible damage to the fisheries, which was the subject of such acute divergence of expert opinion, 'be so great as to operate as a bar to the ... generation of electricity'.[86] Furthermore, the tribunal found that 'no suitable alternative hydro–electric scheme is available or could be brought into effective operation within a comparable period'.[87] Nor would the tribunal sanction the recommendations of the Statutory Committees on Amenity and Fisheries that certain parts of the Board's proposals should be abandoned: 'We are satisfied that acceptance of [their] recommendations would entirely emasculate the Scheme ... [which] must stand or fall as a whole'.[88]

(b) *The Scheme before Parliament*

In accordance with the recommendation of the tribunal, an Order confirming the Scheme was made under Section 5 (5) of the Act which created the Board. This Order was to lie before Parliament for forty days. If during that period either House was to resolve that the Order be annulled it became of no effect. After the unambiguous decision of the tribunal, the Board must have entertained the hope that Parliament would simply acquiese but, if so, they were to be disappointed. On 14 November 1945, Willilam Snadden, the member for Perth and Kinross, moved a Prayer in the Commons for the annulment of the Confirmation Order. All the old animosities were reawakened; all the familiar arguments, so recently and exhaustively investigated, were paraded. What had taken ten days in Edinburgh was compressed into four crowded hours in Westminster. The opposition to the scheme seized upon the setting aside of the recommendations of the Amenity Committee, the very committee 'specifically appointed for the very purpose of giving us adequate protection against the destruction of amenities ... the bulwark against ... engineering irresponsibility'. 'When this deed is done the beauty of the heart of Scotland will be forever broken', Snadden predicted. It was, he said, 'too stiff a price to pay even for power ... it was never the intention of Parliament, in giving powers to the Board, to allow them to endanger a countryside so lovely and so famous'. He painted a horrifying picture:

> Whether we like it or not, we have to admit that a complete breakthrough has been achieved by the Board's mechanised forces, and ... there is nothing whatsoever to stop them fanning out over the whole of Scotland, like a gigantic squadron of bulldozers ... and eliminating everything, including statutory committees and local authorities ... all that is necessary is for the Hydro-Electric Board to get a certificate from the Central Electricity Board to the effect that they are short of power. When they have got their certificate they can push through any scheme, because then it is held to be in the public interest to do it ... No part of Scotland is now safe, and any further inquiries will be a waste of time.

Snadden appealed to the House to regard the Order as a 'great test case, not only for the Hydro-Electric Board but for other people. We know that the statutory committees are as dead as the dodo. No county councils in Scotland are powerful enough to oppose this scheme, and all inquiries are a farce and a waste of time ... it is clear that far more oppressive powers than were ever intended have been given to this all-powerful corporation. It is our duty to refuse to approve the scheme'.[89] Colonel Gomme-Duncan, the member for Perth, in seconding the mention, developed this theme, emphasising that 'What we have to decide tonight boils down to this: shall Parliament be paramount in this matter, or the Electricity Commissioners?', and he continued by predicting the ruin of the fisheries, the devastation of Central Perthshire, and the diversion of water supplies from agriculture, afforestation and housing. But above all, he was afraid of the government, and he quoted with approval the words of Donald MacPherson, the Leader of the Labour Party in the Highlands: 'The country is today virtually in the hands of engineers thinking only in terms of concrete, machinery and volumes of water.'[90]

Other members of the House reinforced these points. The horrors of Lochs Laggan and Treig were described; the use of Highland power to benefit the Lowlands repeatedly critised; the damage to the fisheries was a constant theme, and the tyrannical powers of the Electricity Commissioners endlessly discussed. Indeed, Henderson Stewart, the Liberal National member for East Fife, felt that the Hydro Electricity Board was being treated as 'merely another power station for the Central Electricity Board', that 'power lay not in the Highlands but in London', and that Lord Airlie, of whom he was 'ashamed', should resign his office immediately, 'in view of the pressure put upon the Board':

> I am appealing on behalf of those ordinary folk in the Highlands who expect this Bill to give them light and heat and warmth, but who have been defrauded. This is a test case. If we pass this particular scheme, and in so doing give our approval to this domination by the Electricity Commissioners of the activities of the Board, I am certain that it will be regarded as a precedent, and will be followed, in scheme after scheme. The Board will go on seeking profitable schemes, will go on submitting to the demands of the Central Board for more power; and the cause of the Highlands folk will go on being neglected.'[91]

But while the Board was being accused of timidity towards the Electricity Commissioners, it was being castigated for its maladroit relations with the local authorities which were said by Alexander Anderson, the member for Motherwell, to be so dictatorial, unconciliatory and tactless that the Board had brought upon itself much of the opposition to which it had been subjected.

Lord Airlie, who was listening to the debate, had to derive solace from the arguments of those in favour of the Order, but there is no doubt that he was deeply hurt by the nature of the attacks upon the Board and upon himself. He received some consolation from Malcolm MacMillan, the member for the Western Isles, who lambasted 'the Sussex Highlanders ... the fellow who comes up to the Highlands of Scotland once a year, or once in two years, to do a spot of hunting and fishing, like an elegant Eskimo' and who was constantly bleating about the amenities of the Highlands. The Highlanders cannot live upon scenery and amenity alone, MacMillan reminded the House. They

needed 'full employment, a sure livelihood, and a decent standard of living', which
hydro-electricity might go some way to providing.

> It will be a blessing when we can supply the domestic users with electricity, so that I shall
> see, before I leave this House, the time when it is not necessary for women in the Western
> Isles to go out cutting peat and carting it home—a burdensome and primitive toil—in
> order to get fuel for their homes. I hope to see the day when the people of the Western
> Isles will no longer have to use paraffin lamps, with all their dirtiness and expense and
> danger of fire, especially to children[92]

Other members took the same line. To Mr Thomas Cook, the member for Dundee,
one of four making their maiden speeches in the debate, 'All this question of amenities
is so much balderdash'. He claimed that 100,000 people in Dundee had signed petitions
in favour of Tummel-Garry, and he asked the

> Members to look at the progress of Scottish history and to think of the beautiful scenes.
> One can go to Ullapool and see the beautiful crofts on the side of Loch Broom, lovely
> things, with white-painted walls and red roofs, with aching hearts inside them; women
> compelled to plough and furrow the land while the men go and do jobs at sea, grubbing
> for a living. All as a result of this so-called amenity and nothing else.
>   We have to have a true perspective of what we mean by amenities. If we mean the right
> of deer-stalkers to pay £50 for guns and to hire and 'fire' gillies as a seasonal occupation,
> let us have it. If we mean also that these same salmon fishers should be hired and 'fired' in
> a seasonal occupation in the cause of amenity, all right, then, let us have it ... I am trying
> to show what amenity has meant to the Highlands of Scotland—glens darkened, villages
> depopulated ... All those people who talk about amenities have never travelled further than
> Pitlochry; they ought to extend their visits a good deal further'[93]

And, as a one time employee of the electrical industry, Mr Cook stressed the great
need for additional electrical power, as did Alexander Anderson and the Joint Under-
Secretary of State for Scotland, George Buchanan.
    But perhaps the most lucid and telling speech in favour of the Order was that by
Colonel Errol, the member for Altrincham and Sale, who suggested in his maiden
speech 'that the Scots ought to realise what a very good bargain they are getting out of
this scheme. They do not seem to realise ... that the Scottish Lowlands and England are
going to pay for cheap power for the Highlands'.

> The scheme is so arranged that the Lowlands and the much-maligned Central Electricity
> Board are going to take all the surplus power which is produced, and the profits from the
> sale of that power will be used for financing uneconomic schemes in the far North of
> Scotland .... Furthermore, as and when development in the Highlands is stimulated, so can
> the Highlands draw more and more from the Tummel-Garry scheme and reduce the
> amount supplied to the Central Electricity Board. The Highlands therefore get it both
> ways; in the initial stage when it is uneconomic, and in the later stages when they are able
> to take more power . .... Finally ... this scheme produces a link-up with the Fannich scheme
> and with other schemes further off still. These are some of the good bargains which the
> Highlanders will get out of this scheme.

Col. Errol, with considerable prescience, also suggested that 'it is at least a moot point that the amenities of the River Tummel will not be improved by its being changed into a winding loch', and that those who disagree and will no longer visit the area might well be outnumbered by those who will come to see the engineering works themselves. He also reminded the House that

> everybody connected with the scheme is a Scot. The Hydro-Electric Board members are all Scots. The tribunal were all Scots. The civil engineering consultants are Scots. Although not entirely a Scottish firm, the partner concerned with the scheme is a Scotsman. These men are not combining together to do irreparable harm to the Highlands. They have come out in favour of the scheme and it would be a great mistake if we overturned their decision too lightly[94]

In the end, the Prayer for the annulment of the Order was overwhelmingly rejected by a vote of 248 to 63, but whether the vote in favour of Tummel-Garry would have been quite so high in the absence of the Whips is problematical.

Since Lord Kinnaird, who had intended to move the annulment of the Order in the House of Lords, was persuaded by Lord Westwood to postpone his motion, the Tummel-Garry scheme became operative from the 19 November 1945. Even this brought but temporary relief to Lord Airlie. Although the date for annulment was past, Lord Kinnaird insisted on introducing a debate in the Upper House on the operation of the Hydro-Electric Development Act, 1943. Tummel-Garry was, he said, a test case which would determine all future developments under the Act and, as such, it must be fully debated. And so it was, on 22 November and 3 December 1945.[95] Although few new arguments emerged during its protracted course, the debate did permit Lord Airlie to set out the case for Tummel-Garry and to explain the nature of the Board's policy and the constraints to which it was subject. Numerous references were made to the relationship between the Board and the Electricity Commissioners, the Central Electricity Board and the Amenity and Fisheries Committees. Much of the criticism of the policies underlying the Board's Second Constructional Scheme turned upon precise interpretations of the 1943 Act; what was said by Tom Johnston in introducing the bill; and the recommendations of the Cooper Committee.

The Lords' discussion was less acerbic than that of the Commons but its legalistic tones could not disguise the passionate beliefs of the participants. The amenities and fishery issues were nicely balanced by a profound fear of the powers of the State. This, of course, was not novel. Where the noble Lords gave a new slant to the topic was in their advocacy of atomic power. Where the attitude of the defenders of Pitlochry had been 'Go anywhere but do not come here', the position taken by many of the Lords was 'Don't develop hydro-electricity *at all* because it has been superseded by atomic power'. The words of the Earl of Rosebery were typical:

> I think it would be ghastly to find in three years' time, when the Tummel-Garry scheme has taken the water away from the Tummel and the Garry, that there was no need whatever for the Hydro-electric Board[96]

It was left to Lord Westwood, the leader of the House, to emphasise that 'the development of atomic energy as a source of power is a matter for the future, whereas the need for the production of additional electricity is an urgent and present necessity',[97] and for Lord Airlie to point out that

> If atomic energy is harnessed to produce power for domestic or industrial use it will ... be harnessed in the form of heat. In order to produce electricity that heat would still have to be employed in raising steam in boilers and the whole paraphernalia for the production of electricity would remain as it is today. Consequently, even if that atomic fuel were to be free of cost, the Tummel–Garry Scheme would still be more economic.[98]

Like much else of what Lord Airlie said, this too was regarded with considerable scepticism, but even bitter opponents of the Tummel–Garry scheme and of the Hydro-Board acknowledged that Lord Airlie's speech on the 20 November had been 'eloquent ... sincere, fair, frank and forceful'.[99] And at no point had Lord Airlie been more earnest than when he said:

> I am satisfied in my own mind, as is my Board, that this so very controversial scheme is vital to the provision of electricity in the Board's area, and that there is no alternative scheme which will be either so suitable or comparable in efficiency, and that in the best interests of the Highlands it is right that it should have been allowed to go forward ... I sympathise with [all the opponents of the scheme], and I think I can claim to do so because I am connected with the land myself in some measure. I clearly recognise that the Board must do everything it can to mitigate any defacement of the countryside. Believe me, I have given this matter heart-searching thought by day and by night. It is not an easy row to hoe being Chairman of this Board. But I am confident that it will not be destruction that we shall see but change, and though that change may possibly not commend itself to all who know these places as they are now, yet to those who come after, in forty, fifty or sixty years time, it really will be as natural as the railways and telegraphs are to us today'.[100]

Nevertheless, this did not save Lord Airlie from venomous attacks in the resumed debate two weeks later, particularly from the conservative peer Lord Rushcliffe.[101] While more moderate, Lord Lovat was particularly incensed by the 'unfortunate remark' of 'the noble Earl's second in command, Mr McColl ... when he said recently in Edinburgh that all that stood in the way of the Hydro-Electric Board were salmon and amenities'. And he made the point that

> Do not let anybody think that the Highlands are going to become repopulated and revived by an influx of generating stations. That is wholly false. Industry on a heavy scale will never come to the Highlands, because it is common sense that it is easier to bring current to industry than industry to current[102]

In the end, after Lord Westwood had stoutly defended the actions of the Board and Lord Kinnaird had had his final say, the latter's 'motion for papers' was negatived. The Board had survived. It seemed that it could now concentrate on fulfilling the function for which it had been created. Indeed, during the course of the Lords debate, Lord Westwood mentioned that all the objections to the Board's third constructional scheme, the Fannich project, a development of the upper waters of the River Conon in Ross-shire, had been withdrawn after negotiations between the Board and the objectors. This scheme had the full approval of the Amenity and Fisheries Committees and was before Parliament at the time of the debate in the Lords. But there was one more blow to come.

7   Findhorn-Duntelchaig

Detailed planning of what became known as the Duntelchaig scheme had begun in the summer of 1944.[103] Loch Duntelchaig formed a natural high level reservoir about 640 feet above Loch Ness and less than two miles from it. Although the catchment area of Loch Duntelchaig itself was relatively small, it was believed that it could be greatly enhanced by water from the River Findhorn. If a dam was built on the Findhorn below Tomatin the water in the Findhorn would be maintained at a suitable height for it to flow by gravity, via a tunnel, into Loch Duntelchaig. In addition to the generation of power (the annual average output was estimated at 120 million kWh), the scheme would, it was believed, bring certain incidental benefits. A dam at Tomatin would help to control the exceptionally severe floods which occasionally ravaged the Findhorn. At the same time, a reservoir at Loch Duntelchaig could be a source of compensation water which would naturally supplement the deficient flow of the river during times of drought. Furthermore, if the two tributaries on the right bank of the River Nairn were tapped to feed into the tunnel from the Findhorn to Loch Duntelchaig, compensation water would also be released down the River Nairn in times of drought. If the level of Loch Duntelchaig was raised, the Loch would form the source not only of water power for the Board but of water supplies for the Burgh of Inverness.

These features made Duntelchaig a most attractive project and every effort was made to secure its approval. The Amenities Committee was fully consulted and the Board's adviser, W L Calderwood, carried out intensive research into the fishery aspects of the scheme. These left him 'fairly well satisfied, although not entirely free of anxieties'. Certainly, the Board's detailed proposals took full cognisance both of his recommendations and those of the Fisheries Committee.[104] To avoid those accusations of undue secrecy which had bedevilled many of the Board's earlier activities, all the proprietors of lands and fishings affected by the scheme were kept fully informed.[105]

In April 1945, Lord Airlie addressed a joint meeting of the Town Council of Inverness and representatives of the Board, to whom he submitted proposals for the joint water supply and water power development of Loch Duntelchaig. These proposals were confirmed and amplified in a letter sent to the Town Clerk of Inverness in July in which it was emphasised that the Board's plans could be 'the means of saving the Council a very considerable capital expenditure on water supply'.[106] It was to no avail. The Town Council of Inverness would have none of it. 'They want[ed] Loch Duntelchaig entirely for themselves'.[107] There is no doubt that the Town saw Duntelchaig as a source of pure water, whereas the Board's scheme envisaged delivery of a constant supply of 'not so pure' water at Loch Ashie that would involve purification treatment;[108] but it is difficult not to believe that Inverness Burgh Council were partially motivated by a detestation of the Board's activities and by a desire to strike a blow for the protection of the

Highlands against Lord Airlie's 'bulldozers'.[109] Consequently, the Council promoted a Provisional Order under the Private Legislation Procedure (Scotland) Acts to develop Loch Duntelchaig solely as a water-supply scheme. This left the Board no alternative but to appear as objectors to prevent the loch's hydro-power potential from being 'sterilised'.[110] In the event, the Joint Parliamentary Commissioners, meeting in Edinburgh, found the Preamble proved, thus giving the Council exclusive powers to utilise Loch Duntelchaig. There was no appeal and the Board relunctantly decided to abandon the scheme.[111]

8   The Departure of Lord Airlie

It was a bitter blow to the Board. For Lord Airlie it was the last straw. The venomous personal criticism to which he had been subjected during the struggle for Tummel-Garry had left him shocked and dispirited. Now Duntelchaig, which was to have been the Board's sixth constructional scheme, had been lost. The future seemed to be one of wearisome acrimony. Many of Lord Airlie's former friends refused even to speak to him, regarding him as an enemy of his class. He was prepared to tolerate this behaviour, believing that the Board's policy would finally be vindicated, but 'when the abuse began to be spread over his relatives (his son was blackballed from membership of the Perth hunt), he felt he had had enough'.[112] He determined to resign and, with his colleagues on the Board, began to look around for some new figure who could be persuaded 'to attract the forked lightning from the vested interests'.[113] Not until Tom Johnston had agreed to take on the task did Lord Airlie depart. He did so with characteristic dignity, expressing regret that other public duties made his resignation necessary, and extending a warm welcome to his successor, whose 'appointment had given the Board such pleasure'.[114] He could not have known that the Board was about to experience over a decade a remarkable growth and achievement, and to establish itself in the affections of the people of the Highlands, but even had such an unexpected turn of events been clear to him, it is doubtful if he would have stayed on. He had done his work. Under his leadership the Board's future course had been clearly charted. He had never doubted the correctness of the Board's policies. To have been the first Chairman of the Board was for Lord Airlie an honour and a privilege:[115] that was reward enough.

CHAPTER 5

Setbacks Overcome: The Board under Tom Johnston and Edward MacColl, 1946-1951

1 Tom Johnston as Chairman

In his autobiography, Tom Johnston claimed that he accepted the chairmanship of the Hydro Board only after some persuasion from Neil Beaton, Sir Hugh McKenzie, Sir Duncan Watson, and his own successor as Secretary of State for Scotland, Joseph Westwood,[1] but it is difficult to believe that he put up much resistance. As the political architect of the 1943 Act, he was fully committed to the objectives of the Board and it is patently clear that in the negotiations on post-war reconstruction he had done everything in his power to secure its continued existence.[2] The 'perverse and fatuous antagonisms' engendered by the early constructional schemes had distressed him, and his fears for the future of the Board were heightened by the loss of Duntelchaig.[3] If he could become the focus of attacks upon the Board, he reasoned, the engineers might be permitted to get on with the dams and the power stations.

Although it is unnecessary completely to accept the retrospective rationalisation of a politician's behaviour, especially one with as much guile as Johnston, there is little doubt that at this critical stage of the Board's development, he *did* see himself as fulfilling the functions of a lightning conductor. He could bring little or no technical or economic expertise to the Board, but he did possess enormous political experience and a consummate ability to achieve his objectives. Furthermore, his unswerving integrity of purpose 'commanded the whole-hearted respect of his political opponents as well as of his colleagues in the Labour movement'.[4] It could not be doubted that he believed passionately in the benefits that the development of Scotland's hydro-electricity potential could bring to the ordinary people of the Highlands. His ambitions for the Board were boundless, and he was always ready to address meetings, write letters and pamphlets and provide information to convince others who were less enthusiastic.

Edward MacColl may have assured the new chairman that his duties would occupy only about one day a month, but Johnston had no intention simply of presiding over the monthly meetings. He was forever dreaming up novel applications for hydro-power, new plans for the better utilisation of the Board's assets and ingenious ways of securing the political acceptance of the Board's policies. He refused to draw a salary for his post; nor at first would he accept the use of a private office at Rothesay Terrace, preferring to work in the Board room, where he sat enveloped in a long black cloak

PLATE 2   Edward MacColl

with a white scarf around his neck. There was something of the actor manager about him: he tried at all times to involve the public, to get those about him to share his own excitement.

To the engineers of the Board, he was an endless source of encouragement; but he did more than just reassure, he eased their endeavours by preliminary negotiations with his many political friends, not just in Whitehall but at the local level; and those whom he failed to convince, he often disarmed with his abiding sense of humour. Behind a craggy, unyielding countenance, he possessed 'a devastating sense of fun'.[5] To Tom Johnston the harnessing of Scotland's hydro-power was an adventure. This was a feeling which seems to have permeated the Board from its senior officials down to some of the humblest mud-caked labourers.

2 The Loch Sloy Scheme

(a) Preliminary Works and Supply Problems

When Tom Johnston became chairman, work on the Board's first constructional scheme had already started, though headway had been dispiritingly slow. Indeed, within a few months of the scheme becoming operative in March 1945, it was already apparent that the chances of Sloy producing electricity by the scheduled date of 1947 were extremely slim. Work had begun with a typical flourish. On 11 June 1945, Mrs Thomas Johnston had 'cut the first sod' on the site of the temporary diesel power station using, not the usual polished spade, but an 18 ton bulldozer, confirming both the magnitude of the task and the apprehensions of Lord Airlie's worst critics. For the next few months, the Panel of Technical Advisors plaintively reported, progress was 'negligible'.[6]

The immediate constraint was acute shortage of labour. Despite increasingly desperate requests for men by the contractors to the Labour Exchanges, none was available. Representations were made to the Scottish Home Office, the Ministry of Works and the Ministry of Labour, and the result was the allocation to the scheme at the end of October of 200 German prisoners of war. By the end of the year the labour force consisted of 45 British workmen and 398 prisoners of war. Initially, they were mainly employed in the construction of the main access road up to Loch Sloy and the subsidiary access roads to the outlying works, the provision of camp accommodation for the labour force, and the building of railway facilities: stations, sidings and a bridge to carry the West Highland line over the main pipelines.

Preparatory and site work continued throughout 1946, by the end of which $11\frac{1}{2}$ miles of access roads had been completed; camp accommodation provided for 750 men, and a quarry at Coiregrogain had been opened up sufficient to provide 1,500 tons of aggregate a day for the construction of the dam.[7] Perhaps the most difficult of these essential preliminary tasks was the construction of the steep road along the eastern face of Ben Vorlich, which became known to the workers as the 'Burma Road'. Over 15 miles of access roads were eventually required to complete the Scheme. But such were the difficulties of the terrain and the vast quantities of constructional materials required, especially for the dam, that road access had to be supplemented by additional transportation facilities. It was estimated that 400,000 tons of crushed stone would be needed, and as it was specified that this material was to be delivered at the rate of 200 tons per hour; it was decided to carry it by a conveyor system, about $1\frac{3}{4}$ miles long, constructed round the shoulder of Ben Vane, rather than to use road haulage. This conveyor line, the installation of which was a major undertaking in itself, was built by the well-known makers of underground coal haulage machinery, Mavor and Coulson of Glasgow. The first six of the twelve sections of conveyor belt—which often had to be supported by light bridges over the many gullies—were laid on an average gradient of 1 in 6 and each was driven by a 25 horse-power engine (see Fig. 8).

Having reached the summit of the conveyor run, the crushed aggregate was deposited on huge stock piles whence it was carried, again utilising conveyors, to separate service bunkers on top of a mixing tower. This tower also carried bunkers for sand; sand obtained from a natural deposit at Balloch at the southern end of Loch Lomond, about 22 miles from the dam site. The road along the west bank of Loch Lomond was narrow, winding and busy. To circumvent the difficulties involved in making one hundred or more return runs daily on this road, it was decided to use barge transport on the Loch. Two tugs of 60 tons displacement were used, each drawing three 50-ton capacity barges. Because the River Leven, the natural outlet from Loch Lomond which flows to the River Clyde, is not navigable over part of its length, even the tugs and barges had to

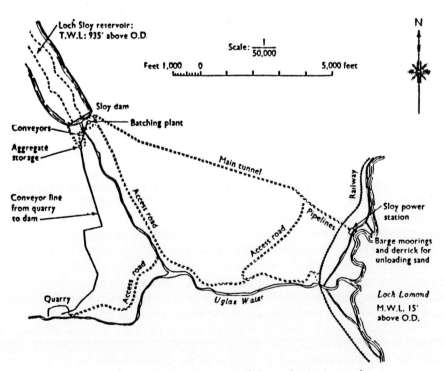

FIGURE 8   Loch Sloy: location of the preliminary works

be transported overland to the Loch. Unloading at Inveruglas Bay was by grab crane to a storage hopper. From the hopper the sand was carried by 5-ton tipping lorries three miles along the access road to a stockpile adjacent to the batching plant at the dam site.

Even the supply of the remaining constituent of concrete, Portland cement, was not without difficulty. Because local suppliers did not possess the facilities necessary to guarantee continuous delivery of the large quantities of bulk cement that would be required, the contractors had to accept delivery in bags. This was to add to the handling costs, involve the construction of a large storage shed close to the batching plant, and increase the density of traffic on the access roads.[8]

The acquisition and assembly of the essential raw materials constituted only the first of an integrated sequence of operations. The crushed aggregate, sand and cement had to be accurately measured, water added, mixed and conveyed to the site of the dam. The mixing station was equipped with weigh-batching plant and cement mixers, the contents of which were transferred to skips. These skips were carried to the site by means of two electrically-driven aerial cableways erected by J M Henderson & Co Ltd. of Aberdeen. The cableways spanned the site of the dam and were capable of depositing a skip containing 4 cubic yards (or approximately ten tons) of concrete at any point over an area of 8,700 square feet.[9]

Not until these essential preliminary works (which included the erection of a temporary diesel-electric power station of 3,600 Kilowatts installed capacity) had been largely completed were the contractors able to concentrate on the main works of the Loch Sloy scheme: the tunnel, dam, pipe-line and power station. It was already 1947. The lack of realism implicit in the optimistic and politically-inspired forecasts of 1944 and 1945 was cruelly exposed. Indeed the year opened with the very national fuel crisis that it had been expected—or, more properly, hoped—that output from Loch Sloy would help to alleviate.[10]

There was no lack of energy on the Board's part to meet the agreed timetable. Everywhere Edward MacColl and the contractors were encountering shortages: of steel, cement, heavy mechanical and electrical plant, timber and men.[11] Even the initial problems of recruitment of labour and its housing had been but partially overcome, and this represented a major constraint at a time when the work was necessarily so labour intensive. Prisoners of war constituted a significant proportion of the labour force until 1948. They were at least stable; the native labour force tended increasingly to be restless, prone to strike action and generally difficult. Balfour, Beatty & Co., the main contractors, reported plaintively in September 1948, 'We have now been on the site for a period of 22 months ... during that period we have had a turnover of 1,884 men in order to maintain an average of 200 men on the site'.[12] Part of the trouble was the appalling weather. Report after report spoke of blizzards or incessant rain, a cold prevailing north-west wind of considerable force, and frequent gales. Such conditions often interrupted work, reduced the length of the working week, adversely affected morale, and created situations in which agitators were able to foment trouble.[13]

Dissatisfaction with the quality of catering and housing were major sources of discontent. No one had envisaged just how difficult it would be to obtain the necessary supplies of timber, building materials and fittings. It was a problem to which the new chairman specifically addressed himself. It infuriated Tom Johnston to see war-time camps, some of them in splendid condition with baths, wash basins, and so forth, all complete, but abandoned. When we offered to purchase the best of these camps we had first to find the appropriate sub-department in charge: then that sub-department would have difficulties in discovering who could give any authority for disposal: then it would be discovered that the camp had not yet been 'declared redundant' or 'de-requisitioned', or some other evasive mouthfiller like that ... there was nothing else for it but that the Board must serve notice to all whom it might concern, that with or without permission, we were sending contractors to lift a camp *holus bolus*: that we would keep careful tab of every bolt and nut taken away, and that we would be ready to pay cash whenever proper and arbitrated demand was made of us. Technically perhaps it was larceny ... but at that time we had on the Board two knights and a privy councillor, and once everybody on the Board was assured that there was no hamesucken involved, and that we would be defended if need be by an ex-Lord Advocate, we decided gaily that the risk of prosecution was worth the taking.[14]

Although the use of such strategies helped to overcome the physical problems of housing the growing number of workers,[15] their care and management were not so easily solved. For example, all the advice of catering specialists failed to reduce the resentment of the labour force—especially the tunnellers—that they were not to be awarded the special food concessions made to the miners in the winter of 1947. Nor could the Board do anything to resolve the conflicts created by differences of working conditions among joiners from their classification as either Building Trade Operatives or employees of members of the Federation of Civil Engineering Contractors, where Civil Engineering Works conditions prevailed.[16]

It was all very trying, but evidence that progress was being made was provided by the increasing number of heavy vehicles along the road that winds by Loch Lomond: lorries with bulldozers, diggers and dumpers; mobile cranes, air compressors, drilling machinery; spiral casings, turbine parts, transformers; all converged on the site. All day long the vehicles moved up and down the access roads which even in the worst winter snow-storms were kept open.

(b) The Main Works

(i) The Loch Sloy Dam

The dam at Loch Sloy was designed by James Williamson. It was of the massive buttress type, first described by Williamson in a paper delivered at the Second Congress on Large Dams in Washington, DC, in 1936. It made use of the principle of reducing the detrimental effects of uplift—to which solid gravity dams are susceptible—by removing material which made no substantial contribution to stability. Not only was this form of dam admirably suited to geological conditions of the site but, in comparison with a solid gravity dam, it made possible significant savings in materials (particularly scarce and expensive cement) and hence cost. The total concrete in the Sloy dam was to be just over 200,000 cubic yards, and it was thought that a mass concrete gravity dam would have required at least 50,000 cubic yards more. Furthermore, the relatively smaller masses of the buttresses, of which there were thirteen at Sloy, restricted the

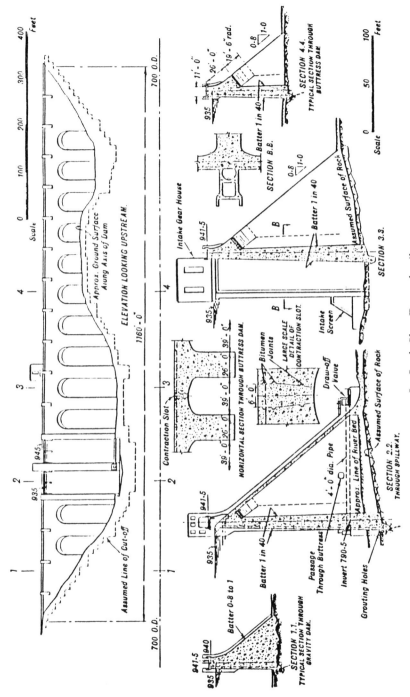

FIGURE 9   Loch Sloy Dam: details

deleterious rise in temperature of the concrete and allowed more rapid cooling than would have been the case with a solid gravity dam.[17] The essential details of the design are shown in Figure 9.

The dam was to be built between two shoulders of rock at a fall in the Inveruglas Water. Overlying the mica–schist rock on which the foundations were to rest was much peat, sand and gravel. This had to be removed, as did those parts of the schistose rock which were heavily fissured and weathered. A major fault was discovered at the eastern end of the site; this too had to be cut out to a depth of about 75 feet below the normal level of the rock. In all, 36,000 cubic yards of peat and sandy loam and 56,000 cubic yards of rock were excavated. The anticipated and actual foundation line is shown in Figure 10.

Since many of the fissures had to be cleared out by hand and the excavated rock loaded into the skips manually (because of the difficulty of using machines, especially in the latter stages of the work), the creation of a satisfactory foundation for the dam was a lengthy process. Not until the Spring of 1948 was it possible to begin placing the concrete of the dam itself. The concrete was poured into great moulds, or formwork. These were formed by steel shuttering, the use of which was dictated by the expense and scarcity of timber and the shortage of skilled joiners. Indeed, the design of the dam—involving as it did thirteen independently standing, almost identical buttresses—lent itself to the use of steel shutters. Formed of long rigid panels, these were ideally suited for handling by crane with a minimum use of manpower, and could each be used 20 or 30 times on a single buttress before being transferred to the next buttress to be built. Sir Andrew MacTaggart was later to pay a tribute to those whose job it had been to erect the shuttering: 'even to hold on to the structure [in the awful weather] was difficult enough without having to do ... work to which they were not accustomed. [It had to be remembered that there had been] an average of twelve real carpenters on the job, when there ought to have [been] fifty or sixty'.[18]

The quantity of concrete placed each week was much influenced by the weather, far less progress was achieved in periods of excessive rainfall and frost than during *relatively* dry and warmer periods. The word 'relatively' deserves emphasis because throughout the *entire* period of construction, work on the site was greatly hampered by atrocious weather. In the years 1947, 1948, and 1949, rainfalls of 106 inches, 163 inches, and 153 inches respectively were recorded, giving a weekly average of 2.75 inches. The maximum weekly rainfall recorded was 11.36 inches and the maximum daily rainfall 4.10 inches. These statistics are graphic enough, but to appreciate the conditions fully it must be realised that 'the rain was invariably coming in horizontally with gale-force winds'. Only three weeks of the entire three years of construction were recorded as being without rainfall. The wind and rain had a less adverse effect on the actual concreting than on the morale of the labour force and on the manipulation of the shutters. The difficulties confronting the shutter-lifting gangs were such that it proved to be 'rarely possible to do serious concreting for more than four days in a week'.[19]

About 600 cubic yards of concrete were placed per week in the Spring of 1948, when mass-concreting began. This volume increased to a maximum of just over 4,000 cubic yards per week during the summer of the following year. As the amount in each lift declined, the weekly totals fell to about 2,000 cubic yards during the Spring of 1950.

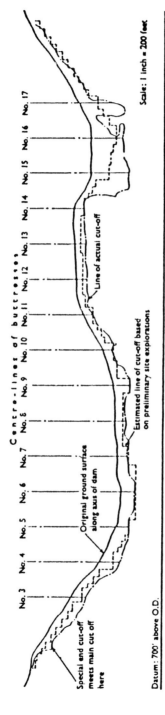

FIGURE 10   Loch Sloy Dam: anticipated and actual foundation line

Mass concreting was completed by the end of June. The general progress, by six-monthly intervals, is depicted in Figure 11.

During 1949, it had become increasingly clear to the main contractors for the dam, Balfour Beatty & Co., that with the extremely adverse weather conditions and the continuing acute shortage of skilled labour the use of complicated shuttering at the higher levels of the dam would be unacceptably slow. It was therefore decided that certain units, such as the components of the arches between the heads of the buttresses, should be pre-cast at ground level under more sheltered conditions using only semi-skilled labour.[20] These units were then lifted into position using the cableways. This method of construction was a complete success and, in all, over 3,000 cubic yards of concrete were eventually pre-cast.

Figure 9 shows that the buttresses of the Sloy dam assumed the form of a series of Ts, each of which was separated from the adjacent buttress by a contraction gap (see Plate 3). It was these very gaps that permitted work on each buttress section to be entirely independent and thus rendered unnecessary the co-ordination of the various stages of construction over the entire length of the dam. This was an important consideration when working on an uneven foundation with unskilled labour. To complete the dam—in other words, to join up the heads of the series of Ts so that the upstream face of dam was continuous—all that remained to do was to fill the 6 foot contraction slots. This was done when sufficient time—about three months—had elapsed to permit the concrete in the main masses of the adjacent buttresses to cool and shrink. The sides of the slots themselves were keyed, they were then coated with bitumen, and the wedge-shaped gaps filled with concrete. As the water level of the reservoir was slowly allowed to rise—water was stored to a depth of 40 feet by the end of 1949—the hydrostatic pressure on the upstream face of the dam acted upon these wedges, and this pressure, combined with the bitumen seal, ensured watertightness.

The flow of water from the Loch Sloy reservoir was to be controlled from a gate house on top of the dam. This house, situated directly above the main intake located on the bed of the Loch, contained all the equipment necessary for controlling two gates: an emergency guard gate, to be used to cut off the water when, for example, the control gate needed maintenance or in the event of a failure of the valves on a pipe line and, downstream of the guard gate, the main control gate. This was of the counter-balanced type and was normally to be under water at all times. The entrance to the main intake was protected by a series of screens designed to prevent the passage of debris. The general arrangement is shown in Figure 12.

(ii) *The Tunnel and Surge Shaft*

The main tunnel through which the water was to flow from the reservoir to the pipe lines was begun early in 1947. Once again, acute difficulties in recruiting labour were encountered and this was exacerbated by the contractor's (Edmund Nuttall Sons & Co) decision to abandon the original 12 hour shifts after two months and work almost entirely on 8 hour shifts, because of the severity of the work and the relative inexperience of the labour employed. This put further pressure on the available camp accommodation since the consequence of Nuttall's decision was to expand the number of men employed

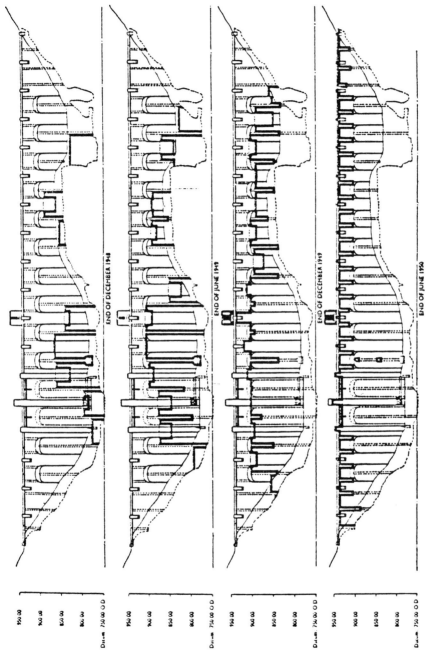

FIGURE 11 Loch Sloy Dam: concrete placing progress

PLATE 3   Loch Sloy Dam: buttresses under construction

91

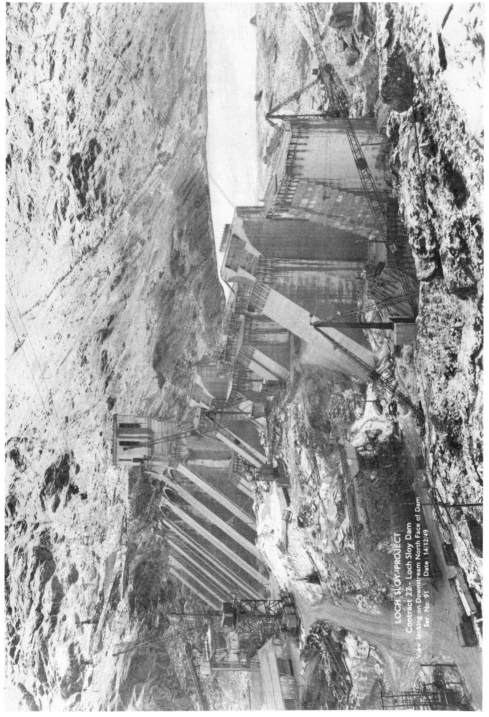

PLATE 4   Loch Sloy Dam under construction

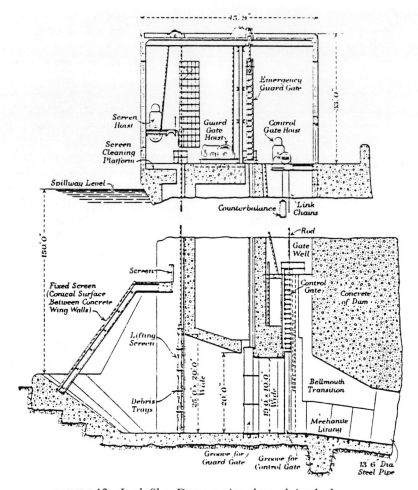

FIGURE 12   Loch Sloy Dam: section through intake house

by the firm from 250 to about 370. Other problems were caused by the contractor's inability to obtain suitable air compressors.[21]

Nevertheless, by May 1947 fair progress was being reported. The tunnel was driven from four faces: the exit portal end, two intermediate faces proceeding in opposite directions and reached by an adit driven into the heart of Ben Vorlich, and from a short tunnel adjacent to the dam itself. The main faces were driven by means of drill carriages mounting nine high speed compressed air drills, an average of seventy 9-foot. holes being drilled into the contorted mica-schist rock at each operation. Using gelignite, these faces were then blasted and the spoil removed by mechanical loaders which discharged into narrow-gauge waggons hauled by diesel and electric locomotives. At one point the tunnel entered loose material formed by the intersection of two major faults and a cavity about 60 feet high resulted from a series of roof falls. It was decided to by-pass this cavity by diverting the tunnel about 75 feet from its original line.[22] In spite of this diversion, the tunnel faces joined with an error of less than one inch. In other parts of the tunnel where loose rock was encountered, the walls were supported by arched steel beams and pressure grouted.

The main tunnel has a total length of about 10,000 feet. The first stretch, about 700 feet long, is circular with a diameter of 13 feet 6 inches and, because there was little rock cover, was strengthened with concrete and reinforcing steel. This part of the tunnel, now well into the great mass of Ben Vorlich, makes a gradual transition to a 15 feet 4 inches-diameter concrete lined horse-shoe section, the length of which is 8,200 feet. Five hundred feet from the exit portal, the 'horse-shoe' tunnel was divided into two smaller, 10 feet-diameter steel-lined tunnels. As these pipes emerged from the hillside, a second bifurcation took place, each 10 feet pipe dividing into two 7 feet pipes which were led into a valve house at the top of the steep slope above the power station.

The driving of the main tunnel had been remarkably successful. All the work was done in free air and the average rate of progress had been about 64 feet per week, though in one week 103 feet had been achieved. Nuttall's had not been able to meet their completion date of mid-July 1948, but in this they fared no worse than the other contractors, all of whom had been impeded by shortage of labour, steel, cement and specialised machinery. Few difficulties had been experienced from water, and no major accidents were reported to the Board, yet over 180,000 tons of rock had been excavated, involving 1,700 blasting operations in which 220 tons of gelignite had been used. When it is remembered that the majority of the men were initially so inexperienced that the contractors had to establish a training school at Sloy providing three weeks of intensive instruction before sending the workmen to the tunnel face, the magnitude of their achievement is apparent. Early efforts to recruit coal miners had proved unsuccessful. Colliers would not work in the tunnels because of the lack of timbering.[23]

In addition to the main tunnel, Nuttall's were also contractors for the surge shaft. This shaft is located about 1,000 feet from the exit portal of the tunnel, and its associated surge chambers are designed to assist in the control of the large volume of moving water as the load on the turbines varies. If, for example, the load on the generating sets is abruptly reduced, a rapid rise in the water level in the surge shaft takes place, it also limits the effects of water hammer. The shaft is 26 feet in diameter and 273 feet high from the tunnel to the arched roof of the top surge chamber which is itself 90 feet long, 38 feet wide and 28 feet high. The lower, smaller expansion chamber at the bottom of the surge shaft is divided into two equal halves, one at each side of the shaft a short distance above the roof of the main tunnel.

The construction of this important safety feature was necessarily complicated. The top surge chamber was excavated after an adit had been driven into the mountain from a point above the main tunnel exit. When this large chamber had been lined with concrete, a small shaft was driven up to it from the tunnel below. This working shaft was used to remove the spoil created by excavation of the circular surge shaft proper. This was carried out from the top downwards, the rock that was removed being dropped down the working shaft and carried away through the main tunnel. To reduce risk from falling stone, which occurred periodically, excavation was stopped after a certain depth had been reached and the shaft lined with concrete. The shaft was completed by alternately sinking and lining lengths of about 20 feet. The construction of the two lateral chambers of the base of the shaft presented far less difficulty and when the entire task had been completed over 2,400 tons of rock had been excavated from the surge chambers and the shaft. Some idea of what was involved in fulfilling the contract for the construction of the tunnel and the surge shaft and chambers can be seen from the diagrammatic section (Figure 13).

(iii) *The Pipelines*

From the valve house the four pipelines convey the water to the power station, 1,500 feet away. Each pipe supplied one of the four main turbo-alternators. They were constructed by Sir William Arrol & Co. Superficially simple, their design (especially the bifurcation at the exit at the end of the main tunnel) was complex,[24] and their erection required careful planning. Great pains were taken to minimise and to simplify the work performed on the site, with its gradient of about 1.5 to 1, and to make sure that the pipes were able to withstand the enormous pressures involved in supplying the power station—when operating at full load—with 220,000 tons of water per hour. Allowance had to be made for the expansion and contraction of the pipes and the design embodied numerous safety devices and facilities for proper inspection and maintenance.

The internal diameter of each pipe diminished from 7 feet at the top of the line to just over 6 feet at the entrance to the power station, while the thickness of the steel from which the pipes were made progressively increased from $\frac{11}{16}''$ to $1\frac{9}{16}''$. The pipes were made in 24 feet lengths of mild steel plate bent to circular form and welded electrically along the longitudinal joints. The welding was carefully checked by means of x-ray photography and fully tested at Sir William Arrol's Glasgow works to nearly double the anticipated maximum pressure of 400lbs per square inch. It was the erection of the pipes—the thickest of which weighed 15 tons—that involved the greatest ingenuity. They were secured to massive blocks of concrete, the uppermost of which formed the foundation of the valve house and the lowest block, part of the power station. The intermediate blocks anchored the pipes at changes of direction and inclination. The weight of these blocks varied between 1,700 and 3,600 tons. Between the anchor blocks, the pipes rest on curved saddle pieces surmounted by bronze bearing strips, which permit the pipes to make a certain amount of longitudinal movement. The saddle pieces were themselves fixed to concrete piers.

The huge pipes were delivered to a railway siding near the power station, unloaded on to a bogie by a 20-ton derrick crane, laboriously hauled up the face of the mountain on an electrically operated inclined railway and placed into position by means of cranes and a travelling gantry. Working from the power station end, the pipes were jointed by riveting, everything possible having been previously prepared in Arrol's workshop to facilitate this stage of the work. Welding on the site was kept to an absolute minimum. The pipe line can be seen under construction in Plate 5.

Almost inevitably, the completion date of 30 June 1948 for the contract was overrun. By the end of 1948 the pipeline had progressed just over halfway up the hillside, impeded by the very wet and unfavourable weather conditions and the chronic shortage of steel,

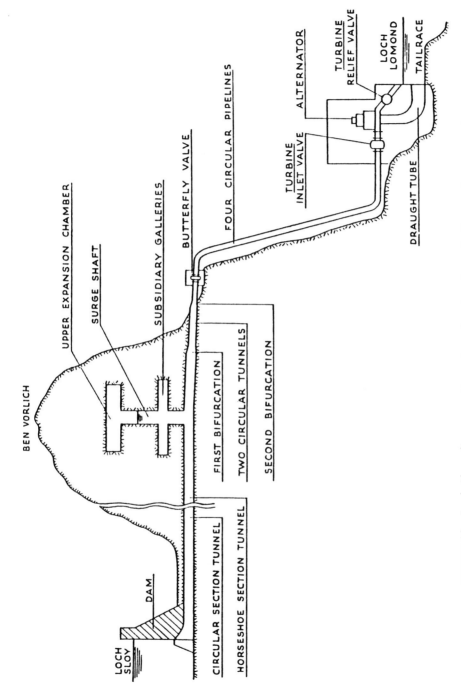

FIGURE 13 Loch Sloy: diagrammatic section, showing dam, pipelines and power station

PLATE 5   Loch Sloy Dam: the pipeline under construction

no less than 3,500 tons being required for the pipes alone. The contract was finally completed in 1950.

(iv) The Power Station and its Equipment

All the expensive and time-consuming activity so far described had but one purpose: to provide the motive power for the huge turbo-alternators that were to be installed in the power station at Inveruglas Bay on the western bank of Loch Lomond. Designed by Tarbolton & Ochterlony, whose senior partner was one of the Board's Panel of Architectural Advisors, the power station was to consist of a turbine hall, repair shop, battery room, control room and offices.

But first the foundations had to be laid, a task involving the excavation of 37,000 tons of rock and earth, for it was essential to provide the firmest of bases for the turbines. Of all the preparatory work, this was the one perhaps most severely impeded by the unceasing rains of 1947 and 1948. Not only did the weather cause unexpected physical difficulties, but in mid-1947 the contractors (Hugh Leggat Ltd) suffered 'an exodus of labour because of the rain and consequent curtailed working week and reduced earnings'.[25] Like the three other principal contractors, Leggat's lost a high proportion of key men 'who through a sense of frustration and of tiredness with strikes and labour troubles ... [often occasioned by] dissatisfaction over the quality of food and alleged inefficiency of the personnel of the catering and welfare staffs ... decided to seek employment elsewhere'.[26] Morale sunk even lower in August 1947 when three employees of Sir William Arrol, who were working on the pipeline, were ... severely injured (one fatally) by blasting operations carried out by Leggat's. The number of employees fell to less than half that required and although concreting for the structural steelwork was started in September it was reported that 'the lack of joiners prevents the attainment of even fair progress'.[27]

Not until the end of 1947 were the monthly reports more cheerful. After a year of endeavour, the contractors had resigned themselves to operating with a labour force the sise of which fluctuated wildly, and had adopted a wide variety of ingenious improvisations designed to reduce the need for skilled men, particularly carpenters and steel erectors. Thereafter progress was more rapid. The draught tubes of the vertical shaft Francis turbines had been placed in position and embedded in the concrete foundations by December 1947. The steel framework of the machinery hall was then erected and a 120-ton overhead travelling crane installed, thereby greatly facilitating the subsequent movement and positioning of the heavy electrical generating plant. Figure 14 shows the general arrangement.

The contractors for the turbine alternators, the auxiliary generator and most of the ancilliary gear were the English Electric Company. Because of the relatively slow progress of the civil engineering work at Sloy, this company—which experienced its own difficulties with skilled labour and steel supplies—was able to design and manufacture the mechanical and electrical equipment by the time installation had been made possible. English Electric's major problem was delivery to the site. Many of the parts were both large and extremely heavy and, after intensive laboratory and workshop testing, special arrangements had to be made to transport them from the Scotstoun Works of Harland and Wolff, where they were constructed for the English Electric

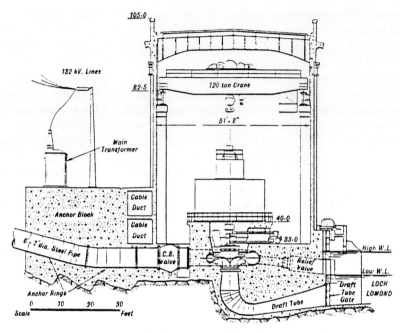

FIGURE 14   Loch Sloy: section through power station

Company, to Inveruglas. Some components, like the spiral casings, were conveyed all the way by road. Their weight (at 42 tons each) was not excessive but their sheer sise considerably exceeded the normally permitted limits, and their carriage was a delicate task involving painfully slow speeds, the provision of a police escort and, for other road users, frustrating delays. Larger parts, such as the alternator rotors, weighing 85 tons each, were carried by rail on specially adapted rolling stock, but even their transfer from the sidings to the power station presented difficulties in the absence of a crane of sufficient capacity for off-loading at Inveruglas, and a system of jacks had to be employed.

The parts had then to be assembled. A retrospective report by English Electric commented, with massive understatement, 'generally, after placing the draught tubes in position very little erection work can be done on the plant until the power station crane is operating and protection from the weather is built. At Loch Sloy, however, the civil progress was such that erection of the turbines had to proceed before the walls were completed, and with the prevailing weather the working conditions were at times not good'.[28] Despite these tribulations, three of the four turbine spiral casings were in position by the Spring of 1949 and the first of the generating sets completed early in the following year. Almost a year was to pass before the fourth and last of the 32,500 kW generating sets had been installed: they were, at the time, the most powerful of their kind in Britain.[29] When the four machines were running at full load, nearly a million gallons of water were to pass through them every minute.

(v) *Additional Collection, and Distribution*

The rising buttresses of the great dam, the lengths of pipeline laboriously snaking their way up the side of Ben Vorlich, and the cladding of the plant-filled, steel-framed power station with pre-cast slabs of Rubislaw and Corrennie granite were those aspects of the Loch Sloy project given most publicity in the Press. Yet in the hills, out of sight of newspaper photographers, isolated gangs of men were driving smaller tunnels and building aqueducts to lead more and more water to Loch Sloy to feed the voracious turbines. It will be recalled that the *natural* catchment area of Loch Sloy was about 6.5 square miles and that it had been originally intended to increase this figure to about 28 square miles.[30] During 1948, however, the Loch Sloy extension scheme was published (Constructional Scheme No.22), which further increased the catchment area of the reservoir to 32.5 square miles and the annual yield of power by some 15 million kWh. MacColl may have been denied his pumped storage system but he refused to be deprived of a single drop of rainfall that could be captured. This involved the construction of about ten miles of pipes and open aqueducts and over 12 miles of tunnels.

From their arduous labour on the main tunnel, Nuttall's men—now working harmoniously in experienced teams—turned in 1949 to the high-level catchment area with such effect that during the week ending Sunday 10 June 1951, the tunnelling gangs, working eight-hour shifts round the clock for seven days drove a distance of 427 feet through the hard diorite rock forming the mountains of the Cobbler Range. This was said to be the first time a footage exceeding 400 feet had been driven in Great Britain from a single heading. Altogether, over a period of thirty-one working days the tunnelling crews, made up of about half British and half displaced European workers, drove a total of 1231 feet. This was nearly a quarter of the total length of the 7 feet square tunnel designed to carry water from above the summit of Rest-and-be-Thankful to Loch Sloy.[31] Meanwhile, Balfour Beatty's were constructing aqueducts either linking the lengths of tunnel or making their own contribution towards capturing the headwaters of the streams that would otherwise have 'gone to waste' into Loch Long, Loch Fyne or, by the way of the River Falloch, Loch Lomond (see Fig. 15).

Long before the first turbo-alternator began to turn, the people of Tarbet and Arrochar were being supplied with electricity from the Loch Sloy scheme. In April 1948, electricity was brought to Arrochar at the head of Loch Long by a line from the temporary diesel station, the switching-on ceremony being performed by Miss Mary MacFarlane, at 96 years old the oldest inhabitant in the village. For their supply of electricity, the rest of the population of Central Scotland had to await not simply the completion of the power station but the creation of a transmission and distribution network.

In step with the work at Loch Sloy and on the banks of Loch Lomond, a small army of men erected the steel towers and strung the high voltage lines that were to carry the electricity produced by the scheme from the main transformers at the power station, via the 132kV switching station at Inveruglas, to the outskirts of Glasgow where, at Windyhill, it was fed into the main lines of the national grid. It proved to be a fearsome task. Army weasels and tractors floundered, and were abandoned, in the peaty quagmires encountered in the mountains between Loch Long and Loch Lomond. One pair of tractors took three days to haul a single load of steel 900 yards up the mountainside,

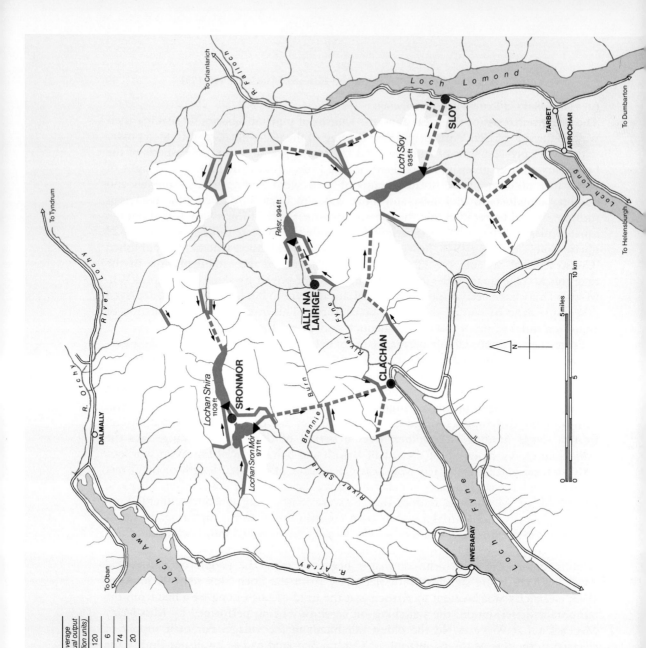

	Year first commissioned	Gross head (feet)	Installed capacity (Megawatts)	Average annual output (million units)
Sloy	1950	909	130	120
Sron Mor	1957	157	5	6
Clachan	1955	965	40	74
Allt-na-Lairige	1956	817	6	20

▲ Dam
● Power station
━━ Aqueduct
┅┅ Tunnel

Reservoir levels in feet above sea level

and just as long to come down again without any load. Pack horses were employed, but they could carry little more than a man up the hills and turned 'stupid' under the strain. Mechanical shovels and bulldozers hacked out much of the 12,000 tons of rock for the pylon sites, but the final stages of preparation had to be done by pick and shovel and small charges of explosives. Working from sunrise to sundown in incessant rain, paid about £8 for a 70-hour week, with 30 shillings a week lodging allowance, the labour force was exceptionally volatile, no less than 1,285 men were taken on during the course of the two year contract to keep a squad of 200 going. The contractor's agent recalled that 'we started at one site at the beginning of last August and I bet the resident engineer a pint that it would be finished before the end of the week. Then the rains came—and we weren't off that site until April [1949]'. To have finished the entire job on time was unanimously agreed to have been 'a minor miracle'.[32]

(vi) *The Opening Ceremony: the Achievement*
At 3.15 p.m. on 18 February 1950, Sir Edward MacColl—he had been knighted only months earlier—set the first of the Loch Sloy generating sets in motion for the first time. Although there had been no previous trial, the set was taken up to full speed and ran entirely satisfactorily. Eight months later Her Majesty the Queen officially opened the scheme. 'It was, almost inevitably, a cold, wet, windswept day, and many guests had to wait a long time in the stands, but they were not cold'. With typical attention to detail, MacColl had insisted on installing an electric light bulb beneath each seat. As usual, there had been many to argue that this simple and effective idea was either unnecessary or would not work. No one had been fully enthusiastic except MacColl, but then he was always enthusiastic. As one of the guests later recalled: 'the memory which remains is his happiness at the opening of the Loch Sloy station. There in the rain he strolled round, unobtrusive and modest, the brain behind the venture, happy in the realisation of one of his dreams and they are not many who have that experience'.[33]

But, in truth, the opening of Loch Sloy, the first of the large hydro-electric schemes of the North of Scotland Hydro-Electric Board, was the realisation of the dreams of several people: James Williamson, principal of the firm of civil engineering consultants who supervised the design and construction and who had examined the hydro–electric potential of the area as early as 1925, was one of them; Thomas Johnston was another. To him, the scheme was

> more than a great engineering achievement ... it has come to be regarded by the people of Scotland as a symbol of the utilisation for the production of electricity of one of the natural resources of our country, the rain that feeds Highland lochs and rivers. It means something more than millions of Kilowatt hours, or thousands of tons of concrete and steel; it crystallises the imagination, enterprise and effort behind the great development being carried out by the Board, which has as its aims improved standards of living, more employment and increased production.

There is no doubt that Johnston fully believed that Loch Sloy was a manifestation of

facing page
FIGURE 15   The Sloy and Shira schemes

'the new spirit that exists where before there was only depopulation and despair ... [it was] an effective answer to any who may lack faith in the future of [Scotland]'.[34] And those who were later to analyse the economies of this and subsequent schemes and find them wanting were to be guilty of ignoring those unquantifiable factors that were so real to Thomas Johnston. To Johnston, Loch Sloy was the first great step in the rehabilitation of the Highlands: as such it was not susceptible to the cold, impersonal and remorseless logic of the accountant or the government auditor.

3   The Tummel-Garry Scheme

If Loch Sloy was the first of the Board's large schemes, Tummel-Garry was one of the most interesting and certainly among the most economical. To provide a detailed account of its construction—as has been attempted in the case of Loch Sloy—would entail considerable repetition. Nevertheless, in its design and execution the Tummel-Garry scheme embodied many noteworthy features that cannot be ignored.

The first stage of Tummel-Garry formed a logical extension to the Grampian Company's works. Loch Tummel was to be enlarged by the construction of the Clunie dam and intake works, and a tunnel was to be constructed to divert the water to Clunie power station. This station was designed to operate on a low load factor, and the flow discharged from it, together with the unregulated flow from the River Garry, was to be evened out by the operation of a power station at Pitlochry. This power station was to be combined with a dam which would form a small narrow reservoir into the upper end of which the Clunie station was to discharge. The working of the two power stations was to be carefully co-ordinated. Clunie, operating on a low load-factor, could safely discharge large volumes of water into the reservoir immediately downstream formed by the dam at Pitlochry. In turn, Pitlochry power station, which was to have a much smaller installed capacity, was to work on a higher load factor, thus minimising sudden variations of water level in the river below the power station.

The second stage of Tummel-Garry was designed to make its contribution to the scheme's total output by impounding the waters of the upper tributaries of the River Garry and a stream known as the Errochty Water by means of a dam situated in Glen Errochty, and by leading the impounded water to a power station on Loch Tummel with an installed capacity even higher than Clunie (75Mw cf. 61.2 Mw). Having been 'used', as it were, at Loch Tummel, the Errochty water would be exploited for a second and third time when it passed through the turbines at Clunie and Pitlochry.[35] (See Fig.16 and compare with Fig 4.)

Tummel-Garry was perhaps MacColl's favourite project. It was large, innovative and—within realistic cost constraints—harnessed every conceivable unit of the potential energy of its huge catchment area of over 700 square miles. J Guthrie Brown, of Sir Alexander Gibb and Partners, was the consulting civil engineer. He worked extremely closely with MacColl in overcoming the many problems which arose during the

facing page
FIGURE 16   The Tummel-Garry scheme

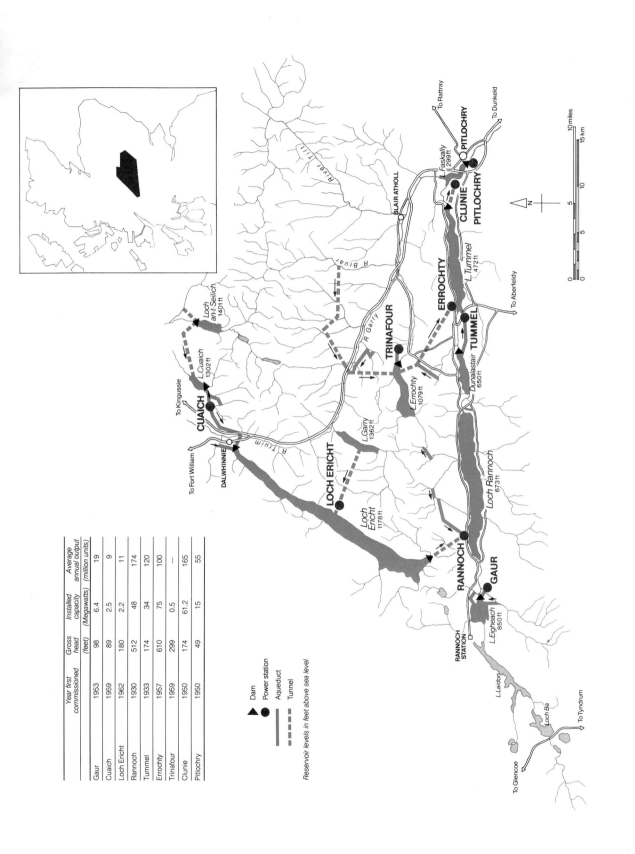

	Year first commissioned	Gross head (feet)	Installed capacity (Megawatts)	Average annual output (million units)
Gaur	1953	98	6.4	19
Cuaich	1959	89	2.5	9
Loch Ericht	1962	180	2.2	11
Rannoch	1930	512	48	174
Tummel	1933	174	34	120
Errochty	1957	610	75	100
Trinafour	1959	299	0.5	–
Clunie	1950	174	61.2	165
Pitlochry	1950	49	15	55

▲ Dam

▲● Power station

Aqueduct

- - - Tunnel

Reservoir levels in feet above sea level

TABLE 1   *Tummel–Garry: Major Dams*

Name of Dam	Type & Year of Completion	Length ft	Height above foundations ft	Cubic Capacity cu. yds.	Main Contractors
Clunie	Mass gravity, 1951	380	70	37,000	George Wimpey & Co.
Pitlochry	Mass gravity, 1951	475	54	43,000	George Wimpey & Co.
Errochty	Diamond-headed buttress, 1957	1,644	162	248,000	A M Carmichael Ltd.
Gaur	Concrete gravity, 1958	361	44	9,200	A A Stuart & Sons

Consulting Engineers:
    Clunie, Pitlochry and Errochty: Sir Alexander Gibb & Partners
    Gaur: Babtie, Shaw & Morton

construction of the scheme.[36] Starting some six or seven months after Loch Sloy, the initial difficulties—involving the acquisition of supplies of aggregate, sand, cement and heavy plant; the recruitment, housing and management of skilled and unskilled labour; unforeseen geological complications and flooding—were almost identical to those encountered by the Board's first constructional scheme and had a similarly malign effect on the timetable.

The numerous contractors were helpless victims of shortages of all kinds. George Wimpey & Co., the main contractors for the Clunie Dam, the construction of which was to require about 37,000 cubic yards of concrete, found that much of the rock in the vicinity of the site was very variable, foliated and interleaved with bands of softer material, so that it tended to flake when crushed. It was not until an area of hard quartz schist was discovered at Bonskeid on the north bank of the River Tummel, and a quarry opened and fully equipped, that the 100,000 tons of aggregate required for the first part of the scheme could be obtained. Similarly, supplies of suitable sand were found only at a considerable distance from the site, at Blairgowrie and from the bed of the Tay between Perth and Dundee. Sand from the latter source was taken by barge to Perth and then, like that from Blairgowrie, delivered by road, an arrangement necessitating haulages of between 30 and 40 miles. It was considered that 'the greater reliability and durability of concrete made with clean, sharp sand, instead of with crushed stone, justified the expense, especially in view of the corrosive action of the peaty water'.[37] Even the Portland cement had to be shipped to Dundee and thence by road. Nevertheless, it is characteristic of the care which was taken of every aspect of the project that a laboratory was established specifically to conduct the testing on site of the different classes of concrete used in the construction of the dams.

But if heavy expenditures coupled with the exercise of ingenuity could overcome the problems encountered in obtaining the basic raw materials, those associated with the supply of labour were for long insoluble. Report after report told of shortages of skilled men, restlessness, strikes and disputes. Carpenters just could not be obtained for any money, and even the creation of a training school for tunnellers by the contractors for the Clunie Tunnel—Cementation Co. Ltd.—failed to stabilise the labour force. The wastage among skilled miners was particularly serious. Even the prisoners of war— who, as at Sloy, initially constituted a significant proportion of the labour force— appear rapidly to have adopted many of the behavioural characteristics of their captors. They could not move; but they could, and did, insist on tea breaks, cinema shows, and the observation of national and local holidays. It is said that not until Polish overseers were employed would German POWs abandon the most blatant of their adopted customs![38] The report on labour at Tummel-Garry for the period 25 July to 21 August 1947 is typical:

> The situation regarding the supply of labour appears to be getting worse. General labour is no longer comparatively easily obtained and, on the whole, the quality is very low. The possibility of employing Polish labour is now being explored.
> The dispute over Carpenters remains unsettled, while The Cementation Co. Ltd. report no improvement in their efforts to obtain tunnel workers. In fact the position with regard to Labour for the Clunie Tunnel Contract has worsened as, although some men have been

taken on during the month, a greater number, including many of Cementation's more experienced men, have left the site. Most of the men now being interviewed by the Contractor are not suitable for the work and are not being engaged.

On other Contracts, too, it has been noticed that some of the 'old hands' have thrown up their jobs for no real reason, although Messrs George Wimpey & Co. Ltd. have reported that the trouble is due to dis-satisfaction with the food in Port-na-craig Camp and the lack of Sunday work.[39]

There is no question that by the Autumn of 1947 'the general shortage of labour and its continued wastage [constituted] one of the principal reasons for lack of progress',[40] and that this was exacerbated by the announcement of the Control of Engagement Order which threatened to lock employees into their current jobs:[41] immediately the labour force at Tummel-Garry fell by 154, or 16 per cent of the prevailing average number of men then employed.

Not until the Spring of 1948 was there any perceptible easing of the labour position, although Wimpey's contracts were still 'handicapped by [the firm's] unwillingness to pay Building Trade conditions to Joiners'.[42] It was this improvement which made it unnecessary to pursue a desperate plan to employ the Italian contracting firm of Astaldi for a major part of the work, though this would almost certainly have foundered because of the necessity of obtaining the consent of the Ministry of Labour, the trade unions, the Home Office and the Treasury. It was not thought that food for the 900 men would present an insuperable difficulty, but doubts were expressed about obtaining the wine, at a cheap price (about 1s. 8d. per litre), that 'would be required to the amount of half-a-litre per man per day'.[43] Had anything come of this proposal, it is not hard to imagine the tenor of Lord Lovat's reaction. Mercifully, although the shortage of carpenters (required for shuttering) proved to be chronic, despite the employment of joiners from the Clyde shipyards, the number of complaints by the contractors about labour recruitment—though not its quality—had diminished markedly by the summer of 1948.

By this time the Tummel-Garry scheme—the first part of which had been expected to be brought into operational service by the winter of 1947, had, like Sloy, fallen grievously behind schedule. Even the foundations of the Clunie Dam, thought to be firm Highland schist, was found to be widely but finely fissured. This involved extensive grouting, and at one point—where a deep triangular hole filled with closely packed gravel was discovered—thorough excavation.[44] In these circumstances, MacColl's tactics of telling Guthrie Brown how much faster James Williamson's work was progressing at Sloy (while at the same time reporting to Williamson what excellent progress was being made at Tummel-Garry) was vain.[45] Both of them were pushing on as rapidly as they could.

We have seen that 'the race' was won by Sloy, but Sloy not only enjoyed a six-month's start, it was in many ways altogether simpler in concept and less constrained by complex amenity issues, the violation of which would have sparked off renewed public furore and gravely endangered the Board's future. Furthermore, Sloy had no fish problem. In partial compensation, the construction of Clunie Dam was greatly facilitated by the excellent water regulation afforded by Lochs Ericht and Rannoch, and the prior existence of the works of Grampian Hydro-Electric scheme. This characteristic of the site made it possible to build the left-hand section of the dam behind a steel sheet cofferdam which was, somewhat unexpectedly, never in any real danger of being overtopped by major floods. After the left-hand portion of the dam had been largely completed the River Tummel was diverted to flow through openings which had been left in the structure, and the rest of the dam constructed within a second cofferdam erected over the right-hand section of the site. This technique was also successfully employed in building the Pitlochry dam and power station.[46]

Clunie and Pitlochry have other similarities. Both were provided with fish passes of the 'pool and orifice' type, the design of which was determined only after painstaking study and research, often using models, to discover the reactions of the fish to different attempts to provide for their needs. At both Clunie and Pitlochry, fish travel up the pass through circular openings constructed at the centre of each of the cross walls forming the 'ladder' of pools. These openings were equivalent to about 2 feet in diameter and were inclined, joining the invert levels of adjacent pools.[47] (See Fig.17). Larger 'resting' pools were provided at intervals where ascending fish could recover from their efforts. This system was believed to give better results than the older passes in which fish jump over each successive weir of the ladder. The Board willingly accepted its responsibility to care for the salmon—indeed, they had no choice—but the cost should not be forgotten. Not only did the provision of fish ladders make a substantial addition to the capital expenditure on dam construction but they occupied a great deal of space (see Plate 6) and required a constant flow of water of about 28 cusecs down the ladder, because instinct drives both breeding salmon and smolts and kelts to follow the current, both up and down. Further expense was incurred, particularly at Clunie, in protecting those perverse smolts who, in migrating downstream to the sea, choose to ignore the fish passes and pursue an alternative route down the main intake tunnel. They had to be prevented from doing so by special screens of fine mesh which, being easily choked

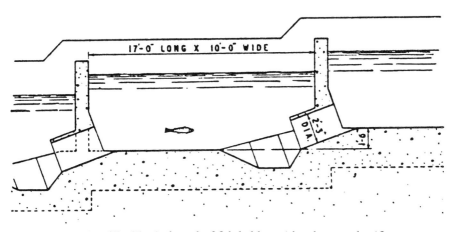

FIGURE 17   Typical pool of fish ladder with submerged orifice

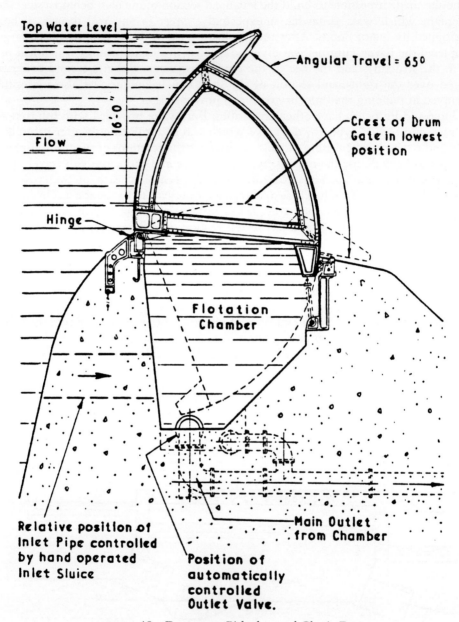

Top Water Level

16'-0"

Flow

Angular Travel = 65°

Crest of Drum
Gate in lowest
position

Hinge

Flotation
Chamber

Relative position of
Inlet Pipe controlled
by hand operated
Inlet Sluice

Position of
automatically
controlled
Outlet Valve.

Main Outlet
from Chamber

FIGURE 18   Drumgate: Pitlochry and Clunie Dam

PLATE 6   Clunie Dam and fish ladder

with debris, require frequent cleaning. At Pitlochry, where the gross head of water was but 54 feet the intractable smolts are allowed to pass through the power station, apparently suffering little inconvenience from their passage through the Kaplan turbines.[48]

Both Clunie and Pitlochry were designed with special attention to amenity. Pitlochry dam and power station is regarded architecturally as one of the Board's successful ventures. It is illustrated in Plate 7. The power station is faced with precast concrete blocks which harmonise with the mass concrete of the dam. The automatic drum gates (see Fig.18) which control the flow of flood water over the crest spillways give a clean appearance, free from overhead operating gear, which was one of the reasons why they were used. Even more important, however, they give a sensitive and effective spill control of all flood flows with virtually no change in reservoir levels, the possibility of which caused such apprehension at the public inquiry and among antagonistic Members of Parliament. These gates—they were also installed at the Clunie dam—are interesting in that they were the first of their type and size to be used in Great Britain. Their design and construction were undertaken by Glenfield & Kennedy of Kilmarnock after a series of experiments had been carried out at Imperial College, South Kensington.[49] Lastly, there are no transformers or power lines leaving Pitlochry power station, the power being transmitted at its generated voltage by underground cable to Clunie power station. Even at Clunie—where water is delivered to the machines through buried pipelines—the transformers and transmission lines were carefully placed in an inconspicuous position. Only one overhead tower is visible from the locality of the power station. This carries the power to the switching station close to the Errochty power station, which forms a major connection in the Highland grid.

Not only were efforts made to create civil engineering works that were visually pleasing, but MacColl insisted that everything be done to allay the very real public anxieties concerning the impact of the project on Pitlochry. In the event, the scheme brought prosperity to the town during the construction period, and the tourist traffic since its completion has been greater than ever, seemingly growing each year, as visitors from all over the world visit the dam, power station and particularly the fish ladder. They are encouraged to do so. Indeed, it was at MacColl's insistence that the Pitlochry dam was opened as a public walk, and an observation chamber built into the first fish ladder so that visitors could see the salmon on their way upstream. MacColl even abandoned the name he had suggested for the reservoir created by the dam. This he wanted to call 'Loch Bailie-Cloich-Righ' from the old Pictish name of Pitlochry, the 'place of the King's Great Stepping-Stones', but he left the selection to the local community, and Pitlochry Burgh Council chose Loch Faskally, derived from the name of the estate on the left bank opposite Clunie Power Station.[50]

Another feature of the Tummel-Garry area much visited by tourists is the large arch which stands near the road leading to the Tummel Falls and straddles the approach road to Clunie power station. The arch is a replica of the cross section of Clunie Tunnel, a horse-shoe shape with a height and width of 22 feet 6 inches, which made it the largest water-carrying tunnel in Great Britain. Guthrie Brown suggested to MacColl that it might be of interest to the public to have some idea of the sheer sise of the Clunie tunnel, the construction of which was a major undertaking in itself.[51] The arch might

PLATE 7   The dam and power station at Pitlochry seen from downstream

also form an appropriate memorial to the men who had died during the driving of the tunnel when a charge placed at the working face was exploded prematurely by lightning striking the hillside immediately above. MacColl gave enthusiastic support to this suggestion as did the six major contractors on the Clunie section when the proposal was put to them, and the arch was built in 1951.[52] (See Plate 8).

The first stage of the Tummel-Garry scheme which comprised the Clunie and Pitlochry dams and generating stations was virtually completed during 1950. At Clunie, the first 20,400 kW turbo-alternator began to operate in April, the second in June and the third in November. The first 7,500 kW set in the Pitlochry station was started up in October and the second in December.[53] The first part of MacColl's second major scheme was finished. He had seen it in operation but he died suddenly on 15 June 1951, on the very eve of its formal opening by Lady MacColl.

4   The Board and its external relations

Guthrie Brown, so closely associated with MacColl in the Tummel-Garry scheme, was later to say that MacColl's death was hastened by over-work.[54] This is almost certainly true. Since becoming Deputy Chairman and Chief Executive of the Board in 1943, MacColl had been working at 'high pressure'. By 1950 much had been achieved, but to MacColl there was still so much left to be done; things that he felt he had to set afoot before he retired, for he had 'little faith' that many of his most cherished ideas 'would be carried on after he went'. He was, in his last two years, 'slowing down'. Grappling with the problems caused by chronic shortages of labour and materials; assuming personal responsibility for the embarrassing delays that made it impossible for Sloy and Tummel-Garry to contribute to the national supply of electricity in 1947-48; increasingly aware that inflationary pressures were making nonsense of earlier cost estimates; and perpetually suspicious of the machinations of Whitehall, which threatened the Board's programme and even its continued existence, MacColl 'was tired and somewhat embittered'.[55]

Part of the problem stemmed from his own character, 'MacColl did not delegate easily. He felt the responsibility was his for the day-today decisions and the load was beyond the ability of any one man to carry. It was clear that he was working beyond his capacity'.[56] Indeed, he had been doing so for some time. The fact is that the management of the Board had always been run on a shoe-string. The senior members of the staff, younger than MacColl but equally enthusiastic, were few in number and similarly over-worked. The Board may have made extensive use of civil, electricial and mechanical engineering consultants and architects,[57] but in the end their proposals had to be considered, evaluated and acted upon by a relatively small group of people— comprising Thomas Lawrie, who became General Manager in 1948, Angus Fulton, Chief Hydraulic and Civil Engineer, W D D Fenton, who succeeded Lawrie as Secretary but retained his post as Commercial Engineer, J J Cargill, Guthrie's successor as Chief Mechanical and Electrical Engineer, and A M Ferrier, the Chief Accountant—at Rothesay Terrace, the burden on whom had been greatly increased by the provisions of the Electricity Act of 1947. Indeed, as some speakers had predicted in the debates on

PLATE 8   Clunie Arch

the Hydro-Electric Development Bill in 1943, the need to satisfy their political masters at nearly every turn imposed an almost intolerable burden on the Board's senior officals. In addition to their 'statutory duties of consulting the Amenity Committee, the Fisheries Committee, the General Post Office, Local Authorities under the Town and County Planning Act, and the Ministry of Transport', the Board suffered from 'an excess of Working Parties'. For example, in 1948, Angus Fulton, 'in as far as his other duties permit ... [had] to attend the Generating Capacity Committee in London (run by the Ministry of Works); the Working Party (in Edinburgh) of the above Committee for the Board's Schemes (run by the Ministry of Works), the Heavy Plant Committee in London (run by the Ministry of Supply); and the Power Station Equipment Committee in London (run by the Ministry of Supply)'.[58]

'The Labour Party's victory in the election of 1945 made it inevitable that the public supply of electricity should be nationalised'. Leslie Hannah has told us, and has demonstrated convincingly that 'Nationalisation was somewhat less of a radical departure for the industry than Labour (and Conservative) speakers sometimes claimed'. Even before Labour came to power, municipal enterprise accounted for two-thirds of the sales of electricity, well over half of which they generated themselves. In bulk supply, the Central Electricity Board—a public corporation established by the Conservative Government in 1927—had controlled the operation of power stations since the completion of the initial national grid in 1933, and the Electricity Commissioners supervised matters such as co-operation between the various undertakings. Thus, 'while rather more than a third of the capital in the industry was still under private control in 1945, public ownership already dominated, and there was a wide degree of public supervision'.[59]

In this context, state ownership and control of the entire industry was, compared with certain other candidates for nationalisation, a relatively small step. Furthermore, in determining the future organisation of the industry, the Ministers most intimately concerned—Herbert Morrison, the Lord President of the Council, who took charge of the nationalisation programme, and Mr Emmanuel Shinwell, the Minister of Fuel and Power—were strongly influenced by the proposals made by Major Gwilym Lloyd-George's Committee of 1944.[60] It will be recalled that whereas Lloyd-George had, somewhat reluctantly, been prepared to accept 'using the Hydro-Electric Board as the distributing authority' for the North of Scotland, he remained adamant that the Board's generating functions should be taken over by his proposed Central Generating Board.[61] Therefore, when the organisation and structure of what was to be the British Electricity Authority was under active consideration in 1946, Tom Johnston was understandably apprehensive. There was, he felt, 'serious danger that our Hydro Schemes would be swallowed up in the new mammoth organisation ... there *were* well-grounded fears that the Hydro Board was ... for the tumbrils: its identity to be lost: its economic development and social improvement purposes for the Highlands submerged or cancelled outright ...'.[62] This could not be allowed to happen. To Johnston, the Board was 'possibly the last hope of stemming the depopulation of the crofting counties'. Yet ranged against him were 'people at the Ministry of Fuel and Power who could conceive of nothing but a unified centralised control by some gigantic machine covering the whole country', and the majority of the engineers at the Central Electricity Board who, since the very creation of the Hydro Board, had become increasingly resentful of its independence and what appeared to them to be its privileges. To the CEB, nationalisation and the establishment of the new British Electricity Authority seemed to offer an ideal opportunity to gain control of a body with whom their relationship had become disharmonious, even hostile.[63]

The origins of these problems lay in the CEB's belief that there was but little scope for profitable development in the Highlands. Indeed, so unpromising did the sparsely-populated North of Scotland appear as a consuming area that no attempt was made to prepare a grid scheme for it. The establishment of the North of Scotland Hydro-Electricity Board did more than hurt the pride of the CEB, they were incensed at the terms under which they were being asked to act as the wholesaler of the Board's electricity in the South under the Act of 1943. In their earlier wholesale purchases of energy from the Grampian Co., the CEB had insisted on sharing some of the benefits of cheap hydro with the company,[64] and when the Bill establishing the Hydro Board was being drafted the CEB expected a similar arrangement with the new Board. They were horrified at the price formula recommended by the Cooper Committee which, they felt, was far too favourable to the Board,[65] and they strongly urged its rejection. Not only did the CEB win their point[66] but Harold Hobson, their chairman, was unremitting in his insistence on tighter CEB control over the magnitude and timing of delivered supplies and the Board's forward planning, to weaknesses in which he unfairly attributed their inability to complete the Sloy and Tummel-Garry schemes on time, thereby exacerbating the national fuel shortage. And if many of the CEB's arguments were both legally correct and economically rational, they betrayed an acute insensitivity to the aspirations and difficulties of the infant Board.

Relations between the two bodies reached their nadir in 1945-6 with the case of 'the points of delivery of electricity to be supplied by the Hydro Board to the Central Board'.[67] The case was highly complex and technical but basically the Hydro Board claimed that since it was the clear intention of the Act of 1943 that 'the benefits accruing from the development of Highland water power [should] be retained for the benefit of District', the points at which they should deliver their surplus energy to the CEB should be those which imposed 'the least possible burden on them'. These points, which would minimise the Board's transmission costs, would be 'in the west on the double circuit line of the Central Board between the Yoker and Port Dundas sub-station' and 'a point in the east at Abernethy'.[68] The CEB would have none of this. They claimed that they should not lose on the cost of transmission and that they required the supplies to be given at those points at which they would otherwise have provided additional generating plant. They demanded therefore that the Hydro Board abide by the strict letter of the 1943 Act and deliver supplies of electricity' at the lower-voltage busbars of each of nine ... selected steam stations in Central Scotland'.[69] The CEB were completely unmoved[70] by the Hydro Board's argument that for them to acquiesce in the CEB's demands would absorb almost *all* the profit which they hoped and expected to derive from sales from Sloy and Tummel-Garry, profit upon which they depended to finance uneconomic schemes.[71] 'The inhabitants of the West Highlands and Islands would not get electricity and the intention of the 1943 Act would be defeated'.[72]

There was no alternative but to apply to the Electricity Commissioners for a determination of the case. It was heard before Sir Cyril Hurcombe, Sir John Kennedy and M H Nimmo on 4 April 1946, both sides being represented by King's Counsel. Although 'the commissioners ... found themselves unable to accept in full the contentions and proposals of either side', essentially they ruled in favour of the Hydro Board. They determined that electricity from Loch Sloy should be delivered at a point on the 132kV main transmission line at or near Drumchapel and up to 25,000kW of that from Tummel-Garry at Abernethy, and the balance at Bonnybridge.[73] The Hydro Board was relieved and delighted; the CEB angry and vindictive.[74]

The Hydro Board's euphoria was short-lived. Clearly, the Electricity Commissioners' ruling was of vital importance to the implementation of their long-term plans, but it made the CEB all the more convinced that Scottish hydro-electricity should be absorbed by a national body and subservient to a national plan. No wonder Tom Johnston feared for the future of 'his' Board. The Scottish Office too were alarmed at the prospect of the Hydro Board being 'administratively disembowelled'. Nevertheless, the Board was not without some winning cards. Although the CEB may have had financial and technical logic on their side and the ear of the majority of the officials at the Ministry of Fuel and Power, the Electricity Commissioners were sympathetic, and they had already invited the Board to submit 'their views about the future of electricity supply in Scotland, bearing in mind the new legislation which is expected on the subject of nationalising and regionalising electricity supply'.[75] The Scottish Office also gave the Board strong support. Joseph Westwood, the Secretary of State, had been Johnston's Parliamentary Secretary in 1943, and was unswerving in his loyalty.

But the Board's greatest strength lay in the personal influence of its new chairman. He was convinced that if he 'could but get ... Mr Shinwell (then Minister of Fuel and Power) and Mr Herbert Morrison up [to Scotland] ... he could make them aware of the tragic blunder that would be committed were the water power assets of our northern counties to be torn from their native economy and made to serve not reinvigorated straths and glens, but already overpopulated industrial areas in the South'. Johnston achieved his objective. Both Shinwell and Morrison came north. Shinwell visited Pitlochry and Morrison, Sloy. 'When they arrived—separately—and saw and listened they both had the vision to declare forthrightly for the retention of [the Board's] autonomy'. Mr Shinwell was so determined to let it be known where he stood that he told the representatives of the Press—whom Johnston had carefully assembled—that 'our Hydro powers would not be impaired in any way by the new Bill. Some of his *entourage* from the Ministry were not ... pleased'.[76] Mr Shinwell fulfilled his promise. In May 1946 he 'told his [Cabinet] colleagues that the Central Generating Board and the Regional Distribution Boards would cover the whole country except the North of Scotland where the Hydro-Electric Board would be suitably reconstituted and would manage both the generation and distribution assets in its area'.[77]

Discussions between the Ministry of Fuel and Power, the Scottish Office and the Treasury continued throughout 1946. The Ministry, much influenced by the advice of the CEB, tried to salvage what they could of their original policy by conceding that the Hydro Board would have generating and distribution functions but insisting that the Board be under the overall control of the new national authority, to whom they should look for their finances. The Scottish office, conscious of the threat to the Board's independence, objected strongly. To agree to the Ministry's proposals would mean that future schemes put forward by the Board would be judged solely on grounds of electricity policy; the wider social objectives explicit in the Act of 1943 would either be ignored or subordinated to strict economic considerations. 'In the end the Scottish Office gained most of its points. Agreement was reached on a scheme which placed the North of Scotland in a special position'.[78]

The arrangements which emerged as a result of these manoevrings were incorporated in the 1947 Electricity Bill. The Board was to take over the sixteen local authority and private undertakings in the North of Scotland and be solely responsible for generation, transmission and distribution within its greatly expanded area of operations. The Board itself was enlarged from five to nine members to be appointed jointly by the Minister of Fuel and Power and the Secretary of State for Scotland; and it was the Secretary of State who would issue general directions to the Board, not the Minister. Well might speakers in the second reading debate on the Electricity Bill suggest that the privileged position accorded to the North of Scotland was due largely to backstairs intrigue between Tom Johnston and his political friends in the Labour Government. This suggestion was rebutted with some indignation by the Secretary of State and, in truth, Johnston did not get everything he wanted. To his intense chagrin, the new British Electricity Authority, staffed by ex-members of the CEB, was to vet the Board's hydro schemes. Although the Minister of Fuel and Power and the Secretary of State for Scotland could arbitrate in the event of disagreement and overrule the BEA, the power given to the Board's 'chief customer' to approve or not to approve the Board's generation schemes infuriated Johnston.[79] It was to cause considerable friction.

Meanwhile, on 1 April 1948, vesting day, the Board's area of operations was extended to include the cities of Aberdeen, Dundee and Perth, the towns of Inverness and Oban, the area of the Grampian Electricity Supply Co., and the undertakings of a number of smaller local authorities and companies.[80] These additions raised the Board's statutory supply area from 17,000 to 21,600 square miles or to 74 per cent of the total area of Scotland. Despite the acquisition of several populous regions, the total population to be served was still less than 1.2 million, with an average consumer density of about 50 per square mile, perhaps one-sixth of the comparable figure for England and Wales. With the increasing number of constructional schemes, no less than twelve of which had been published by the Board and approved by Parliament by January 1948, an ever-growing mileage of transmission and distribution lines, and the manifold problems involved in taking over and co-ordinating the activities of sixteen existing undertakings in the north of Scotland, the pressure on the Board's senior officials grew alarmingly. It was deemed to be both necessary and desirable to devolve some of their responsibilities, and the Board's area was divided into fourteen districts, each having a large measure of local control.[81] This was but one major step in devising an efficient administrative structure for the Board.

But it was the conduct of the Board's external relations that proved most vexatious and time-consuming for its senior officials. It was in this sphere that Tom Johnston made his major contribution, thus permitting the engineers to devote much of their attention to the work of construction and of co-ordinating the Board's accelerating programmes of generating and distribution. Although Johnston 'could always rub along harmoniously enough with [the] chairman [of the newly-created British Electricity Authority], Lord Citrine',[82] with whom he had co-operated in past political campaigns, he could not abide the BEA's officers. They 'might have been experts in steam stations but [they had] no experience in hydro' and yet they tried to go beyond 'the vaguely-worded consultative status legally accorded to them ... and to establish real technical and financial control of the [Hydro] Board'.[83] Johnston and his colleagues were determined to resist any erosion of their autonomy. They made it quite clear from the start that they would appeal to the Secretary of State whenever the BEA attempted to use their vetting powers to inhibit the Board's activities. They provided the BEA with only the minimum of information about their new constructional schemes, and complained bitterly when the BEA would 'only pass [the] schemes with a qualified ... approval in view of the 'limited' information [the Board was prepared to supply]'. Had it not been for Johnston's personal standing and friendship with the ministers, it is doubtful that they would have accepted 'the BEA's limited formula as adequate warranty for passing [the Board's] schemes'.

Having made clear his detestation of outside interference with the affairs of the Board—interference which he saw as but the precursor of ultimate control by London—Johnston adopted a more conciliatory position. Although he refused to vote at the rare meetings of the BEA which he could be persuaded to attend, he raised no objection to the spirit of compromise which is increasingly evident in communications between David Fenton, the Board's newly-appointed Secretary and Commercial Engineer, and the BEA. Citrine too exercised a restraining influence on his senior officials, and relations between the two bodies evidently improved to such an extent that Tom Johnston, looking back in 1952, felt able to say that they were 'on the whole not bad'.[84] Contentious matters remained to be solved and further difficult issues were to arise, but at least they were approached without the posturing which soured the initial months of nationalised electricity.

CHAPTER 6

The Realisation of the Development Plan: Hydro-Electric Development, *c.*1951–1961

In their *Annual Report* for 1951 the Board were able to announce, with justifiable pride, that in the year under review 'for the first time the hydro-electric schemes built by the Board reached the stage of large-scale production. By the end of the year over 280,000 kilowatts of new hydro-electric power were available, producing 576,000,000 units of electricity per annum. The total hydro-electric production, including the output of the pre-war Grampian stations at Rannoch and Tummel and four other small stations transferred to the Board, had reached the rate of nearly 900,000,000 units or kilowatt hours of electricity per annum.... When the hydro-electric schemes now being surveyed, promoted and constructed are in operation, this production will be nearly quadrupled'.[1] There followed, in tabular form, the Board's programme for the development of Highland water power resources as envisaged at the end of 1951 (see Table 2).

That this programme was no *mere* expression of the Board's aspirations is revealed by the detailed appendices to the Report. These showed thirteen schemes already under construction and three more in an advanced state of promotion. MacColl, who died at his work in June 1951, had bequeathed a detailed plan of action to his colleagues, but it would never have been realised had his immediate successors,[2] Tom Lawrie and Angus

TABLE 2 *NSHEB: The Development Programme as envisaged in 1951*

	Total Capacity (kilowatts)	Estimated Annual Output (millions of kilowatt hours or units)
In operation		
Constructed by the Board	282,585	576
Transferred to Board	84,915	297
Under construction	292,000	809
Promoted but not yet under construction	71,100	232
In course of promotion	155,000	568
Under survey	212,000	751
	1,097,600	3,233

Source: NSHEB, *Annual Report*, 1951, p. 7

PLATE 9   Angus Fulton

Fulton, not been infused with as much driving energy and enthusiasm as MacColl himself, and had they not been assisted and encouraged by a Panel of Technical Advisors who had long been fervent advocates of Scottish hydro development, men like Sir William Halcrow, James Williamson, J R Beard and S B Donkin. Furthermore, the money was there. Tom Johnston, chairman of the Board since 1946, had been assured—certainly, he believed he had been promised—that the necessary resources would be made available. MacColl's own attitude was that 'the Treasury has given me £100m and I am going to spend it before they take it away', despite repeated warnings by Sir William Halcrow that by instigating so many schemes at once he was pushing up the price of labour and materials.[3] And if Tom Lawrie, under Treasury pressure, had been

TABLE 3 *NSHEB: Capital Expenditure, 1950-1967*

	Capital Expenditure during year (£m)			Total Capital Expenditure (£m) at end of year		
	Total	on Hydro-Electric generation	$\frac{\text{Hydro}}{\text{Total}}$%	Total	on Hydro-Electric generation	$\frac{\text{Hydro}}{\text{Total}}$%
1950	12.2	10.5	86	57.7★	36.2★	63
1951	14.4	6.9	61	69.1	43.0	62
1952	13.6	8.8	65	82.7	51.8	63
1953	15.9	11.4	72	98.6	63.3	64
1954	19.9	14.8	74	118.5	78.1	66
1955	22.1	16.3	74	140.6	94.4‡	67
1956	19.5	14.2	73	160.0	108.6	68
1957	16.9	12.4	73	176.9	121.0	68
1958	15.4	11.6	75	192.3	132.6	69
1959	13.0	8.8	68	205.3	141.4	69
1960	10.2	6.6	65	215.5	148.0	69
1961	12.5	7.8	62	228.0	155.8	68
1962	15.2	9.4	62	243.1	165.1	68
1963	16.5	7.8	47	259.7	172.9	67
31/iii/1965†	21.9	7.8	36	281.7	180.8‡	64
31/iii/1966	14.3	3.8	27	296.0	184.6	62
31/iii/1967	9.4	1.2	13	305.5	185.8	61

★ Includes acquisitions.
† Period of 15 months to 31 March 1965.
‡ Examples of further disaggregation for 1955 and 1965 (£m):

	1955	%	1965	%
Land and compensation	0.73	(0.8)	1.56	(0.8)
Buildings and civil engineering works	83.77	(88.7)	156.80	(86.8)
Plant and machinery, pipelines etc	9.90	(10.5)	22.40	(12.4)
Total	94.40	(100.0)	180.76	(100.0)

Source: NSHEB, *Annual Reports and Accounts.*

more circumspect, Angus Fulton possessed a fanaticism for hydro development which possibly exceeded even MacColl's.

Thus, the decade of the 1950s did, in fact, see the substantial realisation of the programme drawn up in late 1940s. Whatever doubts may be entertained concerning its economic rationality, it was a remarkable engineering achievement. In the years 1953-58, the Board's annual capital expenditure on hydro schemes was never less than £11m., or over 75 per cent of their total capital investment (see Table 3). At one stage, in 1953, there were 14 power stations simultaneously under construction; and throughout the decade major *new* stations were being commissioned at the rate of nearly four a year (see Table 4). The number of people on the Board's payroll, either as direct employees or as members of the labour force of their numerous contractors, rose to a peak of well over 11,000 in 1954 and, until 1959, was never less than about 8,000 (see Table 5). In addition, the Board's programme provided a significant boost to the establishment and enlargement of several firms of consulting engineers; the demand for qualified civil engineers and auxiliary staff both on site and in central offices was considerable.

It is no exaggeration to say that the 1950s constituted a period of frenzied activity. It was almost as if Tom Johnston, the members of the Board, and the Board's senior officials shared a deep-seated fear that it was now or never. After decades of neglect and perverse opposition, Scotland's hydro potential had to be harnessed quickly before someone in Whitehall called a halt; before the great landowners, temporarily discomfited, regrouped and launched a counter-attack; before the colliery interests, whose standard was kept aloft by Gerald Nabarro, resumed their implacable opposition; before some scientific innovation would be used, fairly or unfairly, to undermine the case for hydro development altogether. Meanwhile, what MacColl had begun would be pushed to a conclusion. In this light, the words of Sir Christopher Hinton, the Chairman of the Central Electricity Generating Board, at the opening of the Glen-moriston scheme in September 1958, acquire a deeper meaning than was perhaps intended at the time: 'In 20, 30 and 50 years hence people looking at the hydro-electric development of Scotland will say how tremendously fortunate it was that this water power development took place when it did.'[4]

TABLE 4   *NSHEB: Hydro-Electric Power stations,* Number commissioned† in each year, 1948-1963

1948	2	1956	5
1949	0	1957	4
1950	4	1958	5
1951	2	1959	5
1952	3	1960	2
1953	1	1961	2
1954	3	1962	6
1955	4	1963	3

* Small stations are not included in this table.

† Dates of *first* commissioning; additional plant often came into service in the subsequent or later years. The date of first commissioning does not *always* correspond with that of the formal opening.

Source: NSHEB, *Annual Reports and Accounts*, and see Appendix Table 21.

TABLE 5   *NSHEB: Number of Employees, 1951-1967*

	Board's own Employees (end of year)	Men Employed by Contractors★	Approximate Total
1951	2,682	5,666	8,348
1952	2,541	6,200	8,741
1953	2,538	7,500	10,038
1954	2,591	9,000	11,591
1955	2,645	8,500	11,145
1956	2,672	7,100	9,772
1957	2,753	6,100	8,853
1958	2,861	4,900	7,761
1959	3,038	2,724	5,762
1960	3,169	3,700	6,869
1961	3,226	2,930	6,156
1962	3,320	2,934	6,254
1963	n.d.	1,851	—
March 1965	3,725	1,668	5,393
March 1966	3,920	1,345	5,265
March 1967	3,986	not recorded	—

★ 1951-1957, at end of year; 1958-1959, 1965-66, average; 1960-1962, maximum at any one time.
Source: NSHEB, *Annual Reports and Accounts.*

Glenmoriston was but one of a number of major schemes completed in the late 1950s. To provide accounts of each of them—as has been briefly attempted for Sloy and the initial stages of Tummel-Garry—would involve much repetition. Instead, some of the more noteworthy planning, technical, construction and economic aspects of the major schemes have been identified and discussed in the following pages. They are followed by some generalisations suggested by these avowedly selective accounts.[5]

1   The Major Schemes[6]

(i)   The Conon Valley (1946-1961)

The Board's plans for the exploitation of the River Conon basin in Ross and Cromarty were from the outset designed comprehensively to develop the entire catchment of about 400 square miles (see Fig. 19).[7] Although each of the component projects was relatively small, in aggregate they made a considerable contribution to the Board's total power production. The entire layout included eight dams, nine tunnels, and six power stations with a total installed capacity of well over 100,000 kW. The Conon development shares one characteristic with the earlier Galloway scheme for there are several examples of successive or cascade development. For example, water from Loch Glascarnoch is passed in turn through machines at Mossford, Luichart and Torr Achilty, dropping in the process about 800 feet, the combined gross head of these three stations. Torr Achilty, the lowest power station in the scheme, is situated just downstream of its dam, with a short connection from Loch Achonachie. While its head is only 52 feet, virtually all the water from the entire catchment area, which has an average annual rainfall of 75 inches, converges on its immediate reservoir.

Such a comprehensive plan, which included numerous diversions to capture the head waters of neighbouring catchments, had to be carried out sequentially. Three distinct stages may be identified: the Fannich scheme (1946-1951) the Glascarnoch-Luichart-Torr Achilty scheme (1951-1957) and the Orrin scheme (1955-1961). The first stage of the scheme, the Fannich section, although simple in layout, presented one spectacular problem. In addition to a number of aqueducts and tunnels designed to increase the flow into Loch Fannich, the major work consisted of driving a sloping tunnel, of horseshoe section, from the hillside above the site of Grudie Bridge power station (on the shore of Loch Luichart) towards and, at its northern end, some 90 feet beneath Loch Fannich. The tunnel was then driven out horizontally under the sloping bed of the Loch until it reached a point where the rock roof between it and the water above was only some 25 feet thick. This rock was cautiously pared away by drilling and blasting until all that remained was a 'plug' about 15 feet thick.

This plug had then to be removed. To do this was a complicated undertaking (see Fig. 20). Beneath the plug the tunnel was deepened to form a deep sump, large enough to accommodate at least twice the volume of the rock remaining in the plug, estimated to be about 500 tons. The upper part of the tunnel was sealed and the gate shaft (a vertical shaft that houses the gates for closing the tunnel) was filled with water to a level 12 feet below the level of the loch. This was done in order to produce a reverse pressure that would minimise the potentially dangerous effects of an inrush of water from the loch, and to encourage the debris from the plug to fall back into the sump. Even further precautions were deemed to be necessary. Three protective bulkheads were installed in the tunnel. The first, nearest the loch, consisted of a slab containing 85 tons of concrete; the second, 36 feet from the main bulkhead, contained 40 tons of concrete, and the third consisted of a wall of steel joists placed at the bottom of the screen shaft. Meanwhile, the plug had been drilled with 120 holes and packed with 200 lbs of explosives. The plug was then blown. Everything went according to plan. The first bulkhead, which it was estimated had been subjected to an instantaneous shock of nearly 10,000 tons, remained undamaged and the shattered remains of the plug settled obediently into the sump. The bulkheads were subsequently demolished. This was only the second time that such a risky operation had been performed in Great Britain; the first, also undertaken by the Board's major contractors, Balfour Beatty & Co., was that at Loch Treig in the Lochaber scheme.[8]

Loch Fannich thus became a natural reservoir. One which, by drawing down its level of 50 feet, was capable of storing 60 per cent of the anticipated annual average output of this part of the overall scheme. Five years later a dam was built. By raising the level of the reservoir by 20 feet this enlarged its storage capacity even further and increased the head at Grudie Bridge power station.

facing page
FIGURE 19   The Conon scheme

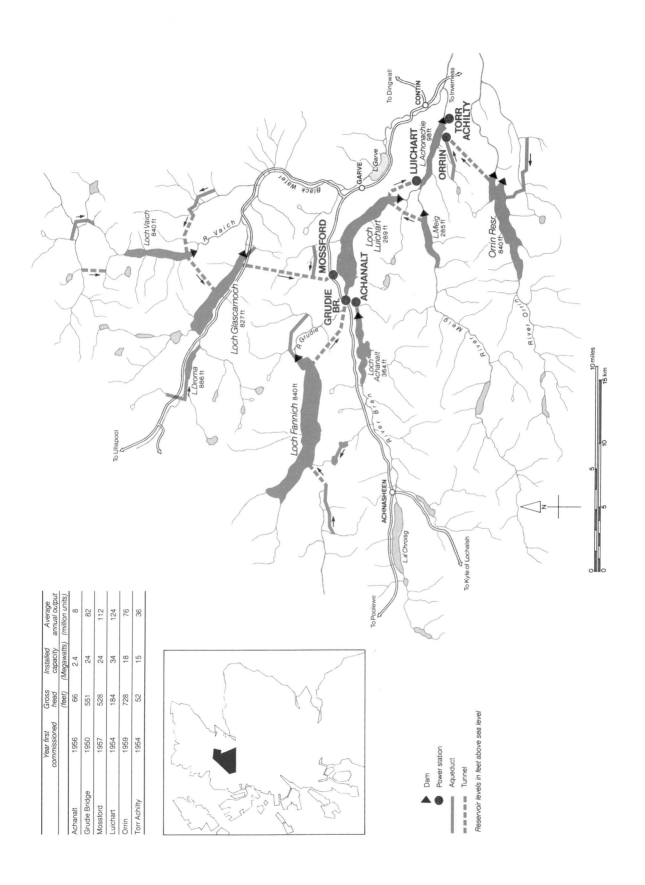

	Year first commissioned	Gross head (feet)	Installed capacity (Megawatts)	Average annual output (million units)
Achanalt	1956	66	2.4	8
Grudie Bridge	1950	551	24	82
Mossford	1957	528	24	112
Luichart	1954	184	34	124
Orrin	1959	728	18	76
Torr Achilty	1954	52	15	36

▲ Dam

● Power station

▬ ▬ ▬ Aqueduct

──── Tunnel

Reservoir levels in feet above sea level

TABLE 6 *Conon Valley: Major Dams*

Name of Dam	Type & Year of Completion	Length ft	Height above foundations ft	Cubic Capacity cub. yds.	Main Contractors
Glascarnoch	Concrete gravity & earthfill, 1957	1,753	141	186,000 concrete 268,000 earthfill	Reed & Mallik Ltd
Vaich	Earthfill with concrete core wall, 1957	843	123	35,000 concrete 400,000 earthfill	Reed & Mallik Ltd
Leuichart	Mass gravity, 1954	718	80	48,000	Reed & Mallik Ltd
Meig	Concrete gravity, buttress & earthfill, 1956	585	86	38,000 concrete 10,000 earthfill	Duncan Logan (Concractors) Ltd
Torr Achilty	Mass gravity, 1953	808	76	48,000	William Tawse Ltd
Orrin	Mass gravity, 1959	1,025	167	233,000	Duncan Logan (Contractors) Ltd

Consulting Engineers: Sir Alexander Gibb & Partners.

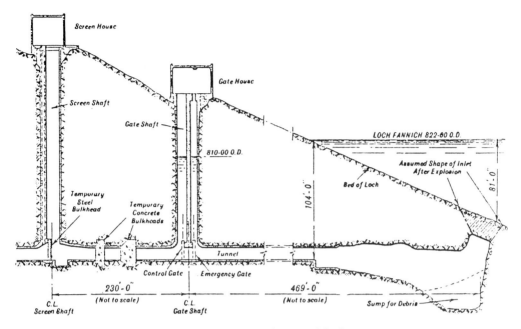

FIGURE 20   Loch Fannich: the tunnel–loch connection

One other feature of the Fannich Scheme is noteworthy. From the portal of the tunnel above Grudie Bridge, the water is conveyed by a single steel pipe-line, initially 8 feet in diameter. This leads to the valve house, whence the main pipe continues steeply downhill, gradually diminishing in internal diameter and increasing in thickness until, within 60 feet of the power station, by which time it is almost horizontal, it bifurcates into two branches to feed the pair of 12mW vertical shaft Francis turbines installed at the power station. Plate 10 shows the lower sections of the 1,500 foot pipeline. It was one of the last constructions of its kind; later in the 1950s the Board felt compelled to adopt alternative designs to reduce or even eliminate the visual impact of such long lengths of surface pipeline.

The six contractors employed by the Board on the second stage of the Conon Valley development—Glascarnoch-Luichart and Torr Achilty—began preliminary work in 1951.[9] In the north, construction of the dams on two tributaries of the River Blackwater, the Glascarnoch and the Vaich, began in the following year. It was decided to use an earth and rockfill form of construction in order to save cement and reduce the need for shuttering (see Plate 11). These dams created the artificial lochs of Vaich and Glascarnoch, whose natural catchments were supplemented by water (from Loch Beag, for example) tapped by tunnels and aqueducts. Another tunnel, almost 4.5 miles in length, takes these waters to Mossford power station on Loch Luichart. To exploit the water power of the western part of the Conon Basin, a small barrage and power station were built on the River Bran at the eastern end of Loch Achanalt only a short distance from Grudie

Bridge. Achanalt power station, like Mossford and Grudie Bridge, discharges into Loch Luichart. A mass gravity dam was built at the foot of Loch Luichart, whose waters were further supplemented by supplies from the River Meig. This was achieved by a dam of concrete gravity buttress and earthfill construction at Curin on the Meig which created the artificial Loch Meig, whence water is carried by tunnel to Loch Luichart. Finally, another relatively small mass gravity dam was built on the Conon itself at Torr Achilty, to create another artificial loch, Loch Achonachie. The principal function of the Torr Achilty dam was to even out the flow of water downstream, in much the same way as the dam at Pitlochry operates on the Tummel–Garry scheme. For this reason it has only a two feet range of level and is fitted with flood gates.

About 1,400 men were employed on this second stage of the Conon development and remarkable progress was made in nearly every aspect of the civil engineering work. Luichart power station was brought into commercial operation in July, and Torr Achilty in December 1954, only $3\frac{1}{2}$ years and 3 years and nine months, respectively, after work began; and A M Carmichael, of Edinburgh, completed the driving of both the Vaich tunnel and the Glascarnoch tunnel by October 1954, an average rate of driving for each face of 476 feet per month. The sheer length of the Glascarnoch tunnel, which involved very long hauls in disposing of the rock spoil, made this progress particularly note-worthy.

The final stage of the Conon development was the Orrin project. The River Orrin falls about 700 feet in the six miles above its junction with the River Conon. Of all the possibilities that were considered to exploit these favourable conditions, it was decided that the most economical would be a mass gravity dam eight miles above the Conon-Orrin junction and, from the reservoir thus created, the water should be diverted through a concrete-lined tunnel, over 3 miles long, to a steel pipeline. This conveys the water to an 18-mW generating station on the shore of Loch Achonachie, the artificial loch produced by the dam at Torr Achilty. Orrin dam, just over 1,000 feet long at roadway level, contains nearly a quarter of a million cubic yards of concrete (see Fig. 21). It raises the water level by 135 feet and forms a reservoir nearly five miles long. This plan involved sealing off a branch of the valley south of the concrete dam by an earth embankment with a reinforced concrete core, also about 1,000 feet long.

A number of features of this project, which was begun in 1955, are interesting. Orrin was the second largest dam[10] built by the Board, its height of 167 feet from foundation to crest being exceeded only by Sloy. Its dimensions were selected not in order to produce the cheapest cost per unit stored, but in pursuance of the Board's policy of determining the size of storage by what was necessary to make the energy firm.[11] The final cost of the civil engineering works (the two dams and the tunnel) was just over £2.8 million and it is apparent that the Board's obligation to avoid damaging the fishing of the Conon Valley had made a major contribution to this figure.

In the initial discussions of the design of the main dam some thought had been given to the possibility of a rockfill embankment for which the site was admirably suited, but *one* reason for the abandonment of this idea was that it could not properly cater for the

facing page
PLATE 10   Grudie Bridge Power Station and pipeline

PLATE 11   Vaich Dam

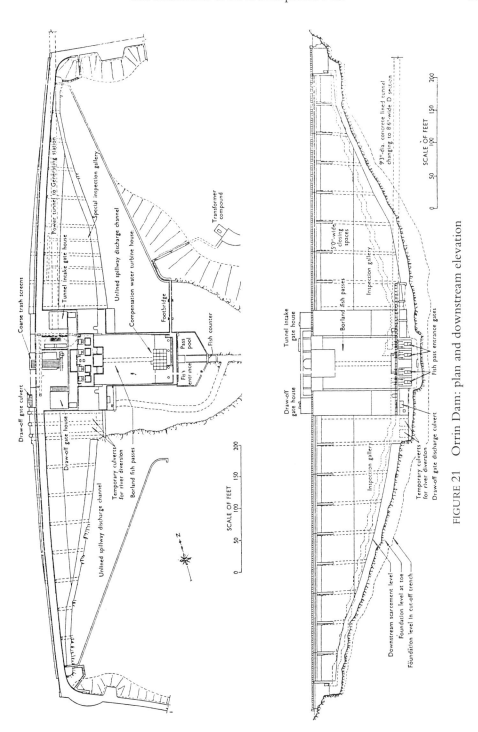

FIGURE 21   Orrin Dam: plan and downstream elevation

needs of migrating salmon. So important was this factor in influencing both the design and the timing of its constructional stages that in a discussion of a paper by the Resident Engineer of the project, one member of the Institution of Civil Engineers fulminated that

> more was said about the fish lock than about anything else ... the whole job was, in fact, built round the fish lock.[12]

There was some truth in this. Such was the height of the dam and the large range of the anticipated water levels that fish passes of the pool and orifice type were ruled out. The only type acceptable to the fishing interests was the Borland fish pass, first used by the Board at Torr Achilty.[13]

This fish pass was developed by J H T Borland, of Glenfield & Kennedy Ltd., the hydraulic engineers. It consists of an upper and lower pool connected by a steeply sloping shaft (see Fig. 22). Fish are attracted into the lower chamber by the flow of water over the upper sluice. The outlet is then closed and as the water continues to pour in, the fish are lifted by the water filling the shaft and either swim or jump into the reservoir ahead of the rising water. Smolts moving downstream are quite content to follow the current into the upper pool and slither down the shaft. The trouble with this

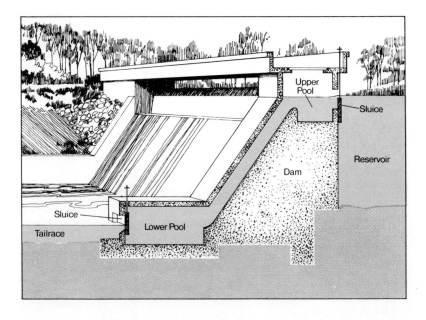

FIGURE 22   Borland Fish Lock

type of fish pass is that it cannot cope with a top water variation greater than about 20 feet because for it to do so would involve the installation of an excessively large top weir gate. It was thought that a modification in the design might overcome this problem but, as Alan Gowers told the Institution of Civil Engineers,

> time was limited and as the salmon is a fish with habits which are still imperfectly known, the adoption of an untried design would have been an acceptable risk[14]

It was therefore decided to provide *four* separate passes to cover the entire range of the anticipated variations in the water level of the Orrin reservoir (see Fig. 23 and Plate 12). Exactly what proportion of the total capital cost of the Orrin project was attributable to the need to look after the interests of the salmon is not known. Indeed, in addition to Torr Achilty, the Board had already installed Borland fish lifts at Luichart, Meig and Achanalt barrage. The opening up of Conon Falls in this way gave breeding fish access to Loch Luichart for the very first time. Salmon could now get right through to Achnasheen, and the Board assisted in the creation of nearly 20 additional miles of salmon fishing by planting 200,000 salmon fry in the Upper Bran.[15]

One final point may be made about the Orrin scheme. In the discussion of the project before the Institution of Civil Engineers, the Board's General Manager, Angus Fulton,

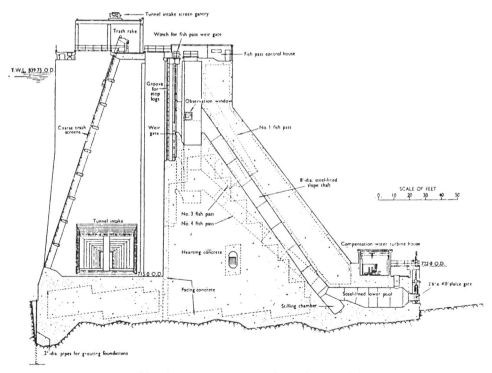

FIGURE 23   Orrin Dam: section through No.2 fish pass

PLATE 12   Orrin Dam: fish pass linings during erection

observed significantly:

> With today's [1964] knowledge of what [is] possible in the way of reversible pump turbines, it [is] interesting to speculate on what might have been done with the Orrin dam if such a convenient method of pumping water had been available at the time it was decided to proceed with it [c.1955]. It [is] now beginning to look as if the extra cost of making a turbine reversible [is] low enough to justify its use to maintain storage in a reservoir. Where conditions [are] favourable, and cheap pumping energy [is] available at nights and over weekends, some lesser height of dam would serve to ensure firm output from the project. In a period where there [is] so much reluctance to make capital available for hydro-electric investment such an opportunity to reduce the cost of capital works [is] one which should not be overlooked.[16]

(ii)   Affric-Beauly (1947-63)

The Grampian Electricity Company had long coveted the hydro-electric potential of Glen Affric. It had been the subject of two abortive bills in 1929 and 1941, but with the creation of the Hydro Board and the war's end, the intense opposition aroused by previous schemes appeared to have moderated. The time was ripe for another attempt to gain Parliamentary sanction for a project which promised to be of great importance to the infant organisation. It was large; it would undoubtedly be 'profitable', in the sense that its operation would produce a surplus capable of 'carrying' the Board's uneconomic schemes; and, carefully planned to preserve the natural beauty of the glen, its successful implementation would sustain the momentum generated by Sloy and Tummel-Garry. The difficult passage of these two major schemes to the stage of confirmation had starkly revealed the continued existence of all the old animosities. Great care was essential. Some have argued that with the approval of Tummel-Garry few obstacles stood in the way of the Hydro-Board. While it is true that no scheme was more likely to raise objections than that which, in the public mind at least, centred on Pitlochry, the Board was by no means complacent. It had been too close a run thing. The Board could not afford to rouse their distractors or play into the hands of their temporarily vanquished enemies. Thus, the Board were prepared to forgo the possibility of fully exploiting the area by producing a plan that would, with luck, secure acquiescence, if not positive enthusiasm.

With the aid of their consultants, Sir William Halcrow & Partners on the civil side and Kennedy & Donkin on the electrical and mechanical side, and advised by James Shearer, one of the Board's panel of architects, a scheme was evolved that would not only preserve the scenic beauty of Glen Affric but would reduce the danger of periodic severe flooding to which the glen and Strathglass were especially subject.

The scheme proposed to utilise the waters of the Rivers Cannich and Affric, both of which are tributaries of the River Glass. This was to be effected by the erection of a large dam across the outlet of Loch Mullardoch and a second, much smaller dam across the outlet of Loch Beinn a'Mheadloin (Loch Benevean). By leading the water impounded in Loch Mullardoch through a tunnel to Loch Benevean, the combined waters would pass through a second tunnel to the main power station at Fasnakyle and be discharged into the River Glass (see Fig. 24). To utilise the difference in level between

PLATE 13   Orrin Dam

the two reservoirs, a subsidiary underground generating station was to be built at the upstream end of the Mullardoch-Benevean tunnel. Unlike the inter-war proposals, which would have involved the conversion of Loch Affric and Loch Benevean, lying further down Glen Affric, into one large sheet of water, the Board's scheme envisaged raising the level of Loch Benevean by only 23 feet—a height that left Loch Affric and Affric Lodge unaffected—by transferring the main burden of storage to Loch Mullardoch. This remote loch, the level of which would be raised by 113 feet (from 704 feet to 817 feet), would accommodate the bulk of the main fluctuations in storage.

Constructional Scheme No.7—the Mullardoch-Fasnakyle-Affric Project—embodying this plan was published in August 1946. Almost unbelievably, no objections were raised on grounds of amenity. There were no fishery problems, and the Secretary of State received only one objection on a technical point, which was withdrawn after negotiation. The Scheme passed through all its stages without opposition and became operative in February 1947.[17] Considerable preparatory work was necessary before the actual construction could begin. Two labour camps, one at Cannich and another at Cozac, near Mullardoch, were built to accommodate a total of 2,100 men, and offices and workshops were also built. A considerable mileage of road construction and improvement was required and four new bridges were built.[18] As the work progressed, and before the level of Loch Benevean could be raised, that part of the road running alongside the River Affric and Loch Benevean had to be diverted and run at a higher level on the flank of the valley (incidentally providing much better views of the surrounding country).

The main features of the Scheme, however, were the Mullardoch Dam and the two tunnels. The Mullardoch Dam, at the eastern end of the Loch, was destined to be the Board's largest dam: 2,385 feet long by 160 feet high above its deepest foundations, its construction required 286,000 cubic yards of concrete to impound no less than $7\frac{1}{2}$ million cubic feet of water. Even more constructional materials might have been required had it not been possible to build the dam in two wings inclined to one another and abutting on an island in the middle of the Loch (see Fig. 25). The dam is of the mass gravity type, and towards the end of 1949, by which time the north wing was well advanced, the Board were forced to accede to urgent government demands to reduce capital expenditure.[19] This posed considerable difficulties. The dam could either be completed to the original crest level, using a cheaper design or form of construction, or by constructing the south wing—which was only at the excavation stage—to a reduced crest level. The first alternative was rejected because although completing the south wing to a buttress gravity design would have saved materials, it would have involved such delays in revising the shuttering and plant lay-out that any economies in materials would rapidly have been dissipated in enhanced labour and logistical costs. The greater number of joiners that would have been required for the construction of a buttress gravity dam was, in fact, the very reason for the adoption of an orthodox gravity dam in the first place. The only way to achieve economies on the scale imposed on the Board was to re-design the south wing of the dam to a reduced height. Detailed estimates revealed that it would be economically irrational to lower the level of the crest below 797 feet OD (i.e. by 20 feet) because to do so would produce a massive diminution in the output of the scheme. Thus, in March 1950, although it was fully appreciated that any immediate savings effected by lowering the height of the mass gravity dam would be far less than the price that would eventually have to be paid to restore the dam to the original, optimum height, it was decided to adopt the 20 feet reduction.

Construction of the south wing of the dam proceeded on this basis for nearly a year until in February 1951 the government's insistence on maximum economy became less acute, and it was decided to complete the dam to the original crest level while the contractor's plant was still on the site. This too involved unique problems. It was necessary both to thicken that portion of the dam already completed and to restore the 20 feet lopped off the height. The first of these two stages was not as simple as it would appear:

> When a comparatively thick mass of fresh concrete is placed on and allowed to adhere to a mass of older concrete, differential contraction caused by drying out and cooling can create considerable internal stresses in the combined mass in the vicinity of the joint, which will be added algebraically to the stresses from externally imposed loads. These internal stresses may even be sufficient to break the bond between two concrete masses and to destroy the homogeneity of the monolith.

It was necessary, therefore, to devise a method of construction which would minimise the effect of contraction; a method, moreover, which would not involve the use of steel anchorages, for these were ruled out by the contemporary shortage of steel.

After intense study of past methods employed to thicken and raise the heights of dams, that used for the Mundaring Weir in Australia was found to be most suitable, chiefly because it too had been accomplished without steel bonds. It was this method that was finally adopted. A concrete blanket 11 feet 6 inches thick was applied to the downstream face of the dam. Over most of its great area this blanket did not come into direct contact with the 'old' dam, but was separated from it by a slot. This slot prevented any immediate bond between the two masses of concrete, helped to cool the concrete in the blanket, and inhibited the transfer of heat from the latter to the old concrete. Only when sufficient time had elapsed to permit most of the contraction in the new concrete to have taken place were the two masses bonded together. This was achieved by filling the slot with dry coarse aggregate and grouting (see Fig. 26). The task was completed by the summer of 1952,[20] some time after partial impounding of water had become possible.

Meanwhile, the tunnels had already been completed. As early as 1948 excavation had been proceeding on seven main faces, and by December almost a third of the total length of the two tunnels had been driven. By October 1949, the driving of the Benevean–Fasnakyle tunnel had been completed and work on the concrete lining begun, and by December almost two miles of the Mullardoch tunnel had been driven. By the end of the following year, 1950, both tunnels, each over three miles in length, had all but been finished. An important feature of the tunnelling was the extensive use of mechanisation by the principal contractors, John Cochrane & Sons. This was said to have been induced by the acute shortage of labour which encouraged the use of lighter

facing page
FIGURE 24   Affric/Beauly

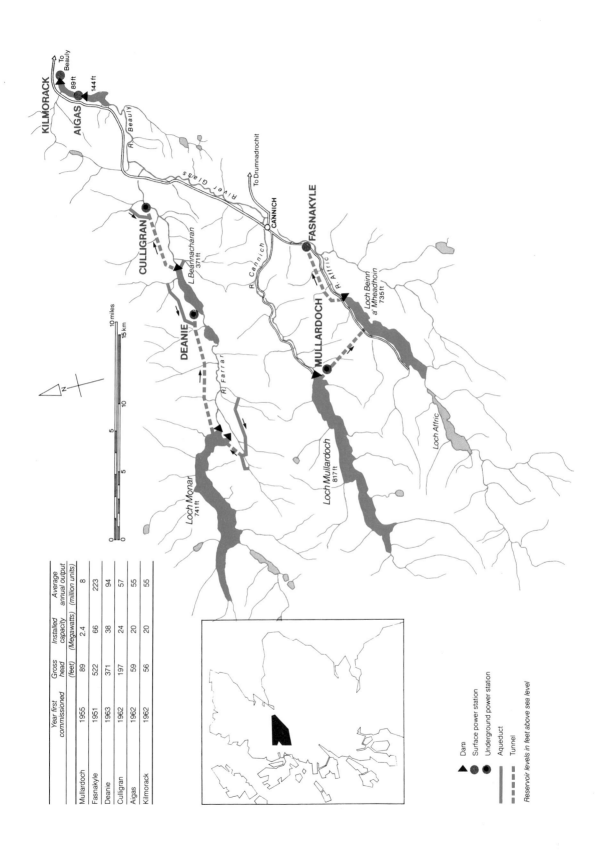

	Year first commissioned	Gross head (feet)	Installed capacity (Megawatts)	Average annual output (million units)
Mullardoch	1955	89	2.4	8
Fasnakyle	1951	522	66	223
Deanie	1963	371	38	94
Culligran	1962	197	24	57
Aigas	1962	59	20	55
Kilmorack	1962	56	20	55

KILMORACK

AIGAS

89 ft

144 ft

To Beauly

R. Beauly

River Glass

To Drumnadrochit

CANNICH

CULLIGRAN

L. Beannacharan
371ft

DEANIE

FASNAKYLE

R. Cannich

R. Affric

MULLARDOCH

Loch Beinn
a' Mheadhoin
735ft

R. Affric

R. Farrar

Loch Monar
741ft

Loch Mullardoch
817ft

Loch Affric

N

10 miles
15 km
0 5 10
0 5 10

Dam
Surface power station
Underground power station
Aqueduct
Tunnel

Reservoir levels in feet above sea level

TABLE 7 *Affric/Beauly: Major Dams*

Name of Dam	Type and Year of Completion	Length ft	Height above foundations ft	Cubic Capacity cub. yds.	Main Contractors
Mullardoch	Mass gravity, 1951	2,385	157	286,000	John Cochrane & Sons Ltd
Benevean	Mass gravity, 1951	582	122	64,500	John Cochrane & Sons Ltd
Monar	Arch constant angle, 1963	528	128	31,400	The Mitchell Construction Co.
Loichel	Mass gravity, 1961	680	65	19,200	Duncan Logan (Contractors) Ltd
Beannachran	Mass gravity, 1962	305	85	27,000	Duncan Logan (Contractors) Ltd
Aigas	Mass gravity, 1962	300	90	64,000	A A Stuart & Sons (Glasgow) Ltd
Kilmorack	Mass gravity, 1962	380	96	55,000	A A Stuart & Sons (Glasgow) Ltd

Consulting Engineers: Sir William Halcrow & Partners.

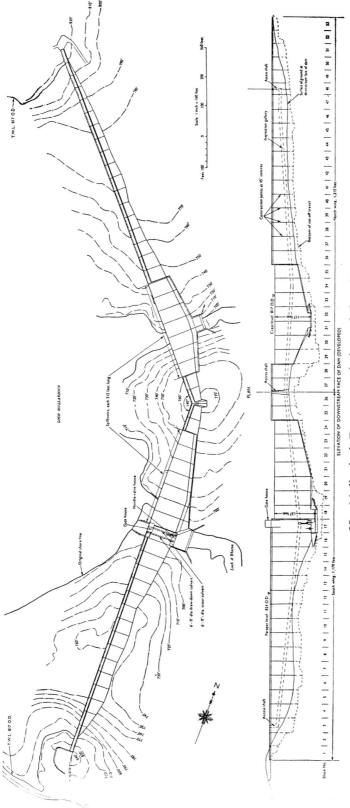

FIGURE 25   Mullardoch Dam: general plan and elevation

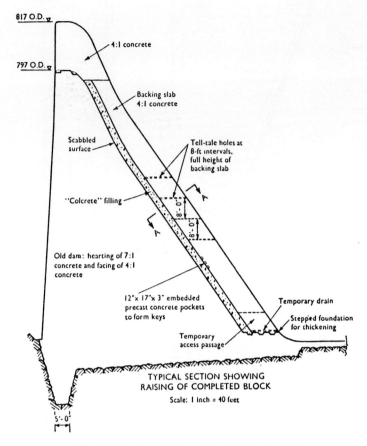

817 O.D.

797 O.D.

4:1 concrete

Backing slab
4:1 concrete

Scabbled
surface

Tell-tale holes at
8-ft intervals,
full height of
backing slab

"Colcrete" filling

8′-0″

8′-0″

Old dam: hearting of 7:1
concrete and facing of 4:1
concrete

12″x 17″x 3″ embedded
precast concrete pockets
to form keys

Temporary drain

Stepped foundation
for thickening

Temporary
access passage

TYPICAL SECTION SHOWING
RAISING OF COMPLETED BLOCK
Scale: 1 Inch = 40 feet

5′-0″

FIGURE 26   Method used for raising Mullardoch Dam

drilling rigs, the employment of special types of mechanical loaders to get rid of the spoil, and the introduction of pneumatic concrete placers to line the tunnels.[21]

The Mullardoch-Benevean tunnel falls about 3 feet over its entire length and is unlined except for a concrete invert throughout and full section lining at the portals and at certain sections of weak rock. The Benevean-Fasnakyle tunnel was more complicated, but few difficulties seem to have been encountered in its construction. The design of the tunnel was greatly influenced by the contemporary steel shortage and environmental considerations. Fig. 27, a longitudinal section of the Affric scheme, shows that the Fasnakyle tunnel has a low pressure section,[22] equivalent to almost three-quarters of its entire length; a high pressure shaft surmounted by a surge shaft; and a high pressure tunnel, falling at a gradient of 1 in 50. Eight hundred feet from its end, the high pressure tunnel divides into three steel-lined tunnels, each of which leads to one of the three 22,000kW vertical Francis turbo-alternators installed in the Fasnakyle generating station. It was the first time in Britain that a high pressure conduit for water had been constructed

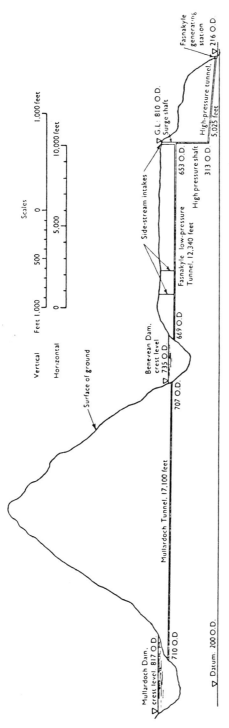

FIGURE 27   Longitudinal section of the Affric scheme

in this way. Fig. 27 makes it plain that an alternative design to that adopted had been possible. Indeed, such a design had been suggested by Sir William Halcrow's firm for the Report of the Water Power Resources Committee in 1918. This would have involved continuing the low-pressure tunnel in the same plane beyond the surge chamber to emerge on the hillside above the site of the generating station, whence the water could have been conveyed by a steel pipeline laid on the surface of the undulating rock platform before plunging down the steep gradient to the power station. This pipe could have been trifurcated before entering the station (or even at the top of the incline), just as in the chosen design. This alternative design, for all its simplicity, was rejected in order to economise on steel[23] and to avoid the criticism that would have been heaped on the Board for the sacrifice of amenity at the entrance to Glen Affric.

The Board were adequately rewarded when, at the opening ceremony on 13 October 1952, the Duke of Edinburgh said that one of his reasons for accepting the Board's invitation had been to see whether there was any justification in the criticism that the Board was wantonly destroying the beauty of the Highlands: 'I am entirely relieved of all anxiety on that score. To suggest that this power house [Fasnakyle] alone destroys the beauty of Glen Affric is being as fastidious as the fairy-tale princess who could feel a pea under fifteen mattresses.'[24] Furthermore, the scheme *did* confer enormous benefit to riverside agriculture, especially between Cannich and Aigas, by the regulation of the headwaters of the River Beauly. As the Board had expected, many hundreds of acres of arable and pasture land were relieved from continual flooding and brought back into regular cultivation.

The second stage of the Board's development of the water resources of the Rivers Farrar, Cannich and Affric, the main tributaries of the River Beauly which drain the eastern slopes of the higher parts of the North West Highlands, was not completed until 1963. No small part of the delay was caused by time-consuming and intense negotiations between the Board and local riparian owners whose objections to the Strathfarrar and Kilmorack Scheme (Constructional Scheme No.30) had first to be satisfied. One private settlement—that with Lord Lovat—involved the payment of compensation 'on account of all damage to fishings, both rod and line, and to spawning grounds' of no less than £100,000.[24] Even then the scheme was the subject of a public inquiry.

This was held in December 1957 and after the Commissioner made recommendations in favour of the Scheme, it was confirmed by the Secretary of State in May 1958. A Prayer for its annulment, moved by the indefatigable Gerald Nabarro and debated in Parliament on 14 July 1958, was rejected by 122 votes to 2,[25] and the Scheme became operative in July.

The scheme is in two separate sections, harnessing the power potentials of the River Farrar and of the River Beauly respectively. Water storage on the Farrar is provided by the Monar dam and supplies a 38MW station at Deanie. This discharges into a reservoir created by Bennachran dam, which in turn feeds Culligran power station, of 24MW capacity. The water is then returned to the Farrar. For the next six miles there are no hydraulic works. The river in this area traverses a plain and falls only 29 feet between the Culligran tail-race and the reservoir created by the first of the dams, Aigas, on the

facing page
PLATE 14   Monar Dam

PLATE 14   Monar Dam

River Beauly proper. By this time the waters of the Farrar have been joined, via the River Glass, by those of the Affric and the Cannich. The Beauly section of the Scheme consists of two 20MW run-of-river stations in immediate succession, Aigas and Kilmorack. The tailwater level at Kilmorack is 33 feet OD, and the total catchment area draining to Kilmorack is 350 square miles.

The Strathfarrar and Kilmorack scheme is particularly interesting for the variety both of the civil engineering works and of the hydraulic equipment.[26] Monar dam, for example, was the first double-curvature arch dam to be built in Britain (see Plate 14), whereas Loichel dam, designed to close an arm of Monar reservoir, is a plain gravity structure. Bennachran, Aigas, and Kilmorack dams are also of the gravity type, but they are far more elaborate than Loichel because they embody provisions for flood control, Borland fish passes, and for passing compensation water with or without power generation. Moreover, Aigas and Kilmorack incorporate power stations within the dam structure (see Plate 15). Indeed, these two dams have been facetiously described by their designers as 'a series of holes with concrete round them' but, as the journal *Water Power* observed, 'they are an ingenious and effective piece of civil-engineering design'. Not only does the entire scheme have an installed capacity of 102kW—achieved, Gerald Nabarro sarcastically informed the Commons, only at an estimated cost of £140 per kW—but a comprehensive system of automatic gates throughout the entire system which provides an effective means of flood control, made all the more remarkable by being designed for remote control from Fasnakyle, the first such scheme in Great Britain, 'if not further afield, to be designed in this way'.[27]

The variety which characterises the civil engineering side of the scheme is also to be found in the generating sets. Deanie station, painfully erected underground after exploratory surveys failed to reveal the existence of deep and dangerous fractures within what was apparently sound rock, is equipped with two Francis sets; Culligran, also underground, was fitted with the first Deriaz machine[28] to be installed in Great Britain; and Aigas and Kilmorack with almost identical pairs of 10MW vertical Kaplan turbines.

A number of the features of the Monar dam warrant rather more detailed treatment (see Fig. 28).[29] If Guthrie Brown, with an unrivalled knowledge of hydro-electric civil engineering practice, could state in the mid-1960s that under British conditions there seemed to be little future for arch dams,[30] why was such a dam chosen for Monar? Two leading members of Sir William Halcrow & Partners, who acted as the Board's consulting engineers for the entire scheme, subsequently explained that the choice was dictated by the shape of the valley of the River Farrar at the projected dam site and by economic considerations.[31] The Board did, in fact, invite tenders for both an arch and a gravity dam, and the price quoted for the former by The Michell Construction Co., who were awarded the contract, proved to be about 9 per cent less than for the alternative gravity type. It is possible, however, that the risk of incurring *additional* costs had not been fully appreciated. After the handsome dam had been erected—and it should be emphasised that only 36,000 cubic yards of concrete were used in its construction—the Board's consultants observed;

> The experience gained ... has shown that an arch dam should be chosen only where the nature of the foundation has been explored to a degree not usual for other types of dam. It

PLATE 15   Kilmorack Dam and Power Station

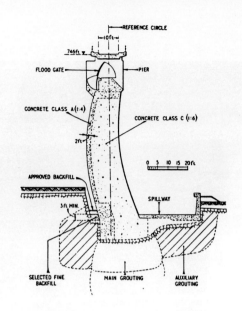

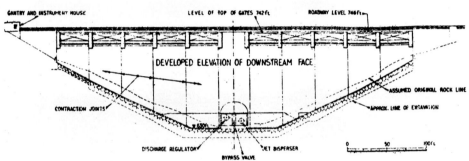

DEVELOPED ELEVATION OF DOWNSTREAM FACE

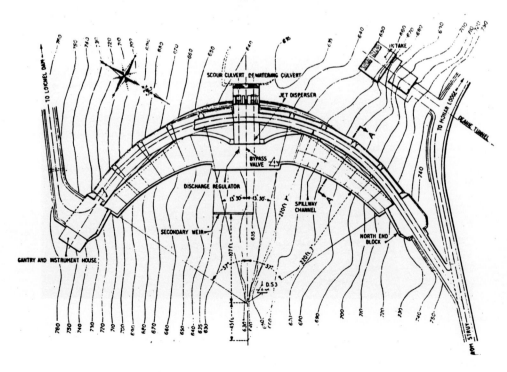

seems desirable to excavate the foundations before designing the concrete arch and deciding on the extent of rock fortification required. Further costs to the promoter may be incurred because of delays in filling the reservoir, peculiar to arch dams only, which arises because the contraction joint grouting should be done in the cold season, before the arch is loaded. Finally the necessity for close observation of the behaviour of an arch dam and its foundation is a continuing burden on the promoter which should not be forgotten. These are onerous conditions which necessitate a greater allowance for contingencies when comparing the cost of an arch dam with a concrete gravity or earth-fill dam on the same site.[32]

This statement gave rise to numerous comments and questions when a paper on the scheme by Robert, Wilson and Wiltshire was discussed before a meeting of the Institution of Civil Engineers at Edinburgh, in 1965. The authors' response makes it apparent that even had the difficulties encountered in building the dam at Morar—difficulties mainly stemming from the unsuspected existence of a faulted dyke—been known in advance, 'it was possible that an arch dam would still have been chosen', given the desirability of utilising the valley shoulder on the left bank of the river.[33] Nevertheless, the suspicion exists that the choice of an arch design was *at least partially* motivated by the Board's consistent policy of encouraging and assisting British engineers and manufacturers to try out new designs whenever appropriate. Certainly, this was explicitly acknowledged to be the reason for the Board's decision to install the Deriaz turbine.[34] In pursuance of this innovative rôle, the Board gave considerable attention to the instrumentation of the dam so that its behaviour in service could be studied. Built into the dam are all manner of strain gauges, resistance thermometers, and other scientific devices to permit the detection and examination of any movements that might occur in the contraction joints, the dam crest, the abutments and the bed rock. These instruments were not intended simply to give the Board's engineers warning of potentially dangerous developments but to provide invaluable data on the complex stresses to which arch dams are subject.[35]

(iii)   *The Great Glen*: *Garry/Moriston* (1949-1962)[36]

Like that of Glen Affric, the water power potential of the Great Glen had long been recognised. It was this area, with its exceptionally heavy average annual rainfall of about 125 inches, that had been the subject of the series of abortive schemes promoted by the British Oxygen Co. between 1928 and 1938.[37] One feature of these earlier promotions that had given rise to intense opposition had been the proposal so to develop the Loch Quoich catchment that its waters, instead of feeding the River Garry and flowing eastward towards the Great Glen, would be diverted towards the west. This would have provided the maximum head for a power station on the shore of Loch Hourn, which is at sea level. However tempting it might have been to have pursued a similar scheme, the Board, anxious not to awaken old controversies, decided to develop the River Garry entirely within its natural catchment and thereby sacrifice about 150 feet of gross head.

facing page
FIGURE 28   Monar Dam: typical cross-section, elevation and plan

Although the Garry and the Moriston schemes were promoted separately as Constructional Schemes 23 and 24 in 1948, they were built simultaneously, and subsequently operated as one group with a control centre at Fort Augustus. Furthermore, they have somewhat similar layouts and a number of common design features. Fig. 30 shows the principal works of the related schemes. It will be seen that the Garry development consists of a large reservoir at Loch Quoich, at the head of the system. Water from this reservoir is taken by tunnel to the upper power station about three miles further down the Garry. This water, together with that from the remainder of the catchment area, passes into a smaller reservoir, whence it is carried to the lower power station at Invergarry. The Moriston scheme differs from its southern neighbour in having two upper reservoirs, the Loyne and Cluanie, joined by tunnel, a subterranean upper power station, Caennacroc, and a lower works which comprise another underground power station (Glenmoriston), built immediately below its associated dam (Dundreggan), and a long unlined tail-race tunnel to the River Moriston close to the point where it flows into Loch Ness. (See the longitudinal sections, Fig. 30). A second catchment on the left bank—the Livishie—was later tapped by a system of aqueducts, the water being delivered to a headpond from which it flows by tunnel into a power station (commissioned in 1962), again built underground, to discharge into Loch Dundreggan and so feed Glenmoriston power station.

The schemes possess a number of noteworthy features. Their planning and construction were greatly influenced by considerations of amenity, the requirements of the salmon, and the ever-present need for economy. In both schemes the upper reservoirs are large and the lower ones relatively confined, so that the effects of draw–down, which can sometimes leave unsightly river banks, are confined to the more remote localities. But another reason for the concentration of storage in the upper reservoirs is that the lower parts of valleys are used as winter grazing for sheep and cattle. During the summer the high grounds and hillsides are used. Flooding of the lower valley land would upset the cycle by diminishing the winter grazing. Thus, the area taken by the lower reservoirs was deliberately restricted.

But the attention given to the needs of agriculture was far outweighed by the efforts to ensure the preservation of the salmon.[38] For example, among the chief protective measures taken on the Garry, the more important river, were the provision of minimum compensation flows between Invergarry dam and power station; a Borland fish pass through Invergarry dam; and an extensive screened intake (requiring constant maintenance) to the power tunnel at Invergarry dam. Because Quoich dam, in the upper part of the catchment, raised the level of the Loch by over 100 feet, it drowned the best spawning reaches. It was therefore necessary to build a fish stopper and trap downstream of Quoich power station in order to trap those fish which tried to go beyond Loch Garry. These fish were kept in pens ready for spawning, when they could be stripped and the fertilised ova taken to a fish hatchery which the Board operated at Invergarry. Furthermore, the fish stopper and trap had to be built two years before impounding began, so that the last smolts bred in the upper waters would pass downstream before the dam was closed. In addition to the permanent fishery protection

facing page
FIGURE 29   The Great Glen: Garry/Moriston schemes

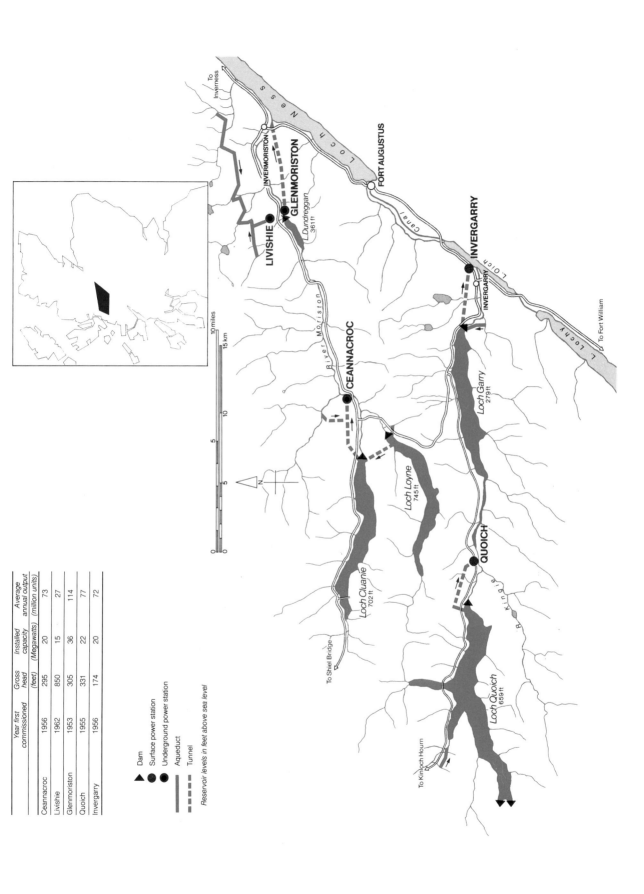

	Year first commissioned	Gross head (feet)	Installed capacity (Megawatts)	Average annual output (million units)
Ceannacroc	1956	295	20	73
Livishie	1962	850	15	27
Glenmoriston	1953	305	36	114
Quoich	1955	331	22	77
Invergarry	1956	174	20	72

▲ Dam
●● Surface power station
● Underground power station
— Aqueduct
--- Tunnel

Reservoir levels in feet above sea level

To Inverness
L o c h N e s s
INVERMORISTON
GLENMORISTON
LIVISHIE
L Dundreggan 361ft
FORT AUGUSTUS
Canal
INVERGARRY
L o c h O i c h
INVERGARRY
River Moriston
CEANNACROC
L Loch Garry 279ft
Loch Loyne 745ft
L o c h y
To Fort William
To Shiel Bridge
Loch Cluanie 702ft
QUOICH
R Kingie
Loch Quoich 659ft
To Kinloch Hourn

10 miles
15 km
N

TABLE 8 *Great Glen: Garry/Moriston: Major Dams*

Name of Dam	Type and Year of Completion	Length ft	Height above foundations ft	Cubic Capacity cub. yds.	Main Contractors
Cluanie	Mass gravity, 1956	2,213	133	232,000	The Mitchell Construction Co.
Loyne	Mass gravity, 1956	1,800	72	66,000	The Mitchell Construction Co.
Dundreggan	Mass gravity, 1957	460	58	23,000+7,000 (west wall of intake)	Duncan Logan (Contrctors) Ltd
Quoich	Rockfill with articulated concrete face, 1956	1,050	126	386,000 rockfill 5,600 concrete	Richard Costain Ltd
Invergarry	Mass gravity, 1956	154	56	8,560	Whatlings Ltd

Consulting Engineers: Sir William Halcrow & Partners.

153

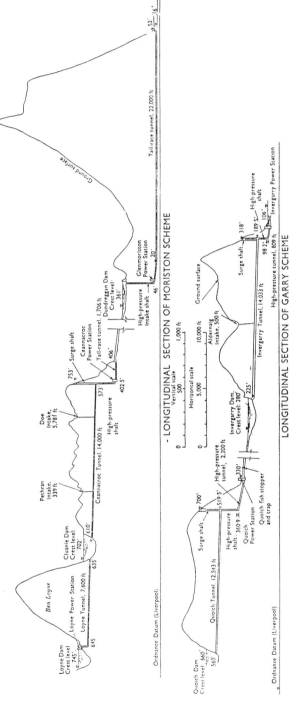

FIGURE 30   Longitudinal sections of the Moriston and Garry schemes

features of the Garry scheme, temporary works, intended to prevent damage to fish during the period of construction, included settling bays and filter tanks to remove the tiny particles of rock flour produced during stone crushing and the washing of rockfill material. As with other schemes, these measures added significantly to the Board's costs.

Of the many interesting technical features of the two schemes, one of the most notable was the rockfill dam at Quoich, the first (and largest) built by the Board.[39] Several types of design for Quoich dam were considered. A rockfill dam was selected because it was the most economical, the price quoted being 10 per cent less than for a gravity dam; because it would save cement, bulk deliveries of which still could not be made to sites in the Northern Highlands, and because its construction required relatively little shuttering and therefore fewer joiners than the Board's usual gravity or buttress designs. The dam, 1050 feet long and 125 feet high, with a cubic capacity of 386,000 square yards, was built in 2 foot layers, each of which was compacted mechanically and washed down thoroughly to secure maximum compaction.[40] No central core was used. Instead, the upstream face was covered with 12-15 inches thick slabs of reinforced concrete, each 20 feet by 20 feet, laid on a base of hand-packed rubble, the thickness of which varied from 7 feet. at the base to 3 feet at the crest. The joints between the individual slabs were sealed by copper strips and filled with a bituminous rubber compound. A cross section of the dam is shown in Fig. 31, and the upstream face of the dam showing the concrete membrane, in Plate 16.

The dam took two and a half years to build, and in raising the level of Loch Quoich by 100 feet and increasing its area from 3 to 7 square miles, necessitated the provision of two further dams to seal the upstream end of the loch. These two concrete gravity structures, known as Cruadhach north and south dams, were themselves of no mean sise.[41] Their construction, in the most remote area of the scheme, involved establishing a special work camp and an access road of $2\frac{1}{2}$ miles. The site had the unenviable record of experiencing the highest rainfall of any of the Board's major construction sites; a record rainfall of 10.2 inches in $22\frac{1}{2}$ hours was measured at the south dam in December 1954.

The design of the two major concrete gravity dams of the Moriston scheme—Cluanie and Loyne—followed well-established practice, but their construction was noteworthy for the use of the Trief process for concrete making and for the precast concrete blocks used to face the dams, which eliminated shuttering. It was said by *The Engineer* that 'the economies effected by these methods ... restored the gravity dam ... as an economic competitor with buttress and rockfill dams'.[42] Be that as it may, in choosing to use Trief concrete the Board were motivated as much by the chronic shortage of home-produced Portland cement and a long-standing resentment that they were being exploited by a 'ring' of cement makers as by considerations of economy.

Trief is a cementitious slag pioneered by Victor Trief, a Belgian. The process involves the replacement of a proportion of ordinary Portland cement in concrete by pozzolanas, in this case blast furnace slag in vitreous form. This has to be ground, and Trief devised a method of increasing the efficiency of grinding by using a wet mill to produce a slurry, which is mixed with the cement in a concrete mixer. Wet grinding produces a finer particle than dry grinding and reduces the power required. Furthermore, fine slags give better mechanical strength after hydration than coarse ones and, after it is ground,

155

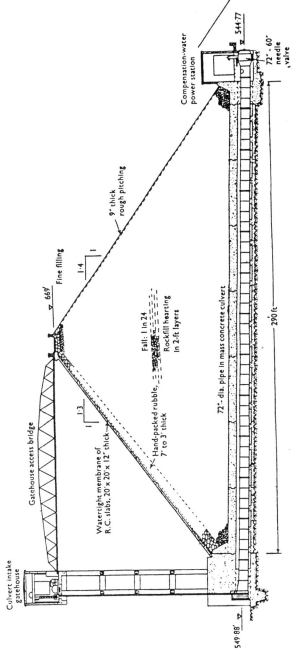

FIGURE 31 The rockfill dam at Quoich: cross-section through scour culvert

156

PLATE 16 Upstream face of Quoich Dam

the slurry can be kept in storage vats without deterioration, provided it is continuously agitated to prevent settlement. Following an early suggestion by Sir Edward MacColl, a detailed study was made by Angus Fulton and Professor W T Marshall of Glasgow University of the use of pozzolanas in concrete, and the Trief process was investigated by the Board's engineers. Tests were made on slags produced at Colville's Clyde Iron Works. The results were satisfactory and it was decided to go ahead. About 270,000 cubic yards of Trief concrete were produced for the Moriston Scheme at the wet-grinding and batching plant erected near Cluanie, the bulk of it using ground slag as a replacement for 70 per cent of the ordinary Portland cement that would otherwise have been needed. That is, about 25,000 tons of cement were saved.[43]

In addition to the use of Trief concrete, the first time that the process had been enployed on a major scale in Great Britain, the Moriston scheme also saw the first use of precast self-supporting facing blocks. Two major types of facing blocks were designed: one for the upstream and the other for the downstream sides of the dam. The essential details are shown in Fig. 32, from which it will be seen that the tail of each block fitted into a corresponding recess in the lower block. After adjustment to secure the correct alignment, these interlocking blocks were wedged, grouted and subsequently pointed. No less than 35,000 of these two-ton concrete facing blocks were required for the Cluanie and Loyne dams. They were made at a suitably equipped site adjacent to Cluanie dam. Although their use did not produce a significant direct saving in cost, the labour employed to make and place the units was much less than the number of joiners

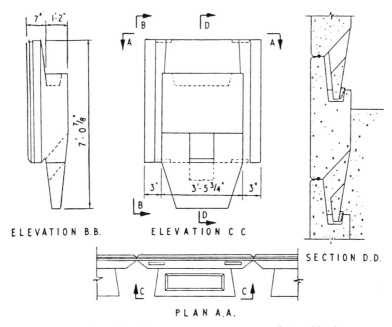

FIGURE 32   Cluanie Dam: precast concrete facing blocks

that would have been required for conventional shuttering, and the rate of progress was much faster.

Of the five power stations of the Garry and Moriston schemes, three are completely underground and one, Invergarry, is partially so. Only the 22MW station at Quoich is on the surface, though even this is somewhat unusual in that for easy erection it was decided to use a *horizontal* Francis turbine. Underground power stations had been constructed on the Continent since 1910, but they were only gradually adopted by the Board. There were good reasons for this apparent lethargy. The geological conditions confronting the Board's engineers were unfavourable, and until improved subterranean excavation techniques had been evolved they were unable to take full advantage of the economic, technical, and environmental advantages implicit in underground stations.[44] Suitable geological conditions, the tunneling and excavation skills and equipment developed by the Board's principal contractors, the perpetual quest to economise on steel and concrete, and environmental pressures, all conspired to induce the Board to adopt underground designs for Glen Moriston. Indeed, Ceannacroc was the first major underground station to be built in this country. Although the roof of the power station was lined with concrete, the side walls are of natural rock and this has greatly enhanced the architectural beauty of the station. The lighting was carefully designed and clear shadowless illumination has been achieved by locating the lights behind the overhead concrete beams which support the crane rails (see Plate 17).[45] The design of the Glen-moriston station is similar to that of Ceannacroc, but because the station is so close to the Dundreggan dam, special arrangements had to be made to overcome the problem of surge in the tail-race. This was solved by building an expansion chamber and two tunnels, as shown in Fig. 33, an arrangement evolved as a result of model tests carried out at Heriot Watt College in Edinburgh.

(iv)   *Shin* (1954–1960)

Shin is the most northerly of the Board's schemes on the mainland of Scotland. It utilises the waters of Loch Shin, the largest of the northern lochs, and its tributaries, the headwaters of the Rivers Cassley and Brora and several smaller streams in Sutherland. Although the catchment area is about 250 square miles, both the average annual rainfall (approximately 60 inches) and the available gross head (some 265 feet) are modest by the standards of the Board's other schemes, but seen in the context of its position and the small and scattered population which it was expected to serve, its power potential was considered to be sufficiently attractive to warrent fairly early consideration. The Shin scheme (Constructional Scheme 32) was published in 1951 and after lengthy negotiations received Parliamentary approval in the summer of 1953. George Wimpey & Co. Ltd. were awarded the contract, and work began in 1954.

The scheme is straightforward (see Fig. 34). The water level of Loch Shin, the main storage reservoir, was raised about 35 feet by the construction of the Lairg Dam, a concrete gravity and earthfill structure (the nature of which is clearly shown in Plate 18) at a point where the natural loch narrowed, west of Lairg. A 3.5MW remotely controlled power station driven by a vertical Kaplan turbine was built into the dam. Water released from Loch Shin through this power station passes into a much smaller

PLATE 17   Ceannocroc underground power station

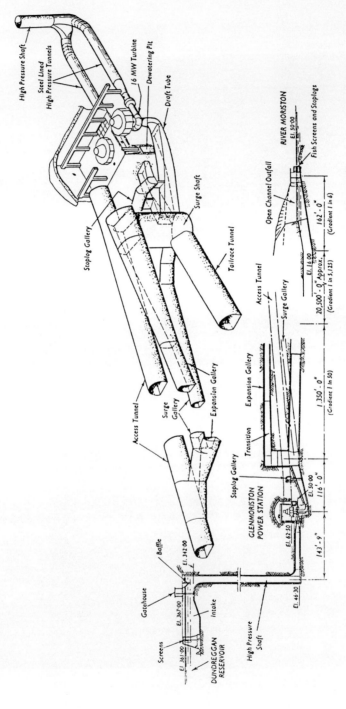

High Pressure Shaft

Steel Lined High Pressure Tunnels

16 MW Turbine

Dewatering Pit

Draft Tube

Surge Shaft

Stoplog Gallery

Tailrace Tunnel

Access Tunnel

Surge Gallery

Expansion Gallery

Access Tunnel

Surge Gallery

Expansion Gallery

Transition

Stoplog Gallery

RIVER MORISTON

Open Channel Outfall

Fish Screens and Stoplogs

EL. 50·00

162' - 0"
(Gradient 1 in 6)

EL. 16·00

20,500' - 0" Approx.
(Gradient 1 in 5,125)

1,350' - 0"
(Gradient 1 in 50)

GLENMORISTON POWER STATION

EL. 50·00

116' - 0"

EL. 67·30

143' - 9"

EL. 46·30

High Pressure Shaft

Gatehouse

Baffle

EL. 342·00

EL. 367·00

Intake

Screens

EL. 361·00

DUNDREGGAN RESERVOIR

FIGURE 33   Glenmoriston power station and its associated tunnels

reservoir (Little Loch Shin) immediately downstream. The level of this reservoir was regulated by a weir across the River Shin. From the weir, water was diverted through a long tunnel—which in its course takes in the water of the Grudie Burn—to the main station at Inveran near the mouth of the River Shin. This power station was equipped with two horizontal Francis turbines each coupled to a 12MW generator. After passing through these turbines, the water is discharged back into the River Shin. A fish screen was erected across the tail-race outlet to prevent salmon from entering and to guide them up the River Shin. Borland fish lifts at Lairg Dam and the Shin diversion weir were also installed to assist their passage up river, the flow of which was maintained by compensation water released through the weir.[46] Even this compensation water was utilised, however, by the installation of a small turbine enclosed in tubular casing built into the weir, one of the first 'compensation sets' of this design in this country.

The major works were completed in 1959. Indeed, the two dams were sufficiently advanced for impounding to begin as early as January 1956. Only the development of the upper part of the scheme was still under construction when the main power station was commissioned. The site of highest section of the scheme, Cassley, is so remote that five miles of new road had to be built to give access to it. This part of the scheme involved the building of two aqueducts to capture the headwaters of the River Cassley and divert them into a headpond created by the erection of the Duchally Weir, whence the water is diverted (via two small turbines installed in a very small power station built into the weir) by a tunnel to the Cassley power station at the western shore of Loch Shin. Power generated by the two generating sets at Cassley, of a total capacity of 10MW is fed to the Cassley sub-station, and partly used to supply the Durness district in the far north west of Scotland. The completion of the Cassley power station in July 1960, the Board reported laconically, 'brought to an end all the work which had been contracted for in the Shin scheme'.[47]

(v) *Breadalbane* (1951-61)

The Breadalbane Scheme exploits the water power resources of the mountainous region around Loch Lyon, Loch Tay and Loch Earn in Perthshire.[48] Although the individual power stations, of which there are seven, and reservoirs are of only moderate sise, the scheme as a whole produces about 360 million units a year from a relatively small catchment area of less than 200 square miles (see Fig. 35). Several features of the scheme are noteworthy: three of the dams, Lawers, Lubreoch and Giorra exhibit successive stages in the evolution of the massive buttress type; in the construction of the second and third of these and of Lednock, a diamond-headed buttress dam, fly ash was used to economise in the consumption of cement; the overall layout called for an intensive use of aqueducts and tunnels, in the driving of which the contractors achieved remarkable standards of performance; and Finlarig, the first of the power stations to be commissioned, is equipped with a Pelton wheel which is the largest of its kind in the country.

Lawers was the first section of the scheme to be promoted. It comprises 'the classical single-stage development of reservoir, tunnel, pipeline and power station, with aqueducts feeding into the reservoir'. Work begun in the Autumn of 1951 and Finlarig power station, fed by tunnel from the reservoir created by Lawers dam, commissioned five years later. It is no criticism of the Board to say that both the design of the dam and the choice of turbo-generator betray their relatively early place in the Board's constructional programme. Lawers dam is similar though not so high as Sloy, the prototype of the massive buttress type of dam, completed in 1950. Lawers was built in the pass between Loch Tay and Glen Lyon to raise the water level of a small loch, Lochan na Lairige, by 90 feet and increase the storage capacity to 460 million cubic feet. The impounded water flows by tunnel and pipeline to Finlarig power station on the shores of Loch Tay. This operates under a maximum gross head of 1,348 feet, the highest available on any of the Board's schemes. The station is equipped with one 30MW Pelton turbine generating set, the largest unit of its kind in Great Britain, and in its report on Finlarig, the journal *Water Power* commented:

> Advances in the design of the Francis turbine during the past few years have been so rapid that it is now the generally accepted practice to use this type of turbine under high heads in preference to the Pelton, although the latter may still be more suitable under certain conditions. It is possible, therefore, that if the Finlarig station were designed today [1959] a Francis unit might well be chosen instead of a Pelton.[49]

In discussing the Garry and Moriston schemes, it was seen that blast-furnace slag had been used in the Trief process to obviate the need for about 70 per cent of the cement which would otherwise have been required. In pursuance of the same objective, the rock-fill dam at Quoich was built. At Breadalbane, the same general policy is evident in the construction of the Board's second large rock-fill dam, Breachlaich, and in the use of fly ash, as an alternative to the Trief process, at Lednock, Lubreoch and Giorra.[50] Fly ash is a fine ash obtained by electrical or mechanical precipitation when pulverised coal is burned in a steam boiler plant. In addition to saving cement, it was said to possess certain advantages in the making of concrete which made its use particularly attractive to the Board's engineers. It was claimed that the substitution of fly ash for some part of the cement traditionally employed resulted in a reduction in the heat generated during setting, and hence in the tendency for shrinkage cracks to form. The consequence was greater impermeability, a quality of over-riding importance in Scotland, where acid Highland waters tend to be very aggressive. Indeed, the desired degree of impermeability had been achieved in the past by maintaining a high proportion of cement in the concrete used for facing dams and in the construction of spillways. The admixture of fly ash into concrete was also said to increase its workability. Its only apparent disdvantage was that concrete made with fly ash took longer than the normal mix to attain its maximum strength and impermeability, though after one year there seems to have been little difference in strength between the two, and the fly ash concrete had become far less permeable than that made with cement alone.

Such benefits could not be ignored. After thorough investigation of the burgeoning literature of the subject, mostly emanating from America; a visit to the United States by A A Fulton and W T Marshall, Regius Professor of Civil Engineering at the University of

facing page
FIGURE 34   The Shin scheme

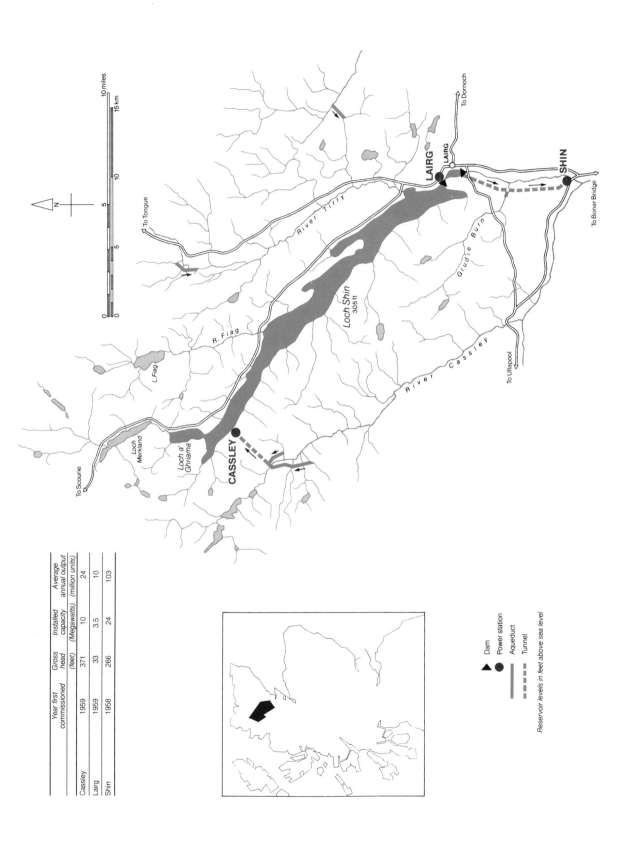

	Year first commissioned	Gross head (feet)	Installed capacity (Megawatts)	Average annual output (million units)
Cassley	1959	371	10	24
Lairg	1959	33	3.5	10
Shin	1958	266	24	103

Dam ▲
Power station ●
Aqueduct ——
Tunnel ----

Reservoir levels in feet above sea level

To Scourie
Loch Merkland
L. Fiag
R. Fiag
Loch a' Ghriama
CASSLEY
To Tongue
River Tirry
Loch Shin
305 ft
River Cassley
Grudie Burn
To Ullapool
LAIRG
LAIRG
To Dornoch
SHIN
To Bonar Bridge

N

0 5 10 15 km
0 5 10 miles

Glasgow, to examine dams built using fly ash concrete in the United States; and intensive research by Professor Marshall at Glasgow University, the Board decided to use fly ash on a 20 per cent replacement-of-cement basis in the construction of Lednock, Lubreoch and Giorra dams.[51] Lednock dam is believed to have been the first major structure in the United Kingdom in which fly ash was used on a large scale. More than 82,000 cubic yards of fly ash concrete were placed, resulting in a reduction of nearly 3,000 tons in the quantity of Portland cement used. At Lubreoch dam a net saving of £17,000 was claimed by the use of fly ash, even though it was not used in the early stages.[52]

But Lednock is notable not merely for the use of fly ash in its construction: it is one of the two diamond-headed buttress dams built by the Board and, unlike other buttress dams in this category, best exemplified in Scotland by the Errochty dam, its upstream face is not markedly sloped, but approaches verticality (see Fig. 36). The design was considered by the Board's consultants, Sir Murdoch MacDonald & Partners, to be the most economical for the particular conditions encountered, and was decided upon only after an extensive comparative analysis of different buttress shapes.[53] In fact, the dam had to be rather more massive than comparable Scottish designs, because of its close proximity to a known earthquake zone, earth tremors having sometimes been caused by movement along the line of the Highland Border Fault, only a few miles distant.[54]

While Taylor Woodrow were completing the Lednock dam in the St Fillans section, James Miller & Partners and Edmund Nuttall's were making good progress with Lubreoch and Giorra in the Killin section of the Breadalbans schemes. James Williamson & Partners, the consulting engineers, had introduced modifications to their prototype Sloy/Lawers design for these later massive buttress dams. These changes—which affected mainly the width of the buttress, the contraction slots, and the sise of the precast arch rings which carry the crest on the downstream side (see Fig. 37)—were intended to effect economies both in the quantity of concrete used and in the need for shuttering. Lubreoch dam represented the first stage in refining the basic Sloy design to attain greater simplicity and constructional speed so that economies in labour supplemented savings in material. Giorra dam carried these refinements another stage. By altering the slopes of the buttress head, the precast arches were eliminated and comparative constructional quantities were still further reduced (see Plate 19a,b,c). Furthermore, the modification of other features of the design achieved an even greater simplicity which cumulatively rendered the contractor's task easier. For example, in conjunction with the use of fly ash, they permitted concreting to be carried out in 10 feet lifts and greatly accelerated the time of construction.[55]

Beause every site has unique problems, and each dam individual ancilliary features, comparisons between dams are inevitably inexact. Nevertheless, by the use of realistic assumptions and simplifications (including the adoption of certain standard dimensions), E J K Chapman and D F Campbell attempted to make meaningful cost comparisons between two representative solid gravity dam designs and the massive buttress designs evolved for Sloy, Lubreoch and Giorra. The result of their calculations are presented in Table 11. It will be seen that the Sloy type of massive buttress dam represented a major cost saving over the solid gravity dam of about 30 per cent, and that subsequent

facing page
FIGURE 35   The Breadalbane scheme

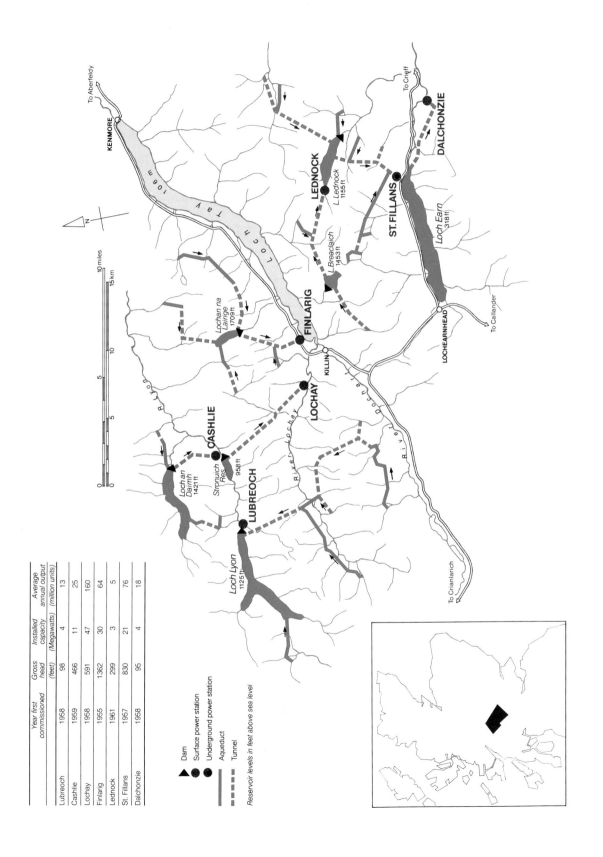

	Year first commissioned	Gross head (feet)	Installed capacity (Megawatts)	Average annual output (million units)
Lubreoch	1958	98	4	13
Cashlie	1959	466	11	25
Lochay	1958	591	47	160
Finlarig	1955	1362	30	64
Lednock	1961	299	3	5
St. Fillans	1957	830	21	76
Dalchonzie	1958	95	4	18

Dam ▲
Surface power station ●
Underground power station ●

Aqueduct
Tunnel

Reservoir levels in feet above sea level

TABLE 9 *Shin: Major Dam*

Name of Dam	Type and Year of Completion	Length ft	Height above foundations ft	Cubic Capacity cub. yds.	Main Contractors
Lairg	Concrete gravity and earthfill, 1957	1,740	66.0	40,000 concrete 76,000 earthfill	George Wimpey & Co.

Consulting Engineers: Sir Murdoch MacDonald & Partners.

PLATE 18   Lairg Dam

TABLE 10 *Breadalbane: Major Dams*

Name of Dam	Type and year of Completion	Length ft	Height above foundations ft	Cubic Capacity cub. yds.	Main Contractors
Lawers section					
Lawers	Massive buttress, 1956	1,130	138	118,700	The Cementation Co. Ltd
St Fillans section					
Breaclaich	Rockfill with upstream concrete facing, 1960	1,420	88	275,000	R J McLeod (Contractors) Ltd
Lednock	Diamond-headed buttress, 1957	950	133	128,000	Taylor Woodrow Ltd
Killin section					
Lubreoch	Massive buttress, 1958	1,740	129	159,300	James Miller & Partners Ltd
Giorra	Massive buttress, 1959	1,518	114	92,000	Edmund Nuttall Sons & Co. Ltd

Consulting Engineers: Lawers & Killin sections, James Williamson & Partners; St Fillans section: Sir Murdoch MacDonald & Partners with (for the Breaclaich dam) Duff & Geddes in association with R H Cuthbertson.

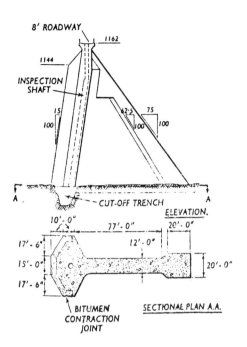

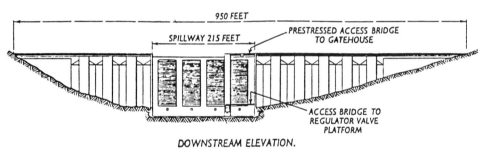

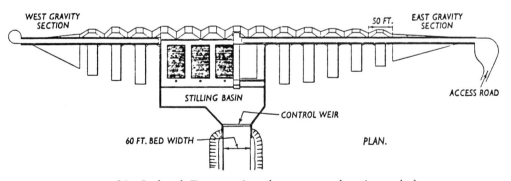

FIGURE 36   Lednock Dam: section, downstream elevation and plan

170

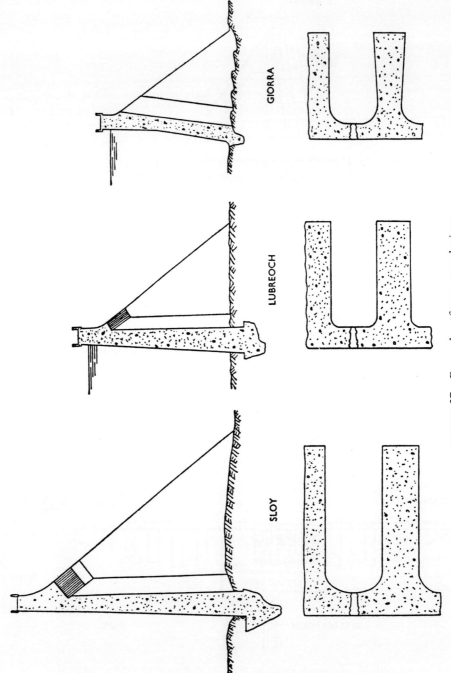

FIGURE 37 Examples of precast arch rings

refinements, exemplified by Giorra, increased this cost advantage so that the unit cost was reduced to about 60 per cent of the unit cost of the conventional solid gravity dam. In relation to the *total* cost of such a project (including earthworks, river diversion, grouting and other common features), real savings of the order of 20 per cent had been achieved during the decade 1945-1955.

Parallel improvements in tunnelling were achieved at Breadalbane.[56] The scheme as a whole is typical of Highland hydro-works in the extent of tunnelling involved in its construction. In addition to the main tunnels joining the reservoirs with the principal power stations, there are extensive aqueducts and connecting tunnels capturing the flow from adjacent catchments. The total length of rock tunnels in the scheme is about 60 miles, and some of the individual tunnels represent major works of contructions. For example, the tunnel from Stronuich to Lochay, in the lower stage of the Killin section, is 25,000 feet in length, and it diameter is 13 feet 5 inches. In the early stages of the Board's constructional programme, great emphasis had to be placed on training tunnelling crews and gradually introducing improved drilling techniques and new methods of tunnel lining. By the mid-1950s, such progress had been made in incalcating skills and adopting technical innovations that tunnelling works could be carried out 'extraordinarily quick-ly'. Among the contractors there was 'a high degree of friendly rivalry' in introducing quicker and cheaper methods.

The tunnelling for the Breadalbane scheme exhibited just how much progress had been made in the previous decade. At one stage a world record was claimed for the speed of driving one of the tunnels. In October 1955, 557 feet was driven in seven days in one of the 8 foot 6 inches diameter collecting tunnels in the St Fillans section. Cutting through a grit formation, with mica intrusions, known locally as Ben Ledi grit, and using conventional equipment which, with the exception of the drill steel, was all of British manufacture, three crews of 14 men worked eight-hour shifts throughout the 24 hours.[57] Ninety cycles of work were completed, the average 'pull' being 6 feet 4

TABLE 11   *Comparison of costs in X units per foot run for dams 120 ft high*

Type of dam	costs in X units		Total cost per foot run of dam
	concrete	shuttering	
Gravity A	209.8	8.9	218.7
Gravity B	209.8	11.4	221.2
Sloy	144.2	11.4	155.6
Lubreoch	137.5	12.5	150.0
Giorra	120.0	12.3	132.2

Note: Gravity dam A is assumed to have a vertical upstream face and a 0.75 to 1 downstream slope, and to have been constructed in blocks of 50 ft length which are concreted alternately. Gravity dam B is assumed to be of the same cross section as A, but to have been constructed in blocks of 45 ft length with five feet contraction slots between each. This method requires additional shuttering for the sides of the contraction slots, but has certain advantages associated with the placing of the concrete and control of shrinkage.

Source: E J K Chapman and D Fraser Campbell, 'The Design and Economics of Massive Buttress Dams', *Fifth International Congress on Large Dams*, Paris, 1955 (Paper code R.61), p. 298.

PLATE 19   Breadalbane: Lawers, Lubreoch and Giorra massive buttress dams

19a.   Three stage in the evolution of the class of dam known as the 'massive buttress' dam, are depicted here. Constructional speed and simplicity were the primary aims in developing these designs. All three dams are part of the Breadalbane scheme. The earliest, the Lawers dam, shown above, was completed in 1957, and is generally similar though not so high as the prototype of this class, which was built at Loch Sloy and completed in 1950.

19b.   Lubreoch dam was slightly more economical in constructional quantities than the Sloy design. Note that the contraction slots between buttresses were carried right up to the crest of the dam, above the precast concrete arches, which carry the roadway on the downstream side. These arches are shallower than in the earlier dam. The illustration shows the gate houses under construction; one controls a gate for the scour culvert, the other a gate for the power station intake. The gate shaft is, in each case, in the body of the dam. There are syphon spillways below each gate house. Precast concrete elements have still to be placed on the crest to form the roadway.

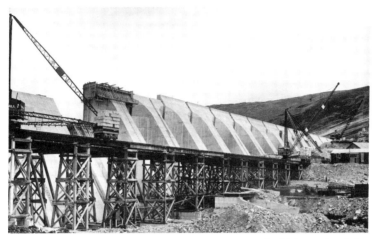

19c.   Giorra dam, part of which is shown under construction, represents the third stage in refining the massive buttress design. By altering the slopes of the buttress head, the precast arches have been eliminated. Comparative quantities were less than for Lubreoch dam. The spillweir was formed by building a length of open-jointed gravity dam, in contrast to the precast concrete planking which spans between buttresses in the earlier dams.

inches. The contractors were the Mitchell Construction Company. Edmund Nuttall, Sons & Co., the contractors for the $4\frac{1}{2}$ mile Lochay tunnel, were not so fortunate. In driving from the northern end of this very long tunnel, a major fault was encountered about 7,000 feet from the portal. The fault was water-bearing, and an inflow of water initially at the rate of 50,000 gallons per hour rushed in and flooded 5,000 feet of the tunnel. After pumping out, a diversion was made, crossing the fault at right angles and using cast iron segmental lining.[58]

Ten years earlier such an unexpected hazard might seriously have disrupted essential tunnelling work. By the mid-1950s, sufficient expertise and specialised equipment had been developed to make such a potential distaster into a frustrating but temporary setback. That this was so was confirmed in March 1959 by the announcement that the driving of the network of tunnels in the Killin section of Breadalbane had been completed nine months ahead of schedule. The Mitchell Construction Co. had begun work on this section on 1 April 1957, when they had been confronted with the task of building 18 miles of access roads, $14\frac{1}{2}$ miles of tunnels and seven miles of pipe aqueducts up to 6 feet in diameter. The work was spread over a mountainous area of about 50 square miles. By using a helicopter and modern instruments, Mitchell's speeded up the surveying, and tunnelling was able to start on 1 June 1957. This was carried out so expeditiously that the *average* speed of tunnel driving, over three-quarters of a mile per month, was equal to the rate for which the world record had been claimed for progress in one week on *one* heading in the St. Fillans section less than four years earlier.[59]

The Breadalbane Scheme was essentially completed by the end of 1959, by which time all the major power stations had been commissioned. Only the small 3MW station at Lednock remained inactive, held up by last minute difficulties with the Breaclaich section, but it too was commissioned in March 1961.[60]

(vi)   *Sloy/Shira* (1945-1959)[61]

The Glen Shira project was designed to harness the headwaters of the Rivers Shira, Fyne, and a number of other streams situated between Loch Fyne and Loch Awe in Argyllshire (see Fig. 15).[62] Like the adjacent Sloy scheme, with which it had many features in common, it was intended to produce energy for the grid to meet peak-load demands. However, it was not, Angus Fulton asserted, ' "just another hydro-electric scheme". It had an individuality of its own". This, of course, could be said of *all* the Board's schemes, but in the case of Shira the words were more than usually justified. 'The wide variety of the work ... was impressive. There were three varieties of dam, and if that was not enough, there were side-stream intakes, free-flow tunnels, pressure tunnels, pressure shafts, collecting aqueducts (both open and closed), a substantial tail-race canal, and an underground power station'. It was typical of Fulton that he should add to this outline of the major features of Shira that these characteristics, 'had given opportunities for experience and training for the many young engineers who had the good fortune to work on the scheme'.[63]

The economic potential of the area—most of which lies above the 1,000 feet contour and rises at the summit of Ben Bhuidhe to 3,106 feet above sea level—had always been appreciated. The Board's preliminary surveys were carried out in 1946 and gauges were installed to permit an accurate assessment of the rainfall of this catchment. Recordings at the gauges, coupled with data from adjacent and broadly similar areas, indicated that the annual average rainfall was likely to be about 105 inches, but the corollary of this promising information was that the rainfall was occasionally very heavy indeed. The maximum weekly rainfall recorded was 8.8 inches and the maximum daily rainfall, 3.6 inches. This meant that although the area may have been admirably suited for hydro-electric development, progress in *construction* on this upland site was liable to be seriously disrupted by torrential rainfall, frost, snow and severe gales. Nor were the geological and topographical conditions entirely favourable; they imposed severe constraints on the choices confronting the civil engineers, and influenced the form and layout of the projected works to a greater degree than was the case in the majority of the Board's schemes.

In the upper reaches of the River Shira the valley was found to be relatively flat. There may have been a good natural storage basin situated at an elevation above the 1,000 feet contour, but this was the *only* suitable site within the region for the creation of a large reservoir. Although the *direct* catchment area upstream of the possible dam site was $4\frac{1}{2}$ miles square, detailed analysis revealed that it was economically feasible to extend this by the diversion of the headwaters of the River Fyne and other adjacent watercourses which flowed either to Loch Fyne or Loch Awe. Again, preliminary investigations showed that there were no attractive sites for additional dams along the valley of the River Shira downstream of the projected main dam site. This meant that a multi-stage development along the course of the river was ruled out, and that the scheme would have to take the form of a high-level main storage reservoir serving an

TABLE 12   *Sloy/Shira: Major Dams*

Name of Dam	Type & Year of Completion	Length ft	Height above foundations ft	Cubic Capacity cu. yds.	Main contractors
Sloy	Massive buttress, 1951	1,170	182	208,000	Balfour Beatty & Co. Ltd
Allt-na-Lairige	Prestressed gravity, 1956	1,395	78	32,900	Maples, Ridgway & Partners Ltd
Shira (Main)	Round headed buttress, 1959	2,380	148	268,600	A M Carmichael Ltd
Shira (Lower)	Concrete gravity and earthfill with concrete core section, 1956	400 600	58 53	18,000 80,000	A M Carmichael Ltd

Consulting Engineers: Sloy, James Williamson & Partners; Allt-na-Lairige and Shira: Babtie, Shaw & Morton.

aqueduct following the shortest possible route to a power station situated at or near sea level. It was equally clear that additional extensive high level catchments could be captured by the diversion of the four main tributaries of the River Shira either into this main tunnel or into a shallow reservoir slightly downstream of the main reservoir.

These factors conspired to produce a two-stage arrangement.[64] This comprised a main reservoir (with an effective storage capacity equivalent to 15 million units of electricity) feeding an upper generating station (Sron Mor) and discharging into a lower reservoir, water from which passed into a pressure-tunnel system supplying a main generating plant at Clachan, near the head of Loch Fyne. Into the main tunnel was diverted the run-off from the Brannie, Kilbaan and Clachan catchments. All this may be regarded as relatively orthodox. Where the scheme was particularly ingenious was in overcoming the topographically-imposed limitations of the lower reservoir. With a top water level of 970 OD, this had an effective storage capacity of only 55 million cubic feet (equivalent to one million electrical units). This was very small in relation to its catchment area[65] and rendered even more inadequate by so arranging the intake levels of the Brannie, Kilblaan and Clachan Burns that, when the main generating station at Clachan was not operating, their waters would flow back up the main tunnel into the lower reservoir.

This was a situation which courted the danger of wasteful, if not damaging spillage. To overcome the problem, the upper generating station, Sron Mor, would be equipped with pumping facilities to raise a proportion of the inflow to the lower reservoir up to the main storage reservoir. This had obvious advantages: the upper reservoir would be reserved for balancing seasonal variations; the top water level of the lower reservoir could be kept close to the spillway level, thus maintaining the maximum head on the main generating plant at Clachan; since the pumping head would be only about one tenth (100-130 feet) of the full head through which the pumped water would be utilised for power at Clachan, the economic advantages would be particularly favourable;[66] and spillage would be reduced to a minimum. Furthermore, because this installation would be the first major scheme of its kind in the United Kingdom, it was hoped that its operation would produce invaluable data on the value of pumped-storage plant in a *system* serving local and peak-load requirements which might one day possess nuclear generating capacity.[67]

This, then, was the scheme. Its implementation proved to be as difficult as its features were novel. About 15 miles of access roads were required to serve the site, and some sections had to be constructed in areas where the stability of the moraine overlying the steeply inclined surfaces of the rock was suspect. The progress on these sections was painfully slow, and for eighteen months, until the roadworks had been completed, little else could be attempted. There were problems too with the constructional materials. The nearest source of natural sand was about 45 miles away, and since fully half a million tons of aggregate would be required, an outcrop of epidiorite situated about half a mile from the main dam site was opened up, and the quarry plant used during the Loch Sloy project installed, much of it modified to produce rock sand. The housing of the 800 workmen involved taking over and re-equipping an abandoned military camp. Not until the Spring of 1951 were these essential preliminaries fully completed.

At the site of the main dam trial borings had shown the geological structure to be highly complex. Because of the unpromising and variable nature of the rock strata not only would it be necessary to excavate 135,000 cubic yards of rock and soil but the design of the dam had to be one which would distribute the foundation pressures evenly within a wide range of loading conditions. Numerous possibilities were considered and the final choice was determined by a combination of technical and economic factors. The form of concrete structure giving the most favourable distribution of pressure on the difficult foundation rock was the roundhead buttress type, a design which also best met the economic criteria. The relative cost of comparable rock-fill, mass gravity, and roundhead buttress dams suitable for the conditions at the Shira site was found to be of the order 1.4 : 1.25 : 1. To allow for shrinkage effects in the concrete and to accommodate variations in the deformation of the different strata under load, the individual buttresses, of which there were 37 built 5 feet apart, the gaps subsequently being sealed with wedge-shaped closing sections that were not poured until sufficient time had elapsed for the contraction of the 'green' concrete in the buttress heads. A typical cross section and plan of one of the buttresses is shown in Fig. 38, and upstream and downstream views of the dam under construction are shown in Plates 20 and 21. Not until December 1956 had the dam reached the stage when partial impounding could be started. A level was reached sufficient to permit the operation of the Sron Mor station late in 1957, and the dam, in the construction of which over a quarter of a million tons of concrete had been used, was finished in the Spring of 1959 (see Plate 22).

Meanwhile, the other major works had already been completed, though these too had had their own complications. It has already been explained that the plan called for a two-stage development involving the provision of a lower storage basin, and that the site conditions were distinctly unfavourable to the formation of such a reservoir. 'The only feasible site involved the construction of a dam in two separate sections, one of

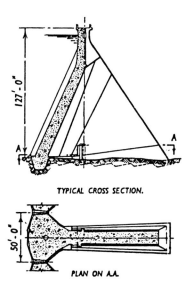

TYPICAL CROSS SECTION.

PLAN ON A.A.

FIGURE 38   Shira Dam: plan and cross-section

178

PLATE 20   Shira roundhead buttress dam under construction

GLEN SHIRA PROJECT
Contract No. 5 - Main Dam
Downstream View of Buttress No. 19
Ser. No. 1/206.   Date 15/12/55

PLATE 21   Shira: downstream view of buttress

PLATE 22   Shira Dam and Sron Mor power station

these being located immediately upstream of a water fall about 40 feet high and separated from the other section to the west by a massive rock intrusion'.[68] The solution was the construction upstream of the waterfall of a concrete gravity dam which incorporated in its design special spilling arrangements to eliminate erosion, which might ultimately endanger the foundations of the dam; and the building (to the west of the rock intrusion) of a 600 foot long earth embankment with a watertight barrier in the form of a thin reinforced concrete core wall supported on a concrete plinth extending into sound rock.[69] A cross section is shown in Fig. 39. All went well until the weather broke in mid-June 1954. The rainfall for the last four months of that year averaged 15 inches per month and made working with earth–fill almost impossible.[70] In some periods progress in building up the embankment fell to less than 2 feet a month, despite the fact that as the height slowly rose the volume of material required steadily diminished. Not until the very end of December could impounding begin.

Progress with the tunnels was much more satisfactory.[71] Within a year of starting work at the end of 1949 nearly three miles of the six miles' long 11 feet tunnel between the lower reservoir and the main power station site or Loch Fyne had been driven. This included a record week's drive of 245 feet made at one face in November 1950. It was then possible to begin work on the main power station at Clachan. 'The decision to adopt an underground power station and inclined pressure shaft (see Fig. 40) was taken following detailed analysis of tender prices received for alternative underground and surface layouts. This investigation indicated that the overall cost for the underground scheme would be of the same order as the surface arrangement. Steel was in short supply at that time and a saving of 350 tons weighed in favour of the underground scheme, which was also preferred on grounds of amenity'.[72]

The Clachan power station was the first large underground station commissioned by the Board. It is equipped with a 40,000kW generating set driven by a vertical shaft Francis turbine, the largest water-turbine-driven set installed by that time in the United Kingdom. The station was excavated by the cut-and-cover method. That is to say, it was carried out by quarrying down to the main floor level, and to accommodate the generator extended downwards by sinking. The hole created was then broken through into the pilot tunnel previously driven for access to the pressure shaft. The concrete walls of the basement section were poured hard against the rock and, after providing a reinforced concrete framework of columns and crane girders to support a large 150 ton overhead travelling crane, a reinforced concrete arch roof was built. This was subsequently covered by rock to reinstate the surface of the hillside.

One last point might be mentioned.[73] At the suggestion of the Fishery adviser the tail-race of Clachan was arranged to discharge into the river Fyne a short distance upstream of the point where the river enters Loch Fyne. It was believed that this arrangement would encourage breeding fish to enter the river. The price paid for the accommodation of these almost ubiquitous fish was the construction of very elaborate tail-race works which required the excavation of 6,000 cubic yards of rock (or about half as much as the power station itself), the building of a 250 feet long tunnel, and extensive model tests in order to make sure that the opposite bank of the river would not be eroded!

This most interesting scheme, only the most outstanding features of which have been

182

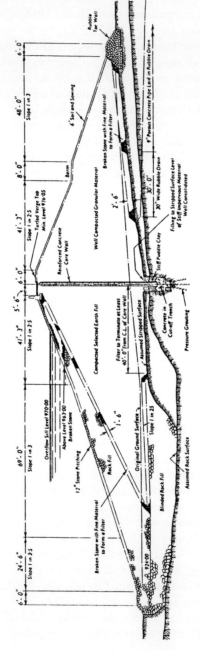

FIGURE 39   Shira scheme: cross-section of earth fill dam of the lower reservoir

183

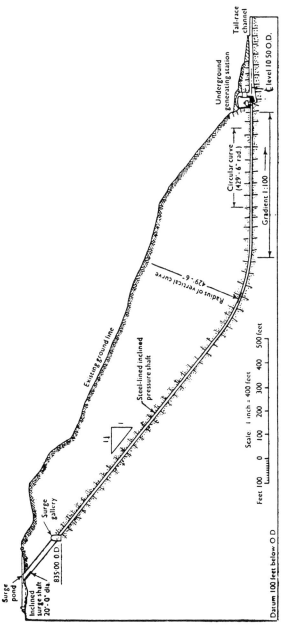

FIGURE 40   Shira: pressure shaft, surge shaft, and underground power station, Clachan

touched upon, began to contribute to the Board's output in January 1955, when the Clachan station was commissioned. The 5,000kW combined generating and pumping set at Sron Mor was put into operation in the autumn of 1957, just over eighteen months before the main dam and the last of the diversion aqueducts were completed. Thereafter, the Shira scheme was to produce about 80 million units annually.

Between the Sloy scheme to the east and Shira to the west, the Board saw an opportunity to develop the catchment of upper Glen Fyne. An appropriate dam site appeared to be available in the valley of the Allt-na-Lairige, a tributary of the River Fyne; the direct catchment of 3.2 square miles could readily be extended by the usual diversionary works; the estimated average rainfall was 125 inches a year; and a power station situated on the River Fyne and fed by tunnel from the storage reservoir would operate under a substantial gross head of about 800 feet. The typical general arrangements, comprising a storage reservoir, dam, pressure tunnel, diversionary aqueducts and a power station, seemed perfectly appropriate. But when detailed investigation of the cost of implementing the plan had been carried out, the economic dubiety of the original proposals was revealed.

The fundamental problem was the dam. As first designed, the scheme envisaged a mass gravity dam, 64 feet in height. With such a dam, the scheme 'had been barely economic and had had somewhat less storage than was necessary to ensure that the full kilowatt capacity of the plant could always be available'.[74] To have increased this limited storage ($7\frac{1}{2}$ per cent of the average annual run-off) by raising the height of the dam would adversely have affected the unit cost of current generated. In searching for a solution to this apparently intractable problem, the idea of a prestressed concrete dam of equal height was suggested. This would have reduced the cost of the works and made its output cheaper, but Fulton, pursuing his endless quest for 'firmness' of supply, argued that instead of reducing the cost of the dam by adopting a prestressed concrete design, a similar expenditure to that anticipated for a mass gravity dam would make possible the construction of a *higher* prestressed concrete dam. This would expand the storage by a third (i.e. to 10 per cent of the average annual run-off) and thus increase the value of the power because of its greater dependability.

This argument convinced the Board, and it was decided to adopt a prestressed concrete design some 14 feet higher than the gravity dam originally proposed. It was acknowledged that there was an element of risk in this decision for it was the first dam of its kind in the world.[75] Furthermore, there was a very real possibility that future maintenance costs could erode the immediate savings. But for Fulton the decision carried with it 'an element of adventure' which he was unable to resist, and it is not difficult to imagine his infectious enthusiasm carrying the largely lay Board with him.[76]

Construction of the scheme began in 1953. No major problems were encountered either with the dam or the driving of the $1\frac{1}{4}$ mile long tunnel to the generating station. In the prestressed portion of the dam (just over 70 per cent of the total length[77]), it was estimated that the volume of concrete used was 40 per cent lower than it would have been had a mass gravity design been built; but against this saving had to be set the cost of high-tensile steel bars and a certain loss of efficiency resulting from delays in their delivery to the site. Each set of steel bars, 138 in all, had to be of a precise length, and their occasional failure to arrive in conformity with the pre-determined timetable caused unpredictable interruptions to the progress of the concreting.[78] But the delays were frustrating rather than serious, and the scheme was completed in the autumn of 1956. (A cross section of the dam is shown in Fig. 41, and Plate 23 shows the dam under construction; the cross section is clearly visible). By the end of the year the reservoir was full, and the power station—equipped with twin Pelton wheels driving a central alternator with a capacity of 6,000kW was commissioned in December.

As with other departures from orthodoxy, the dam was fully instrumented.[79] Isolated sections of the stressing rods were left exposed to check the extension and stress relief under varying loads, and apparatus was devised and installed to measure small deflections or movements of the dam. Such measurements, it was hoped, would provide useful data for future designs, but despite the belief that prestressed concrete dams possessed certain advantages over other types, this successful experiment was never repeated by the Board.[80]

(vii)   *General Observations*

In less than two decades, the North of Scotland Hydro-Electric Board had built 53 dams (See Table 13) and installed a generating capacity of over one million kW in as many major power stations (See Table 4 and Appendix Table 21). By 1963, the Board's 1951 Development Programme had been fulfilled; not perhaps in precisely the form envisaged in 1951, nor at the cost set down in the original Construction Schemes (See Table 14), but it is undeniable that by the early 1960s MacColl's dreams had become reality. Equally remarkable was the fact that the Board's essential targets had been attained without desecrating the Scottish countryside, without exterminating the salmon, and without decimating the tourist trade. Such matters warrant further examination. Here we are concerned simply with certain basic issues of civil and electrical engineering suggested by the foregoing brief survey.[81]

When Angus Fulton commented in 1952 that 'the urgency with which hydro-electric construction has proceeded since the war in order to try and keep pace with the growth of load has not given the designers of the Scottish works many opportunities to strike out on new lines. There are consequently fewer examples of novel civil engineering design in Scotland than in other countries',[82] he was doing himself and his colleagues somewhat less than justice. It is true that gravity dams constituted the overwhelming majority of the Board's programme (see Table 13), but where the topography permitted and economic circumstances dictated, the Board and its technical advisers were, as we have seen, slow neither in adopting variations on an admittedly basic design, nor in introducing innovations. In relation to the brevity of the period during which the major schemes were planned and executed—little more than 15 years—the wonder is that so many original designs and methods were undertaken and such significant strides made in the knowledge and understanding of, for example, the physical properties of rocks, soil mechanics, surveying techniques, the strength and characteristics of concrete made to different specifications, and the behaviour of such an incompressible fluid as water when subjected to control in an enclosed space (e.g. in a pressure aqueduct).

Our all too brief survey mentioned only one or two examples of model testing. It should be emphasised that research, often including models, was conducted for the

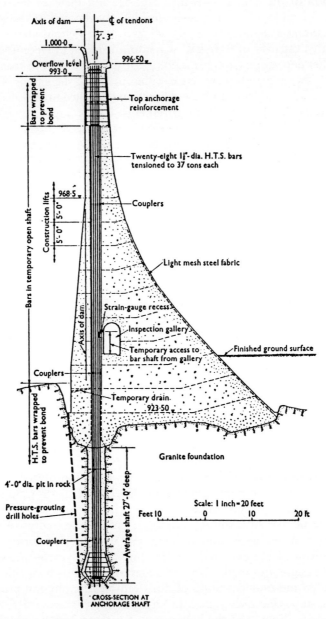

FIGURE 41   Allt-na-Lairige prestressed concrete dam: cross-section

PLATE 23   Allt-na-Lairige prestressed concrete dam under construction

Board at the Universities of Aberdeen, Glasgow and Edinburgh, at Imperial College, London, and at the research laboratories of many of the Board's contractors. From these investigations and those conducted in the Board's own Research Laboratory at Pitlochry there resulted a continuous refinement of dam design, substantial economies in materials, and major advances in catering for the mysterious and often perverse behaviour of the salmon. At the same time, unsightly surface pipelines gave way to subterranean pressure tunnels and shafts, and power stations—once 'boxes to hold the machinery'—were clothed with local stone and properly landscaped, or sunk entirely underground.

During the relatively short period that encompasses the Board's most active period of hydro engineering, the Board rapidly adopted the latest refinements in the Francis turbine, in generating and switching equipment, in remote control mechanisms. The Board was itself a pioneer in devising and installing pumped storage plant, in prestressing, in the use of blast-furnace slag and fly ash in concrete mixes, and the collection of precise data on a range of phenonema as diverse as rainfall, river flows, pore pressures in earth embankments, and the stress, strain and deflexions of dams under varying loads.

This adds up to no mean achievement in a period characterised by shortages of materials and labour. Indeed, the impetus for several of the Board's innovations in design and methods had been provided by scarcities in cement, steel and skilled labour. For example, the intricacy of the shuttering required for the Sloy Dam was rapidly simplified for subsequent massive buttress designs because of the chronic shortage of skilled joiners; not the least reason for the adoption of pressure tunnels was the need to economise on scarce steel in surface pipelines; and the use of local materials, albeit in an imaginative manner, was partially dictated by appalling problems of access on many of the sites. Undoubtedly, the Board was encouraged to experiment—within limits dictated by capital constraints and considerations of safety—by the employment of as many as ten different firms as Consultants, each with its own strengths and prejudices, each jealous of its own expertise, and each vying with the others to secure recognition

TABLE 13   *Number and Types of Dams built by the North of Scotland Hydro-Electric Board, 1945–1964*

Types	Number	Percentage
Gravity	29	54.7
Earthfill	3	5.7
Buttress	9	17.0
Arch	3	5.7
Rockfill	3	5.7
Gravity and earthfill	2	3.8
Gravity and rockfill	2	3.8
Gravity, earthfill and buttress	1	1.9
Prestressed concrete	1	1.9
	53	100.0

Source: J Guthrie Brown, in 'Discussion' of the paper presented to the Institution of Civil Engineers by A A Fulton and L H Dickerson, *Proceedings of the Institution of Civil Engineers*, Vol. 33 (1966), p. 454.

TABLE 14   *North of Scotland Hydro–Electric Board: Cost of Major Hydro Generation Schemes*★

Construction Scheme No.	Name	Generation Sub-Group	Plant Capacity (kW)	Average Annual Output (millions of units)	Estimated Cost Date	Estimated Cost Amount (£000s)	Year of completion of Scheme Works	Approximate Final Cost† (£000s)	Final Cost / Original Estimate %	Final Cost of Installed Capacity‡ (£ per kW)
1	Sloy, Morar and Lochalsh§	Sloy/Shira	132,000	114.0	1944	4,600	1951	8,870	192.8	67.2
12	Glen Shira	Sloy/Shira	45,000	80.0	1946	3,150	1959	8,200	260.3	182.2
27	Allt-na-Lairige	Sloy/Shira	6,000	20.0	1948	620	1956	1,163	262.9	271.7
2	Tummel-Garry, Gairloch§	Tummel Valley	152,675	307.2	1944	6,450	1959	18,500	286.8	121.2
15	Gaur	Tummel Valley	6,400	17.0	1947	650	1954	1,040	160.0	162.5
31	Tummel Valley Additions	Tummel Valley	4,700	35.0	1954	1,340	1962	2,100	156.7	—#
3	Fannich	Conon	24,000	13.5	1944	960	1955	3,500	364.6	145.8
16	Glascarnoch-Luichart-Torr Achilty	Conon	65,980	282.5	1947	8,700	1959	18,500	212.6	280.4
29	Orrin	Conon	18,256	76.9	1954	4,550	1960	4,600	101.1	252.0
7	Mullardoch-Fasnakyle-Affric	Affric/Beauly	68,400	231.0	1946	4,800	1952	9,800	204.2	143.3
30	Strathfarrar and Kilmorach	Affric/Beauly	102,510	263.0	1956	14,250	1963	'underspent'¶	<100.0	139.0
18	Lawers	Breadalbane	30,000	80.0	1947	2,850	1957	5,910	207.4	197.0
25	Breadalbane									
25A	Breadalbane Amendments	Breadalbane	90,260	298.3	1955	20,350	1961	22,000	108.1	243.7
24	Garry	Great Glen	42,665	162.1	1948	4,850	1956	9,580	197.5	224.5
23	Moriston									
23A	Moriston Amendments	Great Glen	72,010	207.0	1953	12,570	1962	12,100	96.3	168.0
32	Loch Shin	Shin	38,050	138.8	1953	7,200	1960	7,600	105.6	199.7
28	Awe★★	Awe	440,886	577.0	1957	24,500	1964	'underspent'¶	<100.0	55.6

★ The Board's smaller schemes with individual capacities of 6,000 kW or less were principally for the supply of local needs and were more expensive than the major schemes in terms of cost per kW installed. Their economic justification stemmed from the very high cost of alternative means of supply (diesel generation and/or very expensive transmission costs from more economical generation). Examples are Loch Dubh (Ullapool), £383 per kW installed, and Loch Gisla (Isle of Lewis), £389 per kW installed.

† It was pointed out to the Mackenzie Committee that over the entire period covered by these data (*c*.1945–1961), costs of labour and materials had risen by about 260 per cent.

‡ It is appreciated that these data are not *fully* consistent with those given in a written answer by the Minister of State for the Scottish Office in 1957 (*HL Deb*, Vol. 201, 22 January 1957, cols. 37–38), but they are broadly similar. The 1957 figures are less accurate than those presented to the Mackenzie Committee.

§ For Constructional Schemes 1 and 2, the component parts are not disaggregated.

In this case, such a calculation is inappropriate.

¶ Expected to be 'underspent' at the time the submission to the Mackenzie Committee was prepared in 1961.

★★In the case of Awe, which includes the Cruachan pumped storage scheme, the Board's records indicate that the cost per kW installed at Cruachan was only £37.8.

Source: NSHEB, Evidence for Mackenzie Committee, Table II(i)H, dated 10 May 1961 (plus additional data).

189

for the imaginative use of materials and the suitability and cost-effectiveness of their designs.[83] This element of rivalry and competitiveness, which extended to the contractors and sub-contractors employed by the Board, made itself manifest particularly in the speed and efficiency with which their work, often in appalling terrain, was accomplished.[84]

Critics may have made great play with statistics showing the frightening escalation of costs between the earliest and final estimates of these major engineering works, but in real terms—allowing for the inflation in the prices paid for labour and materials— the differences were far less serious and, as knowledge and experience accumulated and the fever that gripped the Board in the 1940s moderated with a growing appreciation of the economic realities, predicted and final costs gradually converged. It was, after all, a period of intense excitement and, as we have observed, for the major participants, the development of hydro-electricity in the Highlands took on the character of a crusade. It is important, therefore, to assess the real nature of the Board's achievements.

2 'The Economic Development and Social Improvement of the North of Scotland'

(i) Hopes and Expectations

When Tom Johnston moved the Second reading of the Hydro-Electric Development (Scotland) Bill in the Commons in 1943 he presented the measures as 'a partial remedy' for the illnesses that afflicted the Highlands. It was more than simply a means of harnessing the great latent hydro power of the North of Scotland. Its principal object was nothing less than staunching the haemorrhage of outward migration by the regeneration of the region's economy. Johnston told the Commons that he thought that 'industries ... will be, and ought to be, attracted to locations inside the ... area' as a result of the measure. After the demands of the ordinary consumer for electricity had been met, these 'large power users' would be given priority. When their needs had been satisfied, the surplus output would be sold to the Central Electricity Board and the resulting profit used to subsidise the creation of uneconomic distribution schemes in the remote areas, and 'in the carrying out of ... measures for *the economic development and social improvement of the North of Scotland district*'. This was the famous social clause (Subsection 3 of Section 2) which gave statutory recognition to the fact that the Hydro-Board was conceived in terms broader than that of an organisation simply to supply electricity. It was an instrument to assist in the rehabitation of the Highlands.[85]

The Cooper Committee—upon whose recommendations the Bill had been based— had addressed the question of how best this was to be achieved. It was acknowledged that 'the Highlander could not and should not be separated from his croft or his boat', and that his lot should be ameliorated 'by cheap electricity for lighting and heating ..., attracting summer visitors, and assisting in the working of light home industries and crafts'. It was recognised too that there was scope for considerable development and improvement in agriculture and fishing, forestry and associated industries, quarrying and stone-crushing. But the Cooper Committee had 'little faith' that even the *successful* implementation of such limited objectives would be sufficient to retain the young and more enterprising elements among Highland society, far less 'attract a growing and prosperous population'. It was believed that this could *only* be done by the establishment of the electro-chemical and electro-metallurgical industries. Indeed, the pre-war defeat of the Caledonian Power Bill was regarded 'as a tragic mistake not only for Scotland but for Great Britain'. This mistake could now be rectified, 'provided the electricity [could] be supplied with reliability at a sufficiently low cost', and from centres of industrial development prosperity would gradually be diffused throughout the crofting areas.[86]

(ii) *The Heavy Current Users*

Once established, the Hydro Board lost no time in exploring the industrial prospects. A series of meetings with the Scottish Council on Industry was inaugurated in December 1943, when Sir Steven Bilsland 'intimated that the Council had been making certain investigations as to particular areas which might be suitable for early development involving the establishment of new industries and the extension of existing industries'. Sir Steven had made specific inquiries into the possibilities of attracting metallurgical and other allied industries, but the Board's attention was also directed to the opportunities offered by exploiting raw materials such as Caithness flagstones, feldspar, dolomite, silica, seaweed, slates and the development of the woodworking, woollen, white fish and shell fish industries. Much depended upon the cost at which it would be possible to provide supplies of electricity. It is clear that members of the Council hoped and *expected* the Board to make concessions on price, but all that MacColl would promise at this early stage was that 'the existing tariffs could be taken as the upper limit of the Board's changes'.[87]

Within a month Bilsland was able to report to MacColl and Lawrie that meetings with William Lutyens of ICI, Mr Inman of British Electron Ltd., and officials of the Ministry of Supply had confirmed the belief that so far as heavy current-consuming processes were concered, aluminium and magnesium were 'already overproduced', but that there existed 'better chances' for the manufacture of carborundum, ferro alloys, phosphorous, cyanamide and carbide.[88] In pursuing these leads, it became increasingly clear that the price of electricity was critical. The British Oxygen Company, who had purchased a controlling interest in Odda Smelteverk A/S, a Norwegian factory producing carbide, after the failure of the Caledonian Power Scheme, wanted to establish a carbide industry at Corpach, where they already had land and where there were good facilities for unloading Welsh anthracite and limestone. It all depended on the cost of water power. Before the war, BOC had been able to obtain supplies in Norway at 0.05*d.* per unit. Even in 1936 the Caledonian Power Scheme had not envisaged a cost of production below 0.1*d.* per unit, and BOC's own calculations of future *production costs* of the Board's Tummel project showed an increase of not less than four times the pre-war cost of that abortive scheme. A memorandum by Col. Hardy of the British Oxygen Co. emphasised that the Board had to understand that

> a Hydro-Electric Undertaking, established at today's high costs, places a burden on Users for a long period of years and ... jeopardises the prospects of the establishment of electro-

chemical and electro-metallurgical industries in this country to compete in the International market.[89]

If the Hydro Board *really* wanted to assist in the establishment of such industries, it should postpone the implementation of its constructional schemes until costs experienced a post-war fall; sell electricity at a price that approached that obtaining in Canada, the United States or Norway; and persuade the government to close down its emergency carbide factory in South Wales.

This was too much for the Board. Certain errors in Colonel Hardy's memorandum were pointed out; the Board's duty to begin operations as soon as possible was emphasised; and 'it was made clear that while the Board's tariff would be on a sliding scale, no special cheap rate could be quoted to any one consumer, and the same advantages would be offered to all'. Furthermore,

> if the cost of developing water power after the war could not enable carbide to be produced in the Highlands at a world competitive price, the remedy would have to be sought, not by the Board ... but by carbide manufacturers themselves, either by a safeguarding tariff or an export subsidy[90]

And that, for the moment, was that.

Meanwhile, discussions with other potential heavy current users, such as ICI, the British Aluminium Co., Magnesium Elektron Ltd , Courtaulds, and Albright & Wilson were taking place. They all appear to have foundered on the question of price, though the proposal by Albright and Wilson to erect a factory for the manufacture of phosphorous at Aberdeen also fell foul of the Board's reluctance to transmit large blocks of power to locations outside the Highlands.[91] It was not until 1948 that the Scottish Council on Industry revived the question of large power users, but by this time escalating costs had ruled out any hope of 'cheap' electricity. Tom Johnston told the Council that 'after providing for the financing of losses on distribution schemes (which was essential), the average price per unit sold from the major works would be about 0.7*d*. on the present estimates. If any firm had to have a cheaper rate to compete in foreign markets, it was up to the Government to subsidise the concern and not the Hydro-Electric Board'. A suggestion by the Council's technical adviser that 'the output from one major scheme at least should be allocated to large power users ... at a cost price without any addition to cover losses on uneconomic distribution schemes' was immediately rejected: 'neither the public nor Parliament would accept [such] a scheme'.[92]

Undeterred, Sir Steven Bilsland arranged another meeting between the Board, the Scottish Council on Industry, Colonel Hardy and Mr Watt of the British Oxygen Co. and a group of civil servants from the Scottish Home Department. Neither Colonel Hardy nor the Board would budge. The British Oxygen Co. would not establish works in the Highlands for the production of carbide, acetylene and plastics unless power was made available at 0.15*d*. per unit; the Board, whose first duty was to 'the ordinary consumer', said that this price was 'quite impossible'. Tom Johnston's suggestion that the British Oxygen Co should take up the question of a subsidy to bridge the gap with Sir Stafford Cripps, the Chancellor the Exchequer, was unacceptable:

Colonel Hardy said he would prefer the Hydro Board to be subsidised rather than the BOC, because if the carbide industry was subsidised in Scotland, the Welsh people would want a subsidised industry in Wales.[93]

This time negotiations between the Board and the British Oxygen Co. were not to be revived. Col. Hardy could not forget that power was being produced in Norway at 0.05*d*. per unit, nor could he be convinced of the fact that the conditions which made it possible to contemplate obtaining electricity at 0.10*d*. per unit from the Caledonian Power Scheme in 1936 had gone forever.[94] For his part, Tom Johnston would not jeopardise the prior claims of those who lived in the Highlands, despite appeals by C C Cunningham of the Scottish Home Department, George Boex, the Managing Director of the British Aluminium Co., and Col. Sir Donald Cameron of Lochiel, convenor of Inverness-shire County Council. Lochiel's criticism that 'your Board think only of the Grid, which will be of no use to us in Inverness-shire. And no large Power User will contemplate setting down factories until they know the price they will have to pay for their power', infuriated Johnston. He replied:

> I gather from your letter that you ... want us to offer *now and in advance of precise knowledge of what our construction schemes will cost and in a time of rising prices for materials and labour* a cheaper bulk supply price than 0.3*d*. to some large scale user. Well, let us suppose our experts did have a flying guess at it ... and that they turned out to be wrong, would that be any benefit to the Highlands? Would it not mean that there would be no wherewithal to finance distribution schemes in the rural areas? And who would then be throwing stones at us for our almost criminal folly? Who would be accusing us of financing some wealthy company at the expense of the small consumers in the Highland area?[95]

This letter, written in January 1948, marked the end of the confident hopes of the Cooper Committee that heavy current users would be attracted to and would transform the Highland economy.[96] It was a bitter disappointment to the Scottish Office, The Scottish Council,[97] the Board and to Tom Johnston personally. Let him have the last word:

> Barely had we started operations ere there came upon us pressure—great pressure—to apportion and docket large blocks of power for gigantic electro-metallurgical and chemical corporations at cost price, or even at less than cost price. It was forcibly impressed upon us that some of these concerns must have cheap power if they were to compete with Norway, or Central Africa, or the United States, and that if we failed to supply the power at the low prices desired the great corporations would go elsewhere and the nation would be disadvantaged. But firmly and unanimously we replied that if the corporations aforesaid were of such great national importance, and if they must be subsidised, then the subsidy should be a straight one from the national Exchequer, all British taxpayers sharing in the burden, as *ex-hypothesi* they were to share in at least some of the benefits; but for any sake do not expect us to acquiesce in the scrapping of our Act of Parliament, or evade our social obligations to the Highland population, or connive at placing on the Highland consumer alone burdens which ought to be carried by the nation as a whole. If corporation A had to get 1000 million units at or under cost then clearly there was going to be no fund available from which we could carry, or assist to carry, electricity to the remote consumer, or to the

small (and as we hoped growing) industries in the remote areas. And if to corporation A, why not also to corporations B and C already on our doorstep? So we dug our toes in the ground.[98]

(iii)   *Light and Local Industries*

This outcome cannot be said to have been entirely unexpected. The Board's records relating to the electro-chemical and electro-metallurgical industries betray a growing disillusionment. Meetings with their representatives seemed only to confirm Tom Johnston's suspicions of big business, and MacColl's doubts were evident from his very first encounter with Sir Steven Bilsland. While Sir Steven was extolling the benefits to be anticipated by meeting the power requirements of the British Oxygen Co. and Lever Brothers, MacColl quietly 'pointed out that one of the best means of raising the standard of living for crofters in the Board's area would be to introduce crop drying'. He emphasised that 'the loss of crops after curring due to wet weather is at present enormous'.[99] The contrast between the two attitudes towards Highland development could not have been more stark, and while Lord Airlie was chairman, MacColl had a profound influence on the Board's policy. MacColl wanted to encourage the use of electricity in industries deeply rooted in the Board's area of operations. He was anxious to obtain as large a proportion as possible of the Board's requirements of raw materials from local sources: limestone, cement, granite, and stone. He saw the need for modern refrigeration plant at the fishing ports, and was excited by the possibilities inherent in the timber-based industries.

To many light, labour-intensive industries a supply of electricity was invaluable, even essential, but its simple provision was not calculated to have a major attractive influence. Much greater success stemmed from the Board's own demands for goods and services. When placing orders, preference was given to Scottish manufacturers or to English firms who could be induced to establish branch factories in the north. Where this was unrealistic, the Board let it be known that they would look favourably on those firms in the South who were prepared to sub-contract certain components of major items of equipment to local engineering workshops. Thus, the English Electric Co. had the turbine alternators for Loch Sloy constructed at the Scotstoun Works of Harland and Wolff; Boving and Co. made similar arrangements with John Brown's, and another company, Harland Engineering of Alloa, with no previous experience in hydro-electric installations, was persuaded to manufacture water turbines under licence from the American firm, Morgan Smith. Sir William Arrol & Co. and John Brown's of Clyde-bank were regularly awarded valuable contracts at prices negotiated by the Board after advice from their consulting engineers. Among other Scottish manufacturers to benefit from these mutually-beneficial arrangements were Mavor & Coulson, Glenfield & Kennedy, Bruce Peebles & Co., and British Polar Engines Ltd.

It should be remembered that for about twenty years, between 1945 and 1965, the Board were responsible for a larger share of capital investment in the North of Scotland than any other agency:[100] their economic muscle was considerable. Large firms were prepared to acquiesce in the Board's demands, and having become specialised producers of hydro equipment—in the design of which they had initially to call upon Swiss,

Swedish and American expertise—they developed a symbiotic relationship with the Board. In the case of water turbines, no *competitive* check tenders were called for; the price of every major contract was individually negotiated; and the Board arranged that they should all get a fair share of the work according to their capacity. The Board—though not the Select Committee on Nationalised Industries—were satisfied that these arrangements did not involve them in any extra cost, and they were certainly instrumental in creating what was essentially an entirely new branch of the engineering industry, one that was subsequently to secure major export orders.[101]

But while the acquisition of the Board's heavy mechanical and electrical plant requirements may have helped the *Scottish* economy, it had little direct impact on the Highlands. Here there were pursued a myriad of more modest objectives. The Board succeeded in attracting to the north a variety of new light industries with a high labour content. They included the manufacture of such items as electricity meters, small lamps, transformers, cookers and electric power tools. As a direct result of the Board's approaches, branch assembly and manufacturing plant were established in Peterhead, Buckie, Auchterarder and Inverness by Radiation Ltd., Amalgamated Electrical Industries, the British Thomson Houston Co., and Ferranti's.[102] But far more important were the Board's unceasing efforts to assist small established industrial concerns by connecting them to the Board's distribution system, giving them advice, and by obtaining equipment and materials through them. And when, in order to stay in business, such undertakings (for example, the Herring Industry Board's deep-freezing factory at Lerwick and the Alginate Industries' factory in South Uist) required a supply of current in advance of the Board's spreading network, they were frequently provided with diesel generating plant, most of it made in Scotland.

(iv)   *Maintenance of Local Employment*

In other ways too the Board tried to maintain local employment. In addition to being one of the major employers in the Highlands—at the peak of its building programme the labour force numbered about 12,000 men, and over the period 1945-1965, annually averaged approximately 8,000—the Board's staffing policy was designed to sustain levels of local demand.[103] For example, when the Board took over seventeen 'authorised undertakings' on vesting day 1948 the local managements were essentially retained. The Board recognised that 'in some of the smaller communities, the numbers employed represented a substantial contribution to the community's well-being', and so although some saving—estimated at being about £90,000 per annum—could have been effected by the centralisation of such operations as billing and stores accounting, this was not done.[104]

But the initiative of which the Board—certainly Edward MacColl—was perhaps most proud was that of building in local stone, for this contributed to a revival of the Scottish stone quarry industry in the north and did much to keep alive the craft of the stone mason. The genesis of this policy was recounted by James Shearer, one of the Board's panel of architectural advisers, in a tribute entitled 'A.E.M. and the New Stone Age'[105] Entrusted with the design of Nostie Bridge power station, near Lochalsh, for which the drawings prepared by the civil engineers had indicated a rectangular brick structure with a slate roof, or 'a box to hold machinery', Shearer pondered over the problem of co-ordinating 'these rigid and uncompromising requirements in the design of a building which, however beneficial in purpose, would not in [the] idyllic setting [of Lochalsh] look like a thoughtless intrusion'. It occurred to him that one solution would be to use 'local stone instead of brick, and slates of a colour that would blend harmoniously with the changing colours of the Highland landscape'. He put the case to MacColl, whose response was sympathetic:

> He encouraged me to tell him all that I had in mind. He listened with close attention, saying little, as his habit was, and it was only gradually, during the conversation which followed that I found out, quite accidentally, I had been recommending to him a point of view that he had already made his own.

It was therefore agreed that the power station at Lochalsh should be built of local stone. A suitable source was found and a firm of contractors agreed to recruit a staff of quarrymen and masons to undertake the task.

So successful was it that a similar procedure was employed elsewhere. For example, during 1950, the control houses of the sub-stations of Fasnakyle and Beauly were built of golden yellow sandstone from Burghead and red sandstone from Tarradale in Easter Ross, respectively. Tarradale stone was also used to face the Grudie Bridge power station, and Burghead stone the Fasnakyle generating station of the Affric scheme (See Plate 24).[106] Yet when MacColl and Shearer had first visited the quarry at Tarradale, it was all but derelict and possessed no stone-cutting machinery. MacColl decided that the best and quickest way to bring this and the Greenbrae Quarry at Hopeman, near Elgin, into vigorous production again was to take the risk of placing definite orders, 'in the faith that by so doing he would be supplying an incentive of fresh hope to an industry which had almost given up *all* hope of recovery'. The risk was considerable 'because the orders involved were large, and to ask the stone-building trades to make good in the space of a few months the material and moral damage inflicted by twenty years of almost unrelieved public neglect, was to set them a task of no little magnitude'.

But the plan worked. The masonry industry started recruiting for the first time for decades. The Board continued to use solid stone masonry or stone cladding for its main power stations, sub-stations and staff houses; and as a result of the Board's example, a number of local authorities began once again to build in stone. It was claimed that in the north, where bricks were relatively expensive, the extra capital cost was marginal and that this was partially offset by savings in upkeep.[107] Indeed, in some cases it was positively economical to build in stone. For example, over 1,600 tons of blue whinstone were used to build the diesel generating station at Kirkwall which was given the traditional Orkney square random rubble finish. By the use of stone, the Board was able to save £600 plus £2,000 saving in steel which would have been necessitated by a concrete building.[108]

(v)   *Participation in the development of new forms of power generation*

In addition to sustained efforts to attract new industries to the north and the retention and revival of traditional skills, MacColl threw himself enthusiastically into the devel-

PLATE 24 Fasnakyle Power Station, Glen Affric

opment of new forms of electrical generation. The fact that they ended in failure should not detract from the sincerity of the attempt.

Soon after its creation, the Board examined the possibility of using wind-power as a source of energy. MacColl sought to develop relatively small plants—though much larger than those then being manufactured—for local use. Ever mindful of the needs of the Board's remoter areas, MacColl believed that plants of about 50kW which might operate in parallel with diesel engines, would be of particular value in making electricity available in the outer islands. The Electrical Research Association was also interested, and when this body established a special committee under the chairman of T G M Haldane to investigate large scale wind-power, it won MacColl's immediate support.

Together, the Board and the Electrical Research Association conducted experimental work and made a series of wind measurements at appropriate sites. These culminated in 1949 when the Board entered into a contract with John Browns of Clydebank to build a prototype 100kW wind-generator at Costa Head on the mainland of Orkney, where gusts of wind of over one hundred miles an hour had been recorded. Within a year, the foundations and the steel tower of the windmill had been erected. By September 1950 the machinery had also been completed, bench-tested, and shipped to Orkney, but such was the severity of the weather on the exposed site that it was not mounted on its steel tower until the Spring of 1951 (see Plate 25). Experimental runs were then carried out and a series of modifications made to achieve maximum efficiency.

PLATE 25   The 100 Kilowatt experimental windmill at Costa Head, Orkney

These experiments were continued for six years. They revealed that even if the outstanding technical problems (including metal stress caused by both torsion and centrifugal force) had been fully solved, the unpredictability of the wind's duration and velocity meant that the wind power plant would have to be supported by other sources of power to provide a dependable reserve. The economics of the scheme were not favourable: it was patently cheaper to provide power *solely* by diesel generation. In 1956 John Brown & Co. were released from their contract and the installation dismantled.[109]

The complementarity of hydro and thermal plant has been briefly discussed in Appendix I. From the beginning the Board recognised the need for thermal plant to meet some of their base load and to provide make-up units in time of drought. Because of this, and because of the absence of large coal mines in their district, the Board were attracted by the possibilities inherent in the closed-cycle gas turbine as a source of thermal generation. Once again, it was MacColl who pushed the idea forward. In the gas turbine, 'he saw an opportunity of building up an important Scottish industry and of utilising the energy locked up in the Scottish peat deposits'.[110] The Board's willing partners were again John Brown's, who were the sole licencees for Great Britain of the Escher Wyss patents, and they entered into a contract with the famous shipbuilders and engineers to instal an oil-fired gas turbine of 15,000 kilowatt capacity at the Carolina Port generating station, Dundee. This machine, which was the first of its type in Great Britain, was designed to operate on heavy oil fuel, but as early as 1948 the Board had inaugurated research which would, it was hoped, eventually permit the use of pulverised peat.

Although the original oil-fired turbine soon encountered serious difficulties, particularly in the compressor and in the turbine blade design, and the plant did not achieve its anticipated performance, the Board persevered with the possibilities of a peat-fired closed-cycle gas turbinc. An experimental 500 kilowatt machine ran successfully with powdered dried peat firing in December 1951 and, with the encouragement of the Secretary of State for Scotland, who had set up the Scottish Peat Committee under the chairmanship of Sir Edward Appleton, the Board agreed to construct a 2,000kW pilot plant at Altnabreac in Caithness and to prepare and work the bog which was to provide the fuel. Despite many problems arising from the fact that peat in its natural state contains 90 per cent or more of water and only 10 per cent or less of solid combustible material, MacColl supported the scheme with all his customary enthusiasm. It is significant that of all the officials round the table when this use of peat was first mooted only 'his reactions were ... immediate and unequivocal'. It was a challenge the solution of which could have the most momentous implications. The Highlands were said to have 170,000 acres of peat bog, and if ways could be devised to win and dry the peat, the way would be opened not only for its use as an industrial fuel but for the uncovering of many acres for farmland and afforestation.

After many years of effort, the Altnabreac project failed. While the equipment that had been developed for working the bog and harvesting the peat worked satisfactorily— a stock of about 10,000 tons of milled peat had been accumulated by the summer of 1957—thc 2,000kW gas-turbine installed at the Olgrinbeg station fell far short of its expected performance. The initial trials in 1958 necessitated endless modifications and adjustments, and even when the inevitable teething troubles had been overcome, the test runs in the following year were plagued with excessive vibration. Although the plant was run for over 1,200 hours in 1960, burning in the process nearly 1400 tons of peat and producing 665,400 units of electricity, it became increasingly evident that peat combustion was almost impossible to control, and that substantial modification and expenditure would be necessary to erradicate the many technical problems. Meantime, fuel oil had become cheaper and it had become apparent that the prospects for the economic creation of worthwhile agricultural land were poor. Thus, when grants from the Development Commission were discontinued in 1961 the Board had no alternative but to abandon the experiment.[111]

(vi)   *Improvements to roads and communications*

In examining specific schemes it will have been noticed that in order to provide access to constructional sites it was often necessary for the Board either to build new roads or to strengthen existing thoroughfares, and some roads submerged by reservoirs had to be replaced. By 1960, the Board had been responsible for building or reconstructing some 400 miles of roads at an estimated expenditure of £4.3m. About 100 miles of these new and improved roads were subsequently handed over to the public authorities at no cost to them. And if these roads were of considerable benefit to the local population, so too were the Board's radio communication systems. Installed to permit rapid response to instructions from regional control centres, certain facilities were willingly made available to the police, fire, ambulance and mountain-rescue services.

(vii)   *An Interim Assessment*

In 1961, the MacKenzie Committee sought to determine the exact significance of 'the social clause'.[112] The Board was asked 'to furnish a memorandum setting out in as much detail as is practicable the various ways in which the obligation imposed on the Board by Section 2(3) of the 1943 Act is being discharged'. The Committee was perfectly explicit. It wanted to know just what the Board had done 'to collaborate so far as their power and duties permit in the carrying out of any measures for the economic development and social improvement of their district' and to 'make an assessment for each service of the expenditure the Board have incurred in this connection'.[113]

In composing its reply—essentially embodied in its submission to the Committee entitled 'Collaboration in Economic Development and Social Improvement in North Scotland'[114]—the Board listed the measures so far discussed, together with paragraphs on some of its other activities, such as its support of the Scottish Council of Social Service, the Highlands and Islands Film Guild and the Scottish Craft Centre; the help that it had given in providing piped water supplies; and the regular payments it made to local authorities in lieu of rates. Objectively, even the full catalogue cannot be said to be very impressive. All too many of the measures had failed. The experiments with wind-power and the peat-fired closed cycle gas turbine had been abandoned on economic grounds before complete technical success had been attained; the expectations of the Cooper Committee for the development of industries using hydro-electric power on a large scale had not been fulfilled; and even the Board's sustained efforts to attract light industries must be regarded as disappointing. The Board's discriminatory policy in ordering hydro-electric plant had been instrumental in creating a powerful Scottish presence in this branch of electrical and mechanical engineering, but this benefited the Central Lowlands rather than the Highlands; and even the encouragement of new fishings and an active river- and reservoir-stocking policy failed, some argued, adequately to compensate for the harm inflicted on traditional waters.[115]

And yet as soon as the MacKenzie Committee was set up in 1961 the Board was innundated by letters of support from those who believed its existence was threatened. One such letter exemplifies the sentiments expressed by the vast majority, even those living in the very areas that only a decade or so earlier had been most vociferous in condemning the hydro schemes . This letter, sent by R H MacDonald, observed that 'there is no doubt that the Highlands have been immensely helped by the Board. In fact, there does not seem to have been anything else worthwhile done in the Highlands for generations, and for this every Highlanders should be most grateful'.[116] And it was not simply personal letters of this kind that were written. Fulsome tributes were paid in the newspapers; supportive speeches made at public meetings; and motions affirming their confidence in the Board '*as at present constituted*' passed by, for example, the County Councils of Inverness, Caithness, Argyll, and Ross and Cromarty, and by the Council of the Burgh of Kingussie.

If the implementation of the provisions of Section 2(3) of the 1943 Act had made such an insubstantial impact on the economic development and social improvement of the north of Scotland, how can this spontaneous outpouring of encouragement be explained? Partly it was because the Board had 'always endeavoured to have itself identified closely with most aspects of life and activity in its area. Over the years it ... gained the reputation of being singularly at one with the hopes and aspirations of those Highlanders whose homes and work are in the North'.[117] The local authorities were 'grateful for the *efforts* of the Board to promote new industries, relieve unemployment and construct new roads', no matter that the outcome fell far short of the original objectives. But primarily, those in the north of Scotland were impressed by 'the splendid record of the Board in making electric power available to a majority of residents in the Highlands and Islands'.[118] If the Board *did* help to arrest that 'decay amidst natural beauty' to which Sir Christopher Hinton had referred when he visited the Highlands in 1947,[119] it did so because of its vigorous policy of providing supplies of electricity to the sparsely populated and remote areas of its domain. If anything substantiates Mac-Coll's belief that the Board's activities should be regarded as 'a great social non-profit adventure, which seeks to make available the resources of an area ... for the benefit of the people',[120] it was the Board's transmission and distribution schemes.

(viii) *Transmission and Distribution*

While the Board's hydro schemes possess an obvious grandeur, and even the steel pylons and the main transmission cables seem to march purposefully over the shoulders of hills, through the glens and over the rivers conveying unimaginable power, it was the lesser, lower voltage lines that brought hope and comfort to the general population. It was these lines, strung on wooden poles, that did away with the need to carry paraffin oil from the nearest store, perhaps half a mile away, maybe a mile, sometimes further, to the croft. As MacColl once observed, 'those who live in urban areas, and enjoy the benefits of laid-on services, such as water, electricity, gas and sewage, do not realise the difficulties of life in these remote and isolated places. During the winter months, the islands are rain-soaked and for many days obscured by drifting mists, and there is the restless sea and ... the wind, deadening and numbing in its intensity and constancy and rarely in gentle mood ... . The houses, squat and solid, are well suited for the climatic conditions which they have to withstand, but are notoriously deficient in amenities when measured by standards which prevail elsewhere'.[121]

MacColl was determined to interpret literally those clauses in the 1943 Act that gave priority to the provision of electricity to those who lived in these small and scattered communities; and those who criticised his insistence on going ahead with the Tummel-Garry scheme with its possibility of large 'profits' from feeding the national grid, overlooked the insistent need for the financial resources that he, above all, knew would be required to offset the inevitable financial losses involved in distribution. At vesting day in April 1948 only about one farm in fourteen was connected to the mains in the Board's area, an area of 21,750 square miles or nearly one-quarter of the total area of Great Britain, with but $2\frac{1}{2}$ per cent of the nation's population.

By the end of 1947 320 miles of 132kV transmission lines had been surveyed and contracts placed. They were designed to connect the generating stations of the major hydro schemes with one another, with the existing steam generating stations at Aberdeen and Dundee, with the Grampian Electricity Supply Co.'s Rannoch-Tummel scheme, and with the Grid in Central Scotland. In the following year the Board took over and continued to develop the Grampian 132kV lines (see Appendix Table 22 and Fig. 42), and pressed ahead with both the distribution scheme they had inaugurated in 1944 and that which the Grampian Co. already had in hand. Each year the Board was able to annouce a significant number of hamlets and villages receiving a supply for the first time. By the mid-1950s over half the farms and crofts in the north of Scotland had been connected to the Board's system, and by the beginning of the next decade electricity had been made available to over 80 per cent (see Appendix Table 23 and Fig. 43).

The cost far exceeded the original estimates, especially in the very sparsely populated areas. Between 1949 and 1961, nearly 34,000 consumers were connected by new distribution schemes at an average cost of £262. Some £9 million had been spent on providing 4,100 miles of high voltage and 1,600 miles of low voltage distribution line. To connect *each* of the 3,600 consumers in mainland Orkney had involved a capital investment of £120; to connect a thousand consumers in Banff had cost £$\frac{1}{2}$m or £495 per connection, and some smaller distribution schemes had cost even more (see Table 15).[122]

Although the Board's income from sales of electricity to many of these newly-connected consumers would barely cover the interest charges on the distribution capital investment, far less the cost of electrical generation and transmission, the Board persevered in extending its network:[123] £95 per cent of all farms had received a supply by the mid-1960s and 90 per cent of crofts by 1971/72. And where connections with the Highland grid, even by submarine cables, had proved either impracticable or grotesquely uneconomic, the Board was still, in the 1960s, providing supplies in many of the remoter

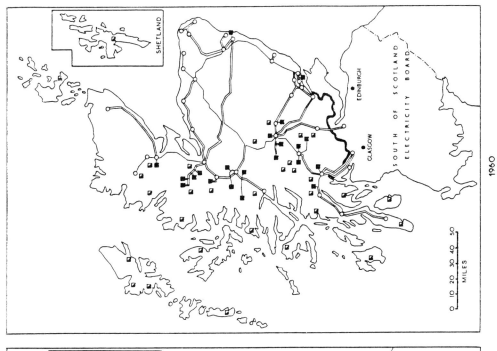

1960

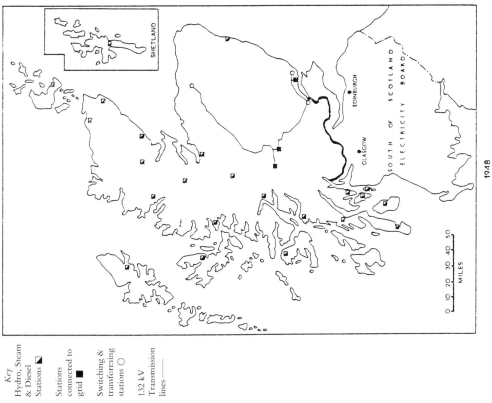

1948

Key
Hydro, Steam
& Diesel
Stations ◼

Stations
connected to
grid ■

Switching &
transferring
stations ○

132 kV
Transmission
lines ——

FIGURE 42   The Development of the Highland Grid System

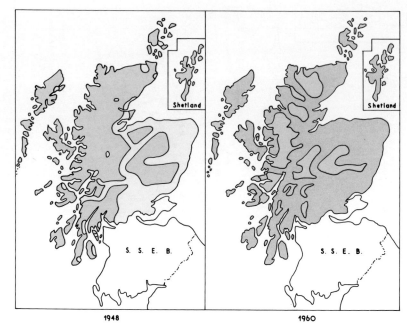

AREAS SHOWN BLUE WERE WITHOUT SUPPLY IN 1948.
AREAS SHOWN YELLOW HAD LIMITED RURAL
DISTRIBUTION AS INDICATED IN FIG.A. BUT SOME
AREAS HAD LOCAL URBAN DEVELOPMENT e.g. DUNDEE,
ABERDEEN,PERTH,etc.

AREAS SHOWN RED INDICATE INTENSIFIED ELECTRICAL
DEVELOPMENT TO THE LEVEL SHOWN IN FIG.B.UP TO 1960
AREAS SHOWN BLUE ARE MOUNTAINOUS OR SPARSELY
POPULATED.

DISTRIBUTION – HIGH VOLTAGE LINES.

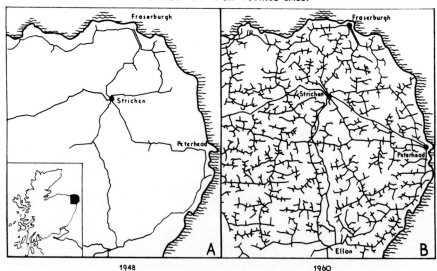

THE AREA ILLUSTRATED COVERS 300 SQ.MILES OF
N.E. ABERDEENSHIRE AND SHOWS AN EXAMPLE OF THE
EXTENSIVE NETWORK OF H.V LINES WHICH THE BOARD
HAS ESTABLISHED IN FARMING DISTRICTS.

FIGURE 43   Distribution, 1948 and 1960

TABLE 15   *Examples of distribution schemes completed 1949-61*

Scheme	Completion date	Miles of Line		Actual Number of Consumers	Actual Cost £000s	Cost per Consumer (£s)	
		H.V.	L.V.			Estimated	Actual
Lochalsh	1949	42.0	14.0	400	71.8	84	180
Morar	1950	33.0	21.0	332	115.1	86	347
Bute & South Cowal	1952	149.5	26.1	2,153	314.0	127	146
Orkney	1953	202.8	122.5	3,559	426.9	81	120
Skye	1955	239.0	118.0	2,144	621.6	109	290
Lewis	1955	233.0	159.0	3,800	592.3	67	156
Arran	1951	76.0	37.0	925	128.7	197	139
Shetland	1960	340.0	160.0	3,149	777.2	194	247
Mull	1958	80.2	11.3	323	185.7	510	575
Kintyre	1953	217.7	38.9	920	304.6	262	331
Banchory, Devenick & Old Machar	1959	82.0	40.0	458	201.3	370	439
Kames/Craignish	1957	16.9	3.1	55	36.3	640	660
Banff	1959	205.5	101.5	1,013	500.9	239	495
Kincardineshire	1960	200.0	74.0	1,950	482.5	267	247
Cassley/Durness	1956	83.5	11.5	278	183.7	447	660
Glen Esk/Glen Clova	1960	161.8	25.3	533	281.7	400	528
Glenshee & Bridge of Forter	1960	18.5	2.8	53	27.2	553	514
Total of 49 schemes	1949-60	4,101.0	1,604.5	33,946	8,889.0	204.5	261.8

Source: NSHEB, Evidence for Mackenzie Committee, Tables II(i)D, dated 10 May, 1961.

islands from diesel stations at a price per unit below even the cost of generation. A further 2,000 consumers in the islands were being supplied with subsidised bottled calor gas until the Board's network, remorselessly inching forward, could reach them.

In less than two decades, the Board had far exceeded the hopes of the Cooper Committee: by 1961 over 210,000 new consumers had been connected. Added to the 188,000 consumers 'inherited' on vesting day 1948, the Board was now supplying about 400,000 homes, farms and crofts, and commercial and industrial concerns. Careful estimates made by the Board's area managers and aggregated by the Chief Commercial Engineer indicated that this represented over 91 per cent of all potential consumers, and that of the remainder well over half had either no desire to be connected or refused to accept the Board's generous terms (See Table 16). To connect the 14,000 premises in areas known to be uneconomic still requiring a supply would, it was calculated, require a capital expenditure in distribution facilities of over £7 millions, or an annual net increase in the Board's financial liabilities of nearly £850,000 (See Appendix Table 25). Although the Board was more than ready to assume this burden, from 1959 onwards it was occasionally suggested that the Government might give consideration 'to the possibility of making grants available ... to prospective consumers who would thereby be able to contribute towards the cost of connection'.[124]

TABLE 16   *Unconnected Premises in the Board's Area, Summer, 1961*

			Percentage
I	Number of potential consumers	434,923	100.00
	Number connected	396,914	91.26
	Remainder	38,009	8.74
II	*An analysis of Unconnected Premises*		
	1. *Economic Areas*		
	No desire for a supply indicated★	17,996	4.14
	2. *Uneconomic Areas*		
	No desire for supply★ or terms unacceptable	5,995	1.38
	Under negotiation, in process of connection, work contracted but not yet started	220	0.06
	Not provided for	13,758	3.16

★ Of the reasons given for a lack of interest in obtaining a connection, the following were suggested as being most important:

   (a) Inability to afford cost of wiring the premises and of meeting any contribution to the cost.
   (b) Elderly couples or widowed persons who had no wish to take a supply.
   (c) Premises either already or expected to be condemned.
   (d) Arguments between owners and tenants over meeting the cost of wiring.

   Source: NSHEB, Inter-departmental letter, J C M Baillie to A A Fulton, 18 August 1961 (G/5, Part 2); subsequently the figures were slightly modified and embodied in the Evidence for the Mackenzie Committee, HEB. M.9(6).

(ix)   Sales to Consumers

No wonder that the Board's customers rose in the Board's support in 1961. After years of neglect, they were fully aware of the true nature of the Board's achievement. If the Board's activities in the 1950s had failed to stem the depopulation of the Highlands and Islands (See Appendix Table 26),[125] those that remained were capable of enjoying a greater number of creature comforts than ever before. Life had become somewhat easier.[126] Between 1949 and 1962 sales of electricity rose at an average rate of 12.5 per cent per annum (See Appendix Table 27). By 1962, 50 per cent of the Board's customers were cooking by electricity, a higher proportion than that attained by any other Electricity Board in the country. The Board's sales of electrical appliances—encouraged by a mobile team of demonstrators and numerous exhibitions—rose sharply, and as the potential market for cookers in some areas became saturated, emphasis was placed on the sale of such equipment as refrigerators, washing machines, food mixers, clothes driers and fires. By the early 1960s, immersion heaters were being fitted in record numbers and off-peak electric heating was fast becoming adopted.

On the farms, following years of research and development, the Board were successful in developing equipment for grain and hay drying which was of especial benefit to the high rainfall areas. The plant was increasingly installed on farms and crofts, for, despite its expense, yields and protein content were much higher than traditional drying methods.[127] Experiments in collaboration with the North of Scotland College of Agriculture resulted in the growing use of electrical equipment in poultry farming, pig rearing and pest control, and a large number of horticultural devices—long available in the South—were taken up. Certainly, the use of electricity on the farms grew significantly faster than the increase in the number of farms connected (See Appendix Tables 23 and 27)[128] and it is not impossible that some small part of the declining employment in the primary sectors (See Appendix Table 26) is to be explained by the substitution of electrically operated devices for human labour.

Although the Board's hopes of attracting heavy current using industries had been dashed, their sustained drive to encourage the development of light industries did not go entirely unrewarded. By 1961 they could claim that over the previous dozen years the number of industrial consumers they supplied had increased from 3,461 to 7,361 and that the annual consumption of this sector had risen from 149 million units in 1948 to 407 million units in 1960 (See Appendix Table 27). It has to be said that most of the firms concerned had long been established and had simply switched from the use of their own generating plant to take a supply from the Board, but the Board had given them every incentive to do so. As the Board's industrial tariffs applied uniformly throughout the North of Scotland district, manufacturers in areas that remained dependent on diesel generation enjoyed a supply of electricity much below cost, especially when connections had been made possible only by uneconomic extensions of supply lines. It was estimated in 1961 that the concealed industrial subsidy provided by the Board in this way was running at an annual figure of not less than £50,000—£60,000, and that had the consumers concerned provided their own plant they would have incurred a capital expenditure of £800,000.[129]

For all that, the share of the Board's total sales taken by industrial consumers never rose above 32 per cent (in 1953) a proportion that had declined to but 23 per cent in 1962, or about half the British figure. Conversely, the share taken by the Board's domestic consumers steadily rose from 41 per cent of sales in 1949 to 55 per cent in 1962, substantially above the national proportion (See Appendix Tables 27 and 28). Nothing better illustrates the fulfilment of MacColl's hopes for the Board. They had taken electricity to the people of the Highlands and Islands, to the fishermen and the crofters, and had done so without requiring them to make more than a modest contribution towards their often expensive and frequently uneconomic connection to the mains. Indeed, at the inception of the Board's distribution schemes no connection charge was made at all provided the consumer was within half a mile of the distribution lines. It was only when nationalisation brought an enlargement of the Board's area and escalating construction costs were encountered in both generation and distribution that the Board were forced to reappraise their policy. Very reluctantly,[130] it was then decided that new consumers, other than those who had been promised free connections, had for each of the first seven years to undertake to use, or pay for, an amount of electricity equivalent to 10 per cent of the cost of connection, a figure that was increased to $12\frac{1}{2}$ per cent in 1950. Even this was considerably less than the figure needed to avoid a loss on the outlay incurred in providing the supply lines (See Appendix Table 25). The series of small progressive increases imposed thereafter was never designed to recoup more than a proportion of the cost of connection which, as the Board's network spread, became exceptionally high, especially in providing for consumers on the Western Isles.

By the end of 1960, over a quarter of the Board's consumers were being supplied on an uneconomic basis, and the estimated annual loss in providing and maintaining services to them was £1.75 million.[131] Furthermore, in the Board's evidence for the MacKenzie Committee, it was estimated that in providing supplies for the *final* thousand potential consumers the cost of each connection would average about £5,000, a sum far in excess of the value of the premises being linked to the system. Nevertheless, distribution schemes in progress in the early 1960s were expected to supply 71 of the most populous islands, when the number of occupied premises on the remaining 64 islands did not exceed 191.[132]

The Board could, of course, have reduced or even avoided the actual or expected annual losses by increasing their tariff, but MacColl had been determined to fix the price of electricity at a price which the majority could afford, and that meant being competitive with the Tilly or paraffin lamp. The inevitable loss was enhanced by the decision to introduce a uniform tariff throughout the Board's area. Although cost increases and the assumption of the responsibility for deficits incurred by Aberdeen and Dundee when these local authority enterprises were taken over in 1948 meant that tariff increases took place in 1949 and in the early 1950s, tariffs were not raised again until 1957, some time after Tom Johnston had responded to a plea by the government to avoid inflationary price increases.[133] It is difficult not to believe that Johnston had been more than willing to peg prices for, like MacColl before him, he refused to dance to the tune of the accountant: the welfare of the people of the north of Scotland came first.

(x)   *The Board's Achievement*

By the early 1960s, it became apparent that the Board was incapable of realising the broader objectives of the Hydro–Electric Development Act. The Highland economy had not been transformed; industry had not rushed into the North of Scotland; the average level of unemployment in the Highlands was persistently at a rate twice that of Scotland as a whole; the flow of outward migration had not been staunched; the standard of living enjoyed by the majority remained below the national average. Shortly before his death, Sir Edward MacColl told his wife, 'Hydro-Electricity is not enough'.[134] This enigmatic statement may have referred to a dissatisfaction with his own personal achievement in life, but it could equally well have been a judgement on the rôle of hydro-electricity in the regeneration of the Highlands, to which cause he had been devoted. By itself, hydro-electricity—which is, after all, only a form of energy capable of manifold uses—could not, and should not, have been expected to carry the enormous responsibilities that Tom Johnston had thrust upon it. For its attainment regional economic growth requires much more than a ready supply of fuel. These other necessary factors—such as large and buoyant internal and external markets, vigorous entrepreneurship, and a comprehensive range of favourable institutional arrangements— were not present, or present only to an inadequate degree. Thus, the Board failed in its deeper purposes, but it can be counted a success in achieving the more modest objectives appropriate to a body of its kind. The Board had harnessed much of the hydro-power of Scotland; had created a generating and distribution system that brought electric power to the great majority of the people; had made the lives of those who remained in the Highlands more comfortable, more enjoyable. Their reward was to come to be regarded as part of the social fabric of the North of Scotland. In the middle decades of the 20th century, the Board became—and remains—more than just an organisation that supplies electricity.

3   Relations with the South of Scotland Electricity Board

When electricity was nationalised in 1948, there had come into being a two-tier organisation comprising the British Electricity Authority, responsible for generation and main transmission, and fourteen Area Boards responsible for distribution. Only the North of Scotland Hydro-Electric Board retained its independence and with it the right to sell bulk supplies, although the *obligation* to purchase them was transferred from the Central Electricity Board to the British Electricity Authority, which the 1947 Act established as the body responsible for generating electricity in the rest of Britain. In effect, this meant that while the BEA purchased the power produced largely by Sloy and Tummel-Garry; it was used in the South West Scotland Electricity Board, one of the two Scottish area boards.

In the elections of 1950 and 1951 the Conservatives had announced their intention to give more independence to the Scottish and Welsh elements of the nationalised industries, and they returned to office committed to hiving off electricity in southern Scotland from the BEA. The Scottish Office were enthusiastic. The civil servants wanted to assume responsibility for electricity throughout the whole of Scotland, rather than merely in the north, and in this they received the support of a majority of Scottish politicians. Thus it came about that shortly after the Conservatives took office in 1951, the new Minister of Fuel and Power, Geoffrey Lloyd, accepted the inevitable and agreed that he should cede control of Scottish electricity from his own Ministry to the Scottish Office. Although Lord Citrine maintained a fervent opposition, the Electricity Reorganisation (Scotland) Act was passed in 1954. This Act combined the South East and South West Scotland Electricity Boards to form the South of Scotland Electricity Board; gave to the new Board the powers of generation and main transmission previously exercised by the BEA, and transferred to the SSEB the obligiation to purchase hydro electricity generated in the north.[135]

John Pickles was appointed chairman of the new Board. A pioneer of rural electrification in Dumfries when he had been the county's Electrical Engineer, he had been chairman of the South West Scotland Electricity Board since 1948. In addition to the assets of the two District Boards, the SSEB took over the Grid transmission system in southern Scotland, twelve steam stations and seven hydro stations on the Clyde and in Galloway.[136] The South Board were, in fact, able to generate about 85 per cent of the power they needed, the remainder being imported through the Grid from the Central Electricity Authority (the successor body to the BEA after the Scottish severance took place in 1955) and the North of Scotland Hydro Electric Board, on whom they depended for supplies to meet peak demand.

The Hydro Board were anxious to enjoy good relations with their newly-created neighbour, and it was therefore particularly unfortunate that in the very first year of the latter's independence, the Board's operations were disrupted by an extraordinary and prolonged drought. This drought, the worst ever known in most of the Board's catchment areas,[137] made it possible to supply only 167.5 Gwh of the 280 Gwh expected by the South Board in 1955.[138] The SSEB were able to make up the deficit by supplies from England, but this disappointing start emphasised the inherent dangers of relying on water power and strengthened the South Board's insistence on negotiating the price agreement with the Hydro Board. In the event, the new agreement on supply prices with the SSEB did not differ materially from that which had previously governed bulk sales of electricity to the BEA, and the South Board's determination to come to a fresh arrangement with the North Board is probably to be explained by a desire to express their new independence rather than to exploit their powerful position as the Hydro Board's major customer.[139] Certainly Pickles, who was sympathetic towards the Hydro Board's policy of rural electrification, is said to have negotiated a 'soft' agreement which left the Hydro Board little worse off than their earlier generous settlement from the BEA.[140]

This agreement on the bulk supply tariff reduced the anxieties of the Hydro Board and satisfied the SSEB. Although the first four months of 1956 were almost as dry as the previous year's period of drought, the weather changed in May and for the remaining months of the year rainfall was well above average.[141] The Hydro Board had little trouble in meeting its export commitments and relations between the two authorities appear to have been extremely cordial. The chairmen met frequently, and there was continuous consultation between the two Boards at all departmental levels on subjects ranging from joint approaches to government departments on financial issues to the consolidation of the Electricity Acts as they applied in Scotland. A Joint Technical Committee was established and first met in 1955 to handle such complex issues as the rules governing the withdrawal from service of old thermal plant; the main requirements for the co-ordinated development of pumped storage; and arrangements for the creation of the 275kV 'super grid' inaugurated in the late 1950s. Problems arising from the working of the price agreement and the interchange of bulk supplies were handled by a Commerical Arrangements Sub-committee, and a Pumped Storage Sub-committee was established to deal specifically with the operation and design of the Cruachan scheme.[142]

Nevertheless, there were difficulties. The Hydro Board had been severely shaken by the drought of 1955 and, seeking to give a greater reliability to their largely weather-dependent generating capacity, planned to install two 60MW coal-fired sets at Dundee. This strategy appealed neither to the South Board nor to the Scottish Office, who argued that it would be more economic to import electricity from the South Board's new Kincardine station, with its 120MW sets. The Hydro Board reluctantly accepted the validity of this argument. Nevertheless, it hurt their pride. More important, a source of potential if not actual friction was the South Board's growing suspicion that they could perhaps generate the electricity that they were purchasing from the north more cheaply themselves but, for all the pooling of statistical data, it was extremely difficult to prove, and a new bulk supply agreement between the two Boards in 1961 reflected this fact, its terms being similar to those of 1955.[143]

4   *The Genesis of the MacKenzie Committee*

It was not the SSEB from whom the Hydro Board had most to fear in the late 1950s but the politicians, the civil servants and the economists. As we have repeatedly seen, from its very inception the Board had been criticised. Bitter attacks had initially been made upon its policies by conservationists, the fishing interests and the coal lobby; subsequently there were those who objected vehemently to Scottish power being sold 'to the South', conjuring up totally false images of lochs desecrated in order to keep Londoners warm. Then there were those who believed that the programme of rural electrification was proceding too slowly, or that the connection changes were scandalously expensive, and that the Board were using Government appeals for investment constraint to evade their responsibilities. A veritable litany of condemnation surfaced during the hearings before the Select Committee on Nationalised Industries in 1957.[144] It is unlikely that Tom Johnston was greatly troubled, accustomed as he was to the denunciation of his fellow politicains, but beneath all the wounding rhetoric there was a more serious ground swell.

There were those who were beginning to question the economic rationality of the Board's policy. In the dismal days of post-war austerity, when shortages of consumer goods and continued rationing were rendered even more unendurable by a coal famine and fuel cuts, the Board made much of the coal-saving potential of hydro power.[145] In this period the real costs could be ignored and, in any case, innumerable (though usually superficial) inquiries seemed conclusively to prove that hydro electricity was cheaper than that produced in thermal stations. The opening salvo was fired by the heretic Conservative MP, Sir Gerald Nabarro, who in 1952 pointed out in a widely-read booklet that 'future hydro-electric schemes, saving as they do only a tiny amount of coal in relation to the vast capital investment envisaged, must be treated with the strictest reserve'.[146] And if many of Nabarro's specific arguments did not stand up to detailed scrutiny, his general case for a *national* fuel policy was irrefutable.

Much more serious were the strictures of Denys Munby, an economist at the University of Aberdeen.[147] Acknowledging that in its task of expanding the production and consumption of electricity in the north of Scotland the Board had been 'outstandingly successful', Munby attempted to determine just how much this success had cost. He then asked whether the Board's use of scarce capital resources could be justified. Although his investigation was hampered by both the inadequacy of the information published in the *Annual Reports* and the inherent complications arising from the relative values to be attached to base and peak load units involved in the exercise, he concluded that 'no further hydro-electric schemes should be built for normal operation; and it may well be doubtful whether some of the promoted schemes should be started'. In arriving at this conclusion, he had drastically reduced the currently accepted periods of amortisation used in calculations of this kind to thirty years for, he argued, the advent of atomic energy suggested the possibility that in fifty years' time 'hydro-electric stations built at very great capital cost may be as obsolete as the horse and carriage'. He also believed that the uniform tariff adopted by the Board meant that consumers in the eastern coastal belt, where distribution costs were relatively low, were in effect subsidising those in much of the rest of the Board's area. This was not only arbitrary and unfair, but inhibited the use of electricity in the 'cheaper' areas. If social considerations warrented the supply of inexpensive electricity to low income groups in 'dear' remote areas, the burden should not fall entirely on the Board's consumers but should be shouldered by the State.

This penetrating and thought-provoking paper might have remained buried in that academic obscurity which is the peculiar fate of articles in the learned journals were it not for the fact that Munby submitted a memorandum enlarging on a number of his arguments to the Select Committee on Nationalised Industries, in whose 1957 Report it was published as an Appendix,[148] and hence given wider currency. Although the Board was vigorously defended by Sir Murdoch MacDonald, Past President of the Institution of Civil Engineers, and J M Kay, Professor of Nuclear Power at Imperial College, on the grounds that the Board's statutory duties were wider than those of the Central Electricity Authority, and that Munby had exaggerated the cost of hydro-electric generation and greatly underestimated that of nuclear power,[149] Munby's analysis strengthened the conviction of a growing number of critics that hydro development was reaching, or had already reached, its limit. Some of the Board's critics were not entirely disinterested. Nabarro gained the support both of the right-wing propaganist organisation, Aims of Industry,[150] and Labour MPs from mining constituencies who were increasingly perturbed by the decline in the demand for coal. The Conservative Scottish Power Investigation Committee argued that thermal stations, fuelled by Lanarkshire coal would be cheaper, less environmentally harmful, and more reliable in times of drought than hydro schemes; and Colonel W H Whitbread, a member of the Council of Aims of Industry, and whose estate was threatened by the Fada-Fionn scheme, claimed that the Board had been guilty of criminal trespass. The Treasury too were concerned that the Board were failing to cut back their capital expenditure to the extent that they had promised.[151]

Meanwhile the Board, undaunted by political sniping, the threats of economists and the wailings of the Treasury, pushed ahead with further schemes: the Awe project, an important element of which was a massive pumped storage development at Cruachan, partially designed to dovetail with the South Board's nuclear station at Hunterston; exploratory work at Loch Laidon and at Fada-Fionn-Maree; borings to ascertain the foundation conditions for dams in the Monadhliath mountains; and the Nevis Project, which proposed to use the water power resources of the River Nevis in an underground power station at Loch Leven. The fact was that Angus Fulton, Tom Lawrie's successor as chief executive, was a hydro fanatic. If water power was available, it should be harnessed whatever the cost.[152]

The Nevis Project—Constructional Scheme No.37—was published in October 1960. Intended to have an installed capacity of 28,000kW an average output of 93 million units at an annual load factor of 38 per cent, the capital cost was expected to be £4.37 million. It was anticipated that eventually much of the Nevis output would be required locally (for example, to supply a projected pulp mill at Corpach) but in the meantime it would be transmitted by 132kV line to Fort William where it would be valuable as a standby for the British Aluminium Company's work near Fort Augustus.[153] Submitted to the Secretary of State for confirmation, the Nevis Project was the subject of a number of objections, one of which was in the name of the National Trust for Scotland, who declared that they would oppose the scheme on amenity grounds. In the ordinary way these objections would have been considered at a Public Inquiry, but on this occasion John Maclay, the Scottish Secretary, decided that no inquiry would be held into the Nevis Project until the report of a Departmental Committee on the arrangements for generating and distributing electricity in Scotland had been received. This Committee, to be chaired by Colin MacKenzie, a former chairman of the Scottish Federation of British Industries, had been appointed as a direct consequence of a decision by the Cabinet's Economic Policy Committee to review the entire question of Scottish electricity.[154]

CHAPTER 7

Mackenzie and After, 1961–1975

1   The Mackenzie Committee and its reception

The Departmental Committee on Electricity in Scotland were appointed by the Secretary of State for Scotland, John S Maclay, on 21 March 1961, with the following terms of reference:

> To review the arrangements for generating and distributing electricity in Scotland having regard to (i) the availability and cost of hydro-electric power and of other sources of electricity; (ii) the rate of increase in the demand for electricity; and (iii) the needs of the remoter areas: and to make recommendations

The Committee was to be chaired by Colin Mackenzie and the other members were E W Craig, chairman of the general council of the Scottish TUC; James L Craig, county clerk of Aberdeen; Sir Josiah Eccles, who had spent a lifetime in the industry, most recently as chairman of the Merseyside and North Wales Area Board, deputy chairman of the British Electricity Authority and, from 1958-61, deputy chairman of the Electricity Council, J S Grant, editor of the *Stornoway Gazette*, J A Keyden, director and general manager of Pressed Steel Ltd. Linwood, and finally Alan T Peacock, Professor of Economics at the University of Edinburgh.[1]

At their very first meeting, held in St Andrew's House, Edinburgh, on 6 April 1961, the Committee invited all who wished to do so to submit written evidence. In addition, some bodies and individuals with a special interest in the inquiry were *specifically* invited to give evidence. In the event, written or oral evidence was received from 67 organisations or persons. In 18 months, the Committee held 26 meetings extending over 46 days and visited numerous hydro-electric schemes, Kincardine power station, the nuclear station in course of construction at Hunterston, and a number of the islands in Shetland which were still without a public supply of electricity and where they heard the views of local district and voluntary bodies.[2] No one could accuse the Committee of slothfulness. It is patently clear that their expressed indebtedness to the Hydro Board and the South Board for providing 'large numbers of facts and figures' was no empty courtesy. Inadequate or evasive answers to their penetrating questions were followed by increasingly specific inquiries. The Hydro Board itself prepared 47 of the 180 memoranda considered by the Committee, and any discrepancies between the information that they contained and that provided by the South Board were tirelessly probed to seek a reconciliation of statistical inconsistencies and anomalies. Sir Josiah Eccles in particular was unrelenting in his pursuit of the solution to technical questions, and Alan Peacock adopted a similar attitude toward the economic problems.

Some of the difficulties stemmed from differences in the postures adopted by the two Boards. While displaying a confidence in the rightness of their policies, the Hydro Board officials were understandably defensive, seeing the Inquiry as part of yet another plan to deprive them of their independence. Conversely, there were those within the South Board who sought to put a rein on their neighbour's exuberance for further hydro-development, and believed that there was no better way of doing so than by the establishment of a Scottish Electricity Board. Because of their larger size, the South Board would dominate the Scottish Electricity Board. This solution would have the additional advantage of putting an end to what some officials of the South Board regarded as their enforced subsidisation of the Hydro Board. The suspicion existed that this course was favoured by the civil servants in the Scottish Office because at one stroke it would both achieve the tidiness that always appeals to the bureaucratic mind and diminish the necessity for them to master and adjudicate between complex technical and economic issues.

And if no one in either the two Boards or the Scottish Office saw the problem in quite such simple terms, there is no doubt that many organisations in the Highlands and not a few members of the public did. We have already noticed the outcry which arose in the Spring of 1961 when the appointment of the Mackenzie Committee was announced. While the widespread manifestations of support for the Hydro Board were completely spontaneous,[3] the Board responded to numerous requests to check and add to the points to be made in submissions to the Mackenzie Committee, in speeches to both Houses of Parliament and to such bodies as the Scottish Board for Industry, and in letters to the Press. It was not necessary for the Board to promote and orchestrate their own defence against what some saw as a long-standing 'campaign of denigration' culminating in an enquiry designed to lend respectability to the Board's extinction. There were many ready to take on this task; people like R MacFarquhar, the Secretary of The Highland Fund, and Major P Hunter Gordon, a member of the Highlands and Islands District Committee of the Scottish Board for Industry.[4] No wonder that the Board's Assistant Information Officer, Hamish Mackinven, was able to inform G M Thompson, MP, that since the announcement of the Departmental Committee the Board had 'never had more friends'. Even 'many past critics, aware now of what they have started, are indulging in second thoughts', especially after Lord Citrine, in the debate in the Upper House on 16 March, had raised the question of 'whether there should be any Scottish Boards at all?' The entire Scottish Press, local and national, with the exception of the Thomson Group in Dundee, were strongly on the Board's side, and it was believed that the great majority of people in the Highlands were of like opinion, seeing the Board 'as an organisation which really does try to help them socially and economically. Unfortunately, this support is, by and large, unvoiced and inarticulate. Only the critics catch the headlines', and one of these, Mr Michael Baillie, the Prime Minister's nephew, continued, like Aims of Industry, 'ceaselessly to level the charge of waste'.[5]

2   *The Questions, the Evidence and the Recommendations*

Meanwhile, the Committee had decided that their duty was 'to recommend what [they] believed to be the best course for Scotland as a whole', and to do this they had to collect the relevant data, estimate future demand, and evaluate the potential sources of electrical energy to meet it. The Hydro Board's abortive experiments with wind power and the use of peat to fire closed-cycle gas turbines led inevitably to the conclusion that the only practical sources of energy available to the two Boards were coal, water, oil and the atom, and that the contribution of each of these to meeting future demands should be determined by relative costs. Immediately, the Committee were confronted with irreconcilable differences between the estimates and projections of the two Boards, and forced to adjudicate between them. To do this led, in turn, to an examination of the rationalilty of the existing arrangements whereby the South Board were obliged to purchase the surplus units of their neighbour at a price determined by a formula which had been controversial since its very inception. Essentially, the Committee had to decide whether these arrangements—legislatively sanctioned as they were—constituted the most economical way of meeting the future demand for electricity in Scotland.

This was a most formidable task, dependent for its resolution on the examination of hypothetical alternatives which required for both their formulation and interpretation detailed technical knowledge; knowledge fully possessed only by Sir Josiah Eccles, on whom the other members of the Committee depended for guidance. The South Board were asked to calculate the cost that they would have incurred by generating the units which had, in fact, been purchased from the Hydro Board during the years 1956 to 1961. This was a peak load supply and the calculations, which involved estimating the cost of installing and operating two thermal stations, were acknowledged by the Committee to be highly complex. The South Board supplied these data and supported their conclusions in great detail. They revealed that the SSEB were losing £596,000 per annum by importing from the Hydro Board rather than by building their own coal-fired stations. These figures were totally unacceptable to the Hydro Board, whose own assessment showed that if the South Board had generated the supplies that they had purchased, it would have cost them, in 1960, £25,000 more than the price they paid.

The Committee's attempt to reconcile this 'wide difference' involved the senior officials of both Boards in preparing a mass of supplementary evidence, each part of which was subjected to searching investigation.[6] Representatives of the two Boards gave oral evidence at St Andrew's House. Much of it was of a technical nature, and this was invariably elicited by Sir Josiah Eccles, but the chairman's own questions and interjections were extremely penetrating. Mackenzie was clearly concerned to discover why, if the South Board's figures were correct, they should have *agreed* to the current price structure. It was, he observed, most 'peculiar'. He could not help entertaining 'lingering doubts about the South Board's figures'.[7] He could understand the Hydro Board's determination to get as much as they could for their surplus power. Indeed, it was their duty to get the 'best bargain that they could', but why should the South Board have accepted a bulk tariff so much higher than they now claim was justified?

The implication of these remarks was that perhaps Sir John Pickles had been too generous. Certainly, this was the belief of the South Board's Chief Engineer, J Henderson, and Chief Financial Officer, E Maxwell, who had a year earlier prepared a paper (at the request of the Scottish Office) that indicated as much.[8] It is significant that Lord Strathclyde, Tom Johnston's successor as chairman of the Hydro Board, felt obliged to 'make a non-technical comment on the South Board's figure' to the Committee:

> I have never found a commercial organisation in Scotland to be a charitable institution, nor, in the course of my long and friendly talks with Sir John Pickles, have I ever found him to be a philanthropist. If the South Board have been giving us a present every year, as is being suggested, I am astonished, because one of the first things I did when I joined this Board was to try to convince Sir John that he must pay us the right sum and, in consequence, he agreed to pay us some £400,000 more. I cannot reconcile that with the figures now produced[9]

Lord Strathclyde would have been even more incredulous had he known that only two months earlier, Norman Elliot, who had taken over the chairmanship of the South Board from Pickles in January 1962, had told the Committee that the real loss to his Board had been infinitely worse than his officers had estimated: nearer £1.5—£2 million, in fact; though when Eccles questioned the derivation of this alarming figure, Elliott had been forced to admit that his method of calculation has been rough and ready.[10]

It is scarcely surprising that the Committee were perplexed by these widely divergent views and sought to ascertain where the truth lay. More information was called for, and it was agreed that representatives of the two Boards should meet in London in July, exchange their detailed calculations, and argue the case anew before Sir Josiah Eccles. More detailed correspondence followed this meeting until by 7 August, after concessions had been made by both sides which *still* failed to effect a reconciliation, Eccles felt that there was no point in pursuing the matter further.[11] If the two Boards could not agree, it was up to the Committee to use their own judgment. This they did, and produced the following tabulated data (Table 17). In presenting this Table in their *Report*, the Committee stated:

> the fact that a difference of opinion of [the] magnitude [that we have encountered] between the two Boards can continue in the face of prolonged and detailed investigation suggests to us how difficult it can be, under the present system, to reach conclusions which are agreed to by both Boards and valid for Scotland as a whole.

Nevertheless, the Committee, were satisfied that the costs set out in column E of Table 17—for it was the assessment of these figures that had proved to be so difficult—represented 'as nearly as may be the true cost to [the South] Board of generating the supplies they obtained from the North'.

Table 17 showed that

> over the six-year period, the North Board's cost of production was less than the South's would have been by about £3m. so that there was an overall saving as a result of generation by water power; but during the same period, the South Board paid the North Board about £3.4m more than it would have cost them to generate the supply themselves. The North

TABLE 17   *Bulk Supplies of Electricity from the Hydro Board to the South of Scotland Electricity Board,*
1956-61

A	B	C	D	E	F
				Cost to South Board of generating like	
			Gain to North Board	supply (as adjusted	Extra Cost to South
	Price Paid to	Cost to	(difference between	upwards by the	Board (difference
Year	North Board	North Board	B & C)	Committee)	between B & E)
	£m	£m	£m	£m	£m
1956	2.095	1.337	0.758	1.775	0.320
1957	2.567	1.563	1.004	2.085	0.482
1958	3.035	1.964	1.071	2.220	0.815
1959	3.578	2.409	1.169	3.065	0.513
1960	3.701	2.765	0.936	3.130	0.571
1961	4.412	2.940	1.472	3.700	0.712
Total	19.388	12.978	6.410	15.975	3.413

Source: Mackenzie Committee Report, p. 87.

Board, from their own point of view, were justified in obtaining the best price they could, while the South Board were obliged to accept the supply, and there was uncertainty of the results which resort to the formula might produce. It is clear, however, that if the proceeds from the sale of current to the South Board had been less, the financial difficulties of the North Board would have been increased, and the extension of their distribution system would have proceeded more slowly.[13]

These findings—even the very way in which they were arrived at—convinced the Committee that 'the best interests of the country will be served, and the most economical production of electricity will be achieved, only if the whole of Scotland is treated as one unit in the planning, construction, and operation of all generating and main transmission facilities'.[14] Take, for example, the question of 'spill units', which figured promently in the discussion between the two Boards. Spill units, as their name implies, are units of electrical power generated (usually during periods of high precipitation) from water which, if not used for this purpose, would spill uselessly over or through the dam. Spill units were, by their very nature, random in nature. No one could predict when, for example, sudden heavy outbursts of rain followed by very rapid run off would augment the normal quantity of water flowing into a reservoir to such an extent that its level rose sufficiently to discharge over the spillway. In such an event, the water can either be allowed to spill over the dam or, more productively, be led to the turbines to produce power. Sometimes it happened that such power was generated when there was no immediate need for it—or at least at a time when its use had not previously been anticipated, perhaps during those hours of the day characterised by a relatively low demand. What was to be done with such power? It would appear that the South Board occasionally took these spill units from the Hydro Board at a price above the cost at which they could, *at these times*, have generated the equivalent units in their own thermal plants. Yet these units had costs the Hydro Boad next to nothing, and had it not been for the helpful attitude of the South Board, the equivalent water *would* simply have spilled over the dam. The Committee's comment is highly significant:

> The South Board have generally taken a co-operative view in this situation but, even so, there must have been occasions when power was not accepted with the alacrity that was necessary if excess water from existing catchments was not to be wasted, and *we cannot commend the continuance of the present arrangements.* The control and load dispatching staffs should be placed in a position to act solely on the economic merits of the problems before them, without having constantly to be looking over their shoulders at the effect a decision will have upon the sectional interest that they serve.[15]

For the Hydro Board, each of the conclusions of the Committee had an ominous ring. Paragraph followed paragraph like the steps of the hangman approaching the condemned cell. On the Cruachan pumped storage scheme, which involved the Hydro Board buying off-peak electricity from the South Board for pumping, and selling the output back to the South during peak-load periods, the Committee believed that 'complexities are bound to arise where one Board has the pumping energy and needs the peak-load power, while the other controls the water and the sites suitable for pumped storage. As we visualise the future, difficulties of this kind are bound to recur as long as there are two Boards ... the matter is far too important to run the risk of incorrect decisions being arrived at between organisations whose primary responsibility must necessarily be to consumers in their own Districts'. And concerning the installation by the Hydro Board of 120 MW sets at Dundee and the South Board's plan to put down 300 MW sets at Cockenzie, the Committee felt obliged to draw attention to the Central Electricity Generating Board's construction of 550 MW sets in England. While Scotland's annual incremental increase in demand for electricity would always fall short of England's, Scotland's disadvantageous position was exacerbated by having its generating system 'parcelled out between two independent Boards'. Even the possibility of a future nuclear station being constructed in the North of Scotland would 'inevitably create complications if the division of Scotland into two generating authorities is retained'.[16]

These considerations led inexorably to the recommendations that

> there shall be established a single authority for the whole of Scotland, to be known as the Scottish Electricity Board, consisting of persons appointed by the Secretary of State; that the two existing Boards shall be dissolved; and that all property, rights, liabilities and obligations of the North of Scotland Hydro-Electric Board and of the South of Scotland Electricity Board shall be transferred to the Scottish Electricity Board'[17]

3   The Reaction to the Report

The fact that the Committee, recognising both 'the place that the North Board have carved for themselves in the affections and esteem of the people' they served, and the mystique and importance attached to the 'social clause' (even though it had been 'less effective than is commonly supposed'), suggested that 'the new Board should [at least temporarily] be called upon to discharge the obligations implicit in the clause'[18], did nothing to lessen the ensuing furore.

The reactions to the Report took many forms, ranging from the purely emotional to the uncompromisingly technical. Just as the announcement of the appointment of the Committee had engendered a wave of support for the Hydro Board, so too did the publication of its recommendations. The majority of those who wrote to the Board seized upon the amalgamation issue. 'I am afraid if they carried it out it would be the death knell of our Highland ambitions', wrote one ex-part-time member of the Board. 'It is quite inevitable that if the south were amalgamated with the north then their extra weight would carry everything. [It] is not that I suggest malice prepense, but just that the weight of numbers inevitably leads to that result'.[19] Others took a similar view. Bruce Millan, the member for Glasgow, Craigton, in the debate on the Electricity (Borrowing Powers) (Scotland) Bill, believed amalgamation to be the 'main recommendation' and he was, he told the House, very prejudiced against it:

> People in the north of Scotland have had very little about which to be optimistic or hopeful during the last ten years, and one of the few things which has given them any ground for optimism has been the existence of the Hydro-Electric Board and the work it has done in the north of Scotland.[20]

The Town Council of Elgin in presenting their views on the Report to the Convention of Royal Burghs expressed a widespread anxiety: 'there is fear, not without cause, that the interests of the industrial areas will take precedence over their remote country cousins ... This tendency to subordinate the needs of the North on purely economic grounds has already been shown by the proposals for cessation of railway lines in the North'.[21]

While there was a certain sympathy with the Committee's contention that the Hydro Board was an inappropriate vehicle for the promotion of 'socially desirable projects', many emphasised that until 1962 there had been no alternative. It was all very well for the Committee to recommend that this function be assumed by some other body, 'yet uncreated and even unvisualised', but 'The Highlands [could] hardly be blamed for their reluctance to lose the albeit imperfect substance they have for the shadow of a recommendation'.[22] Nevertheless, there were those, particularly in the outer Isles who despaired of ever getting connections to the grid, whose loyalty to the Board was severely strained by the possibility of sharing in an interest-free Government loan of up to £8m. to the new Scottish Electricity Board for the purposes of expediting the supply of electricity from the mainland grid.[23] But that they were in a minority was demonstrated by the statement of criticism of the Mackenzie Report approved by the Council of the Highland Fund and by the recommendations of the Advisory Committee on the Highlands and Islands.[24]

Perhaps the most persuasive comment on the *Report* was that prepared by the Electricity Consultative Council for the North of Scotland District, a body whose members, being drawn from all parts of the Highlands and Islands, and from all walks of life, were 'in close contact with opinion in the North'. The Council made it perfectly clear that they opposed any merger with the South. The Council's general impression was

> one of satisfaction with the Board's record and of appreciation of the fact that the faith of those who sponsored the establishment of the Board has been justified in that no other agency has done more to arrest the decline into which the Highlands and Islands have fallen'.

Furthermore, the Board 'is already large enough to comprehend all modern techniques ... [yet] at the same time, small enough to enable consumers, even in the most remote places, to experience a sense of intimacy with it and to regard it as a Highland enterprise with the interests of the Highlands and Islands as its primary objective'. Following these introductory remarks, the Council carefully scrutinised each of the Report's major recommendations.

Among the most interesting of the Council's observations were those relating to a uniform tariff for the whole of Scotland, a proposal which many in the 'diesel districts' initially welcomed. The Council questioned the validity of the Mackenzie Committee's conclusion that a uniform tariff would benefit the North. The Council were

> of the opinion that the history of the coal industry in Scotland over the past few years, and such conclusions as anyone may dare to reach as to its future, provide no ground for the assumption that a uniform tariff would reduce the price of electricity in the North ... On the contrary, there is good reason for urging that ... the North will be best served by the maximum development of hydro power within the shortest possible time and by the retention of a separate tariff ... The Mackenzie Committee appear to have accepted very readily the assurances given them regarding the future stability of coal prices and the ability of the coal industry to produce suitable coal in the quantities and at the prices which the large thermal power station of the future will require.

And on the merger of the two Boards, the Consultative Council had this to say:

> The most dispassionate reader of the daily Press would be bound to conclude that the reaction in the North has been overwhelmingly against an incorporating merger and this view has been endorsed by many of the national dailies and by English newspapers. The suggestion has been made that much of this condemnation is emotional and unsupported by facts. In the Council's opinion, however, the reaction is based upon the elementary fact ... that the Hydro Board have ... accomplished over 90 per cent of their initial task of bringing supplies to the inhabitants of the North of Scotland District, that in doing so they have remained solvent, they have sold their supplies at prices comparable with those of other Boards and are, at the moment, free of debt with a surplus in reserve. It is seldom indeed that an official report refers to a public body as having 'carved for themselves a place in the affections and esteem of the people'. The ... conclusion must, therefore, be that the proposal to abolish the autonomy of the Hydro Board for the doubtful advantage of an electrical economy based on the problematic future of the Scottish coalfields, which might even provide a precedent for a still wider amalgamation, would be directly contrary to the trend of public opinion in the North.[25]

And if the widely-circulated statement by the Electricity Consultative Council for the North of Scotland had most influence on the general public, the article by E J K Chapman, 'The Value of Water Power in a Mixed System',[26], weakened professional confidence in the *Report's* findings, especially those on the limited scope for further hydro development in the Highlands. Chapman disagreed with some of the technical assumptions implicit in the arguments employed by the Committee—perhaps it would be more accurate to say, by Sir Josiah Eccles—in arriving at their conclusions. In determining the economic viability of new hydro plant, Eccles had adopted a comparative approach. The costs of providing electricity by hydro plant were contrasted with those incurred in producing electricity by thermal plant. In such a comparison, the lifetime load factor of the plant is of critical importance. In his calculations, Eccles had assumed a figure of 41 per cent for the average lifetime load factor of thermal plant. Chapman disputed this figure. He argued that in an expanding system, new plant is brought into service at a rate mainly determined by the annual increase in demand— in the early 1960s about eight per cent per annum—whereas it retires from the system at a rate of only one per cent per annum. As a result, thermal plant spends a proportionately greater amount of its productive life than had hitherto been assumed in the medium and low load factor range. This fact profoundly influences the average *lifetime* load factor of thermal plant, which Chapman found to be no more than 27 per cent, or one third lower than Eccles had assumed, and hence increases the unit cost of its output and the relative economic attractiveness of hydro plant.[27]

Chapman, as senior partner of James Williamson's, consultants to the Hydro Board, was not entirely disinterested in the future course of hydro development in the Highlands and, if only for that reason, his article was subjected to detailed critical analysis and comment. The *immediate* response of Sir Josiah Eccles was not to question Chapman's methodology but to emphasise the unreality of the proposition that demand for electricity would *continue* to double every eight to ten years. This was, of course, a key factor influencing the commissioning of new thermal generating capacity. Beyond that, he acknowledged that 'the subject is a very complex one', and took temporary refuge in the explanation that 'it would not be proper for me to enter into public discussion of it at the present time'.[28] Behind the scenes, however, others were sufficiently worried by Chapman's criticisms to instigate intensive investigation of his data. At the Scottish Development Department, Douglas Haddow asked Sir Christopher Hinton at the Central Electricity Generating Board to have them examined. Hinton agreed that Chapman did have a point, but he believed the article to be biased and that any conclusions to be drawn from it could only be tentative.[29] Sir John George, MP for Glasgow, Pollock Division, and until recently Parliamentary Secretary to the Ministry of Power, sought advice from Robert A Moore, the Scientific Director of the National Coal Board, who 'went over the paper' with his electrical engineers. They concluded that 'there seems to be no doubt that the author has substantiated his claim that an individual station has, over its life of 30 years, an average load factor of only 27 per cent and not 40 per cent as stated in the Mackenzie Report'.[30] Moore added that 'some of the new stations of the SSEB are down to half capacity only 10 years after they come into operation'.

It is unnecessary to pursue this highly technical matter. Suffice it to say that although

Chapman agreed with a later assessment by Eccles that the difference between them 'is nothing like as great as one would imagine from the change in load factor from 40 per cent to 27 per cent',[31] the effect of his article was to raise doubts amoung the civil servants and the politicians about the technical underpinnings of the Mackenzie Report, and hence erode their confidence in the Committee's recommendations—a feeling that the indefatigable Bruce Millan, who had been in detailed correspondence with Chapman, did everything he could to intensify by a series of Parliamentary Questions.[32]

As for the two Boards themselves, they maintained a relatively low profile. The Hydro Board disseminated information critical of the *Report* among MPs and vigorously opposed amalgamation (though not closer co-operation) with the SSEB, but at a technical level accepted—with various degrees of reluctance—that the future development of hydro-electricity *was* limited. Only pumped storage schemes seemed to offer the exciting prospects that twenty years earlier had been associated with conventional schemes. Nevertheless, they welcomed the possibility of using water power to contribute 400 MW of Scotland's additional electricity requirements, hoping all the while that the interest rates on Exchequer advances would fall and make the Mackenzie's Committee's estimate of future hydro generation appear unduly conservative.[33] The SSEB, whose prospects of essentially taking over the Hydro Board seemed to have been boosted by the *Report*, were having second thoughts. Not all the officials of the South Board had in any case favoured a merger: now that they were confronted with the possibility of assuming direct responsibility for completing the increasingly expensive programme of rural electrification initiated by the Hydro Board, even the predators paused, though only William Hutton, the Deputy Chairman of the SSEB, went so far as publicly to state that he was and always had been against a merger.[34] His chairman, Norman Elliott, had no such doubts and continued to argue for the creation of a single board.[35]

Meanwhile, the Cabinet, confronted by the almost unanimous opposition of the North of Scotland, somewhat ambiguous signals from the SSEB, a divided Scottish Office,[36] a doubtful Ministry of Power, and a Treasury reluctant to meet the cost of an accelerated programme of electrification of the outer Isles with which to make the Mackenzie proposals more paletable,[37] decided that with a general election in the offing it would be politically inexpedient to implement the recommendations of the *Report*. Thus, on 10 July 1963 Michael Noble, the Secretary of State for Scotland, announced in the Commons that the 'central recommendation' of the Mackenzie Committee that 'the functions of the two electricity boards in Scotland should be transferred to a single authority' would not be acted upon:

> It is ... clear that the proposal to merge the two existing boards is unwelcome to a wide range of interests, especially those who have benefited by the immensely valuable work that the North of Scotland Hydro-electric Board has carried out during the last twenty years ... I do not think that it has been established that the continued existence of the two boards is incompatible with the provision of electricity in the most economic manner, and I intend to see what can be achieved by close consulatation and co-operation between the two boards.

As for the 'subordinate recommendation ... that special assistance should be provided to enable rural electrification in the North of Scotland to be speeded up, and to link the islands with the mainland by submarine cable', this would be considered within the context of a general assessment of the capital investment needs of electricity boards throughout the country.[38]

Once again, the Hydro Board had survived. Only Sir Gerald Nabarro and Sir David Robertson, member for Caithness and Sutherland, and a long time critic of the Board,[39] expressed their grave displeasure, the latter suggesting that the government had unwisely yielded to the opposition 'fomented by the propaganda of the North of Scotland Hydro-Electric Board'. A more representative reaction was that of one of the Board's Area Managers: 'Everyone in Aberdeen delighted with the return of sanity—Board's flag flying at Millburn Street'.[40]

4   The End of Conventional Hydro Schemes: The Public Inquiry into Fada-Fionn

Amidst all the euphoria engendered by the Secretary of State's decision, the Board's General Manager, A A Fulton, remained brutally realistic. To the many people who sent congratulatory messages to the Board,[41] Fulton replied:

> Naturally [the decision] has given us all a great deal of pleasure but I would not like to disguise the fact that we still have a lot of problems ahead of us. Even when we get the 'go ahead' to promote new schemes, we will still have the same virulent opposition to deal with as we have in the past and it may be that our opponents might be even worse than they were before[42]

How correct he proved to be!

Since 1960 the Nevis scheme had been in a state of limbo. Published in 1960, it was the subject of numerous objections. The Secretary of State had decided that no Inquiry would be held into the project until the Mackenzie Report had been received. No scheme had been brought forward in 1961, but the Laidon Scheme (Constructional Scheme No.38) was published in April 1962, and preparatory planning on the Fada-Fionn and Loch a'Bhraoin schemes, both in Wester Ross, were well advanced by the end of the year. Elsewhere exploratory boring work, preliminary engineering studies and numerous other investigations were under way. The overall position at the end of 1962 is shown in Table 18.

In March 1963, the Fada-Fionn and Loch a'Bhraoin projects were published (as Constructional Schemes Nos. 39 and 33 respectively), and the Board pressed the Scottish Office to arrange for the usual Public Inquiries into both their acceptability and those previously published (Nevis, No.37; Laidon, No.38). Since all four Schemes had been costed in accordance with the principles established by the Mackenzie Committee, the application of which revealed satisfactory results when compared with alternative forms of generation, the Board fully anticipated their ultimate approval. Meanwhile, the Scottish Press were urging action. Drawing attention to the Mackenzie Committee's estimate that there was scope for the economic generation of at least another 400 MW

TABLE 18   *NSHEB: Hydro-electric schemes under promotion, survey and preliminary investigation in 1962*

Scheme	Approximate Kilowatt Capacity	Estimated Annual Output (Million Units)
Under Promotion		
Nevis	28,000	93
Laidon	5,000	16
Ready for Promotion		
Fada-Fionn	44,000	142
Monadhliath: Foyers Section	50,000	170
Tarff Section	28,000	86
Loch a'Bhraoin	14,000	48
Under Survey		
Snizort-Bracadale	4,000	14
Caledonian Canal	7,800	50
Monadhliath (remainder)	72,000	240
Kirkaig	14,000	47
Kenmore and Grandtully	18,000	80
Morven	4,000	16
Orchy-Etive	135,000	230
South Awe	25,000	55
Glass-Morie	32,000	83
	480,800	1,370
Under Preliminary Investigation	161,000	469
	641,800	1,839

Source: NSHEB, *Annual Report and Accounts*, 1962, p. 4.

of hydro power, and to the Glen Nevis and Loch Laidon schemes, 'gathering dust on the Secretary of State's shelves', the *Glasgow Herald*, for example, demanded to know whether there was 'to be any further development of water power at all'.[43] If the Scottish Development Department's response two days later to Inverness County Council's request for the immediate action on the Glen Nevis scheme was anything to go by, the answer to this question was doubtful. Writing to Sir Francis Walker, the County Convener, the Department had stated that before any new hydro scheme could be approved, 'it must be clear that it would represent a proper element in the Scottish generating programme as a whole, and this involved ensuring not only that generating costs would be comparable with that of thermal generation, but also that it would produce a return on capital comparable with the corresponding return on thermal generation'. This reply produced the headline 'Hydro stations on way out, North is warned', in the *Scottish Daily Mail*, and considerable anxiety in the mind of Lord Strathclyde.[44] Lord Strathclyde's anxieties would have been intensified had he known that Norman Elliott had refused to endorse the schemes, believing that Scotland's generating needs could be better met by thermal stations of the kind the SSEB were planning at Longannet.[45]

Not until December 1963 did the Secretary of State order an Inquiry into the largest of the four schemes, the 51 MW Fada-Fionn Project—the order of priority requested by the Hydro Board. Later, it was announced that this Inquiry would also cover the Laidon Scheme. The Inquiry opened on 6 January 1964 and heard evidence on 16 days over the period from 6 January to 24 March. The Reporters were J A Dick, QC, and an economist, A D Campbell, Bonar Professor of Applied Economics of the University of St Andrews. The transcript of the proceedings of the Inquiry numbered no less than 2,017 pages! Shortly after the Inquiry got under way, a decision was made that caused consternation among the Board's representatives. Under pressure from the Treasury, the Secretary of State altered the standard to be used in evaluating the economic acceptability of hydro-electric schemes. Instead of requiring a net return of between 6 and 7 per cent on the capital investment involved, the figure used by the Mackenzie Committee,[46] the Reporters were *directed* to employ a rate of 8 per cent.[47] Protests by Lord Strathclyde and Angus Fulton that this figure was unfair and quite unacceptable were ignored by the Scottish Development Department. Nor would the Scottish Office agree that in estimating the comparative costs of Fada-Fionn and Longannet, the SSEB's huge thermal station, a more realistic figure for the cost of coal than 73 shillings per ton should be used.[48] The Board believed that the dice were loaded against them. Calculations made by the Board's Finance and General Purposes Committee, using the figures that the Scottish Development Department were now insisting upon, produced the conclusion that 'even with all other available supporting arguments, it [will] be *almost impossible* ... to find a way of demonstrating that

(a) the Board were right in promoting the [Fada-Fionn] Scheme, and
(b) the Reporters should find in favour of it'[49]

Nevertheless, the Board put forward a powerful case. It was argued that the Fada-Fionn project was an integral part of the forward generating programme which had been already been agreed with the South Board.[50] It was, in fact, the first of number of hydro stations designed to produce a total of 266 MW which would be installed successively up to 1974/75. Fada-Fionn was intended to cater for the annual load growth in the northern half of the Board's area. Without this scheme—and the others that would follow it—some other source of supply would have to be obtained. To argue that this source *could* be a large thermal station in the South of Scotland ignored the very real practical difficulties and expense of transmitting power over long distances in a difficult terrain; it also ignored serious environmental and amenity objections to the overhead lines that would be needed. Moreover, Fada-Fionn possessed considerable merits as a hydro scheme; it would make the most economic use of the water-power resources of the district for it had good storage facilities and a high head. The storage reserves would permit Fada-Fionn to maintain a load factor of 35 per cent even during winter drought conditions. No evidence was submitted to oppose this favourable assessment, which was based on the expert advice of Guthrie Brown, the consulting engineer. Nor was the opposition able to discredit the cost estimates of Fada-Fionn, which they attempted to do by emphasising the Board's inability to complete *earlier* schemes within their anticipated budgets.[51]

The main thrust of the opposition came from the fishing interests: every one of the ten objectors made the impact of the scheme on the fishings the basis of their objections, although three of these also brought in the adverse effect on deer stalking, and one, Col. William H Whitbread, maintained additionally that the schemes were neither economic nor necessary.[52] In no instance was any objector able to produce evidence to show that any effect of the scheme on the fishings would be of material consequence as far as the *public interest* was involved, and damage to private interests—should it take place—would be met by the payment of monetary compensation.[53] Nor were there any serious objections on the grounds of amenity. The Nature Conservancy withdrew their objections before the Inquiry began, and there were no representations on behalf of the National Trust for Scotland, the Association for the Preservation of Rural Scotland, or the mountaineering organisations.

The most serious attack on Fada-Fionn was based on economic considerations. Col. Whitbread led expert evidence against the economic justification of the scheme. He called as witnesses Mr Colin Clark, the Director of the Economic Research Unit in the University of Oxford, and Professor A J Youngson, of the Chair of Economic Science of the University of Edinburgh. An earlier paper by Colin Clark, *Electricity Generation in Scotland: The Economic Factors*, had been prepared for Aims of Industry and formed part of that organisation's evidence to the Mackenzie Committee. In it, Clark had argued that 'proposals for the construction of further hydro-electric (other than pumped storage) plants are *not* calculated to confer a net economic benefit on the country, either in the short run or in the long run, and expenditure on this object should be immediately and finally terminated'.[54] At the Fada-Fionn hearings, he went even further, saying that *none* of the Board's hydro schemes since 1943 had been economically justified. This assessment seemed to be so much at variance with the expert testimony of witnesses before previous inquiries—including the Mackenzie Committee—that it was probably discounted. Even Colin Clark admitted that his views were extreme.

Prof. Youngson was more moderate. In a number of balanced statements elicited by a Queen's Counsel advised by Professor Ronald Meek of the University of Leicester, an economist who had specialised in fuel and electricity questions, Youngson agreed that not all capital intensive projects should be summarily rejected. Capital intensity was a matter of degree. To Youngson, the ultimate test was the cost to the consumer, and he recognised that the Government had to deal with such projects not only as a matter of economics but as a matter of policy. He admitted that a government's policy might be considered to be economically sound by one school of economists and economically unsound by another school of economists. Youngson refused to be drawn on the possible future course of either fuel costs or inflation, nor would he criticise the Board's calculations of comparative costs.

For its part, the Board made it quite clear that on the basis of a 5.5 per cent interest rate the cost of a unit delivered at Beauly from electricity produced at Fada-Fionn would be lower than if produced at any of the other sources with which Fada-Fionn was being compared. It was not until an annual rate of interest of 7.2 per cent was used without any adjustment for the possibility of inflation in the price of coal that, using the principles laid down by the Mackenzie Committee, the cost per unit of electricity from the scheme became equal to that of an equivalent supply from the thermal extension at Dundee. And if a realistically modest rise in the price of coal and the wages of power station staff were allowed, the break-even figure would be reached when interest was taken at 8.9 per cent. What was so irksome to the Board was that in all these calculations the South Board had been instructed to employ a figure for the cost of coal that had been specially negotiated for Longannet by the Scottish Development Department. At 73 shillings per ton, this was below that obtaining in any other power station in Scotland. The Hydro Board were expressly forbidden to question this figure, nor were they allowed to call witnesses from the National Coal Board in order to ascertain either the way in which it had been determined or its more general applicability.[55]

Concerning the Secretary of State's insistence on a minimum net return on capital investment of 8 per cent, the Board could do little except to assert that they were aware of no other public body having been similarly directed. With some justification they complained that it was highly misleading to employ this criterion in the economic assessment of an *individual* power station. If the 8 per cent rate were to be used for purposes of evaluation, it should be applied to the *system* of which the specific project was but a constituent part. Certainly, such an argument had been accepted by the Select Committee on Nationalised Industries, the Central Electricity Generating Board, and even the Treasury itself.

Lastly, the Board pointed to a number of fringe benefits associated with hydro electric projects in the North of Scotland. These included the employment opportunities, the substantial impact on the economy of the region of the regular wages earned by construction workers, and the growing importance of both hydro plant and specialised technical knowledge of hydro electricity in the nation's export trade. The Board concluded with a plea to the Reporters to impress upon the Secretary of State the necessity for an early decision on how they were to be enabled to carry out the functions entrusted to them by Parliament. After all, their development plans had been held in suspense for nearly four years, and they had to know how they were expected to meet the growing demands of their consumers and to continue their uneconomic programme of rural electrification.

Although the last of the hearings took place at the end of March 1964, and the report by John Dick, QC, and Professor Campbell was completed six months later, it was not published until November 1965. The inquiry had been ordered by Michael Noble. It was submitted to him only a week before the general election in which the Conservatives were defeated. Noble's successor as Secretary of State for Scotland, William Ross, was appointed on 17 October, and there is little doubt that he was sorely embarrassed by the recommendations of the two Reporters. They were quite categoric. Neither of the Constructional Schemes (Fada-Fionn, No.39, and Laidon, No.38) should be confirmed. Yet the Labour Party had fought the election on a manifesto which clearly stated that hydro-electric schemes in the Highlands were examples of public enterprise which should be greatly extended.[56] It was, of course, not unknown for the result of a public inquiry to be quietly shelved, but *this* report could not be ignored. Members of Parliament, the general public, the Press and the Hydro Board, all demanded to be told the findings and to have a decision. In the event, after agonising over the report for a year, the Secretary of State refused to confirm the two schemes.[57]

Why had the Reporters and the Minister come to this conclusion? Lord Strathclyde always believed that the Reporters had been deliberately chosen to produce a result biased against the Hydro Board,[58] but what really killed the schemes was the Treasury's insistence on a net return of 8 per cent on capital expenditure. On the very first day of the proceedings, Lord Strathclyde had been asked

> ... do I understand that you ... are quite clear that if this project [Fada-Fionn] were to take place it would not produce a minimum net return of 8 per cent on the capital asset on its depreciated value over its lifetime?,

And his answer was 'It could not, unless the tariffs were very largely raised'.[59] It did not matter that in the course of cross-examination, A N Ferrier, the Board's Chief Accountant, seemed to disagree. The doubt had been planted in the minds of the Reporters, and they had been given no alternative but to use 8 per cent as 'the "right" rate of "interest"', although they felt obliged to explain, somewhat apolgetically, that 'A discipline of this nature is a rational economic method designed to avoid misallocation of resources. Such a discipline is particularly necessary in the next few years when there are likely to be substantial and increasing demands for capital for all sorts of projects in the United Kingdom'.[60]

But if the Treasury was the villain of the piece, the Hydro Board's case for Fada-Fionn was severely undermined, if not utterly destroyed, by the evidence of the South Board. Their chief engineer, Hywel Jones, was questioned for hours on the economics of the scheme. His evidence made it clear that Fada-Fionn would not be required to meet demand in Scotland for at least ten years, nor would it improve the system costs for Scotland as a whole; that Fada-Fionn, which might be expected to work at a 35 per cent load-factor, was below the system load factor for the whole of Scotland, a system which already possessed an abundance of low load-factor plant, and which would gain 400 MW more when Cruachan was commissioned in 1965 or 1966; and that, because of its relatively small capacity (51 MW), Fada-Fionn could not be a substitute for a new unit in a large thermal station and, by itself, would not defer the necessity for the installation of additional thermal plant. In effect, Hywel Jones argued that Fada-Fionn was completely unnecesary. Indeed, if its construction caused a delay in the erection of transmission reinforcements from ever larger and more efficient thermal stations to remote load centres, it could have a positively detrimental effect on the *Scottish* system as a whole.[61]

And it was the needs of the Scottish system as a whole that dominated the thinking of the two Reporters. The adverse effect of the scheme on the area's amenity and fisheries, to which so much time was devoted, was likened to 'the small dust' in the balance. The real issues were economic. The argument of the Board's advocate, Mr W R Grieve, QC, that 'With two Boards in operation ... it is proper to look at the separate systems ... of the Boards ... you don't test [Fada-Fionn] against the needs of the system as a whole and see whether it is going to be necessary or unnecessary in the whole Scottish system', was swept aside as irrational. Indeed, it was subversive of the view expressed by both Lord Strathclyde and Angus Fulton that 'the policy of the Board was to find the least-cost solution for supplying electricity whether that involved a hydro station, or imports from the South Board'. In the opinion of the Reporters, 'the supply of electricity in Scotland, in regard to generation and transmission, ought to be planned and developed as one system, and Fada-Fionn should be tested against the needs of that system, even though there are two Boards and even though the results of the test were to mean greater imports of electricity by the [Hydro] Board'.[62]

Seen in this context, Fada-Fionn and Laidon were doomed, since the Reporters were convinced that there were great economies of scale to be won if a system were large enough to assimilate the most efficient plant; and that should be *not* 'a succession of Fadas', but large generating sets operating in large thermal stations, stations such as that planned for Longannet, that proposed by the South Board for Irvine, and even those nuclear stations, with capacities of 1,000 MW, envisaged for the 1970s.[63] In effect, the Reporters accepted the argument by Hywel Jones that Fada-Fionn was not required to meet demand in Scotland in the period up to 1974/5. Alternatively, the capacity that might be required could 'more conveniently [be met by] larger thermal units more nearly matched to the growth of demand'.[64] The Reporters concluded, then, that

> on economic grounds ... the generation and transmission of electricity in Scotland should be planned and developed as one system. Fada-Fionn should therefore be tested against the nature and needs of the whole system. From the preceding cost analyses, made in accordance with the Mackenzie Committee proposals at an 8 per cent return, Fada-Fionn emerges as a relatively expensive method of meeting a particular demand in the north which could be met more cheaply from other sources even after making allowance for transmission costs.[65]

Against this, 'the benefits that might be attributed to Fada-Fionn under such headings as employment, exports, and the "social clause" of the 1943 Act' were felt to be of 'little weight'[66]. The Reporters recommendations were inevitable: 'the [Fada-Fionn] scheme should not be confirmed'.[67]

The reluctant acceptance of the logic of the Dick/Campbell report by the Labour Secretary of State, William Ross, a year after its publication, marked the end of conventional hydro electric schemes in the North of Scotland. If the Fada-Fionn scheme could be rejected, there was little or no hope for the Board's other schemes (See Table 18). Indeed, the Reporters stated as much. 'It is probable that because of natural conditions any future conventional hydro schemes in Scotland are also likely to be of relatively small capacity ... [Not one of these "succession of Fadas" could] match a year's growth [even] in the Board's own district'. And any further increase of demand would *reinforce* the desirability of meeting it by means of 'new thermal plant or, more speculatively, by nuclear generation'.[68] It was the end of an era.

5   Pumped Storage: Cruachan and Foyers

(i)   Cruachan

The letter conveying the Secretary of State's decision not to confirm Fada-Fionn and Laidon contained just one crumb of comfort to those members of the Board who retained their devotion to the development of hydro-power. It hinted at the future possibility of a 'fuller exploitation of pumped storage'.[69] It will be recalled that Sir

Edward MacColl had envisaged a huge pumped storage scheme for Loch Sloy in 1936, but nothing had come of it. Nor was the idea revived in 1944. It was not until 1957, with the publication of the Awe Scheme (Constructional Scheme No.28) that the Board provided for the construction of the first large-scale pumped storage hydro-electric development in Scotland. Although the Awe scheme included two conventional and self-contained hydro stations at Inverawe (25 MW) and Nant (15 MW), its centrepiece was the Cruachan pumped storage project.

By the late 1950s, the time was right to put forward such a proposal.[70] The Board—driven forward by Angus Fulton—realised that the solution of civil, electrical and mechanical engineering problems involved would require intensive preliminary investigation, and that the successful implementation of the scheme would take many years. If the many difficulties anticipated could be overcome—as was confidently expected—and the civil engineering works were pushed ahead in accordance with the Board's provisional programme, it was hoped that the pumped storage project would be available to meet the growing Scottish load by 1965/66, by which time the South of Scotland Electricity Board expected to have sufficient surplus high merit generating plant capacity at nights and or weekends to be able to provide the essential low cost electricity for pumping.[71] In a sense, the Cruachan project was one of the first tangible results of the increasing cooperation between the Hydro Board and the South Board. But another impetus towards pumped storage in the late 1950s was the increasing expense of conventional hydro schemes. Pumping seemed to offer the possibility of providing the storage needed to ensure firm output from peak load hydro plant at a much lower capital cost than the construction of large dams. Furthermore, by its need for electrical energy, pumped storage plant was capable of improving the performance of the thermal plant that produced that energy.[72]

It was in this context that Cruachan was considered for inclusion in the Board's future generating programme, though only after joint technical and economic studies by the two Boards had fully demonstrated its justification. The site was selected because it offered the best prospects of low capital costs. This object could be attained if a high head was available and if the horizontal distance between the upper and low reservoirs was relatively small. The greater the head : distance ratio the more economic the scheme was likely to be.[73] In these respects, the steeply rising rock slopes above the northern shore of Loch Awe and the presence of a small stream flowing from a corrie beneath the main peak of Ben Cruachan, seemed particularly attractive. Examination of the apparently favourable conditions confirmed this impression. Detailed investigations revealed an excellent dam site on the Cruachan burn at an elevation of about 1,160 feet OD, and the small flat corrie upstream of the dam site, not apparent from Ordnance Survey contour maps, provided an excellent storage basin. Moreover, the horizontal distance between the dam site and the nearest point on the northern slope of Loch Awe was 4,700 feet, giving a head : distance ratio of about 1 : 4. It was therefore decided to take advantage of these highly promising conditions at Cruachan and to link the pumped storage works with the two conventional schemes at Loch Awe. (See Figure 44).

For all its potential economy, Fulton was always conscious of the need to keep the capital costs of Cruachan to an absolute minimum.[74] These capital costs had to be in line with those which characterised the ever larger thermal plants being installed

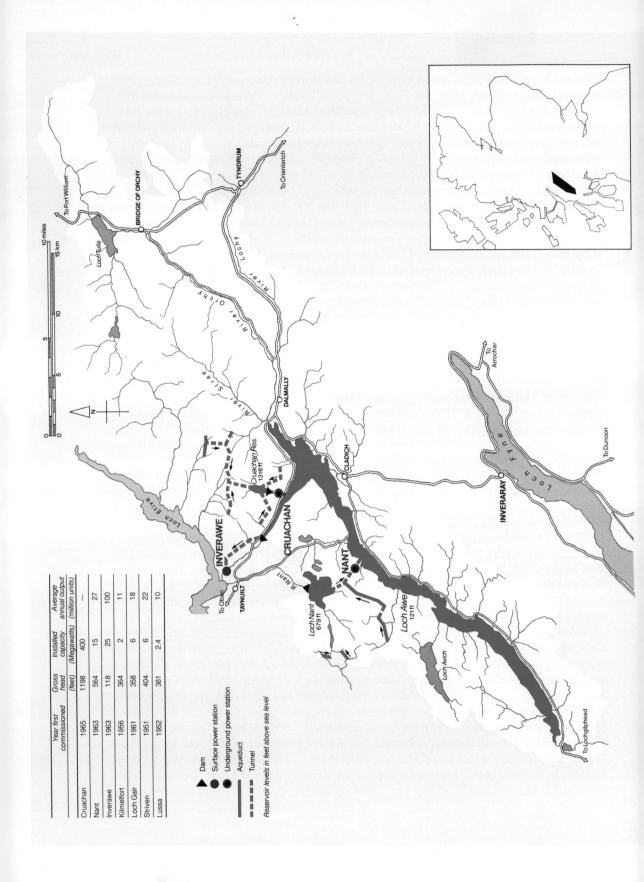

	Year first commissioned	Gross head (feet)	Installed capacity (Megawatts)	Average annual output (million units)
Cruachan	1965	1198	400	—
Nant	1963	564	15	27
Inverawe	1963	118	25	100
Kilmelfort	1956	364	2	11
Loch Gair	1961	358	6	18
Striven	1951	404	6	22
Lussa	1952	381	2.4	10

Dam ▲

Surface power station ●

Underground power station ●

Aqueduct

Tunnel

Reservoir levels in feet above sea level

10 miles
15 km

N

To Fort William

Loch Tulla

BRIDGE OF ORCHY

TYNDRUM

To Crianlarich

RIVER LOCHY

River Orchy

River Strae

DALMALLY

Loch Etive

Cruachan Res. 1316ft

INVERAWE

CRUACHAN

CLADICH

To Oban

TAYNUILT

R. Nant

NANT

Loch Nant 679ft

Loch Awe 121ft

Loch Avich

To Lochgilphead

INVERARAY

Loch Fyne

To Arrochar

To Dunoon

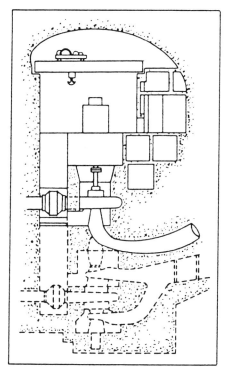

FIGURE 45   Cruachan power station: section through main chamber

throughout Great Britain. It was therefore decided to provide a total plant capacity comparable in scale with that of the large thermal plants with which it was destined to work, and with the costs of which it would undoubtedly be compared. Until the late 1950s, separate pumps had been a feature of all high head pumped storage projects throughout the world. Fulton argued that if these separate pumps could be eliminated, substantial savings (perhaps of the order of £1 million) would be made, not only in the plant and machinery, but also in civil engineering, for there would be less extensive plant to house. An indication of the saving in plant and space is given in Figure 45. The leading British manufacturers of hydro electric machinery were therefore invited to undertake the development of a reversible pump-turbine with an acceptable performance.[75]

This was no mean task. Nothing existed in the literature concerning the special problems involved in starting and operating a reversible machine working under such a high head. To solve these problems Boving & Co conducted an extensive programme of research in the KMW Laboratory at Kristenehamn in Sweden, and The English Electric Company undertook similar experiments at the company's hydraulic lab-

facing page
FIGURE 44   Loch Awe scheme

oratories at Rugby. Not until the consulting enginers, Merz & McLellan, were satisfied by the results obtained in model tests and the design perfected could the project proceed.[76]

However suitable the Cruachan site may have been for meeting the overall economic and hydraulic requirements of the scheme, the very nature of those requirements meant that the location possessed severe physical limitations. Between the corrie to be used as the upper reservoir, high on the flanks of Ben Cruachan, and Loch Awe, the lower reservoir, both the trunk road and the railway line to Oban made use of the narrow Pass of Brander. There was no room for a power station on the confined space available. Indeed, it was doubtful if there was even sufficient access and working space for contractors' men and equipment. These were very cogent reasons for putting the Cruachan power station deep underground in the heart of the mountain, and these arguments were strengthened by a desire to avoid erecting pressure pipelines on the steep slopes of the Pass. This, then, was what was decided.[77]

No such problems attended the determination of either the position or the type of dam which was to convert the corrie above Loch Awe into the upper reservoir.[78] The profile of the dam site was too flat for an arch dam, nor could a 'fill' type of dam be contemplated because, even if sufficient fill had been available, all too little was known about the behaviour of such a structure in conditions of fluctuating water levels. These considerations led to the selection of a massive buttress dam. This well-tried type of dam had in earlier low load factor projects safely withstood the sort of stress fluctuations that could be expected from the regular rise and fall of water which would characterise

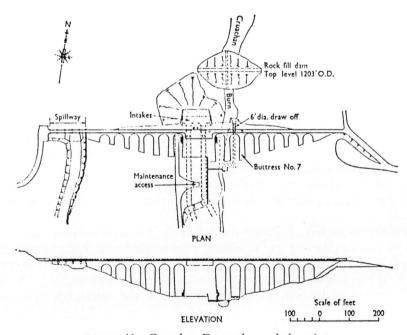

FIGURE 46   Cruachan Dam: plan and elevation

a pumped storage scheme. It also offered the prospect of economies in materials and those other advantages, such as reduced heating and shrinkage, which were discussed in connection with Sloy. The final design comprised six buttresses to the east side and five buttresses to the west side of a central gravity block which would accommodate two intakes, the gate shafts and the outlet pipes. An elevation and plan of the dam is shown in Fig. 46, and the layout finally adopted for the entire project in Fig. 48.

The Awe scheme was confirmed by the Secretary of State and received Parliamentary Approval in May 1959. Work began almost at once on the Inverawe power station and barrage and the Nant project, but the two conventional schemes were quite overshadowed by the immensity and importance of Cruachan. The most difficult constructional work in the Cruachan project was the excavation of the caverns required to house the main machinery and the transformers. But before this major work could even begin, it was necessary to drive the access tunnel and the seven adits which were to be used 'as extra points of attack' for the excavation of the main machinery hall, the draft tubes, the surge chamber and the tailrace tunnel. Such a huge undertaking, comprising the removal of 330,000 cubic yards or rock, would never have been contemplated had it not been believed beforehand that the rock which was likely to be encountered would be a fine-grained granite. It was, therefore, particularly unfortunate that when the main access tunnel had been driven from a site on the shore of Loch Awe and part of the main chamber had been opened up, a crush zone was exposed, traversing

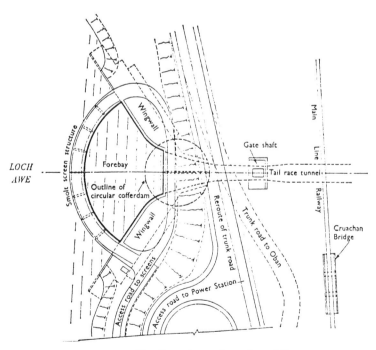

FIGURE 47   Cruachan: plan of outfall

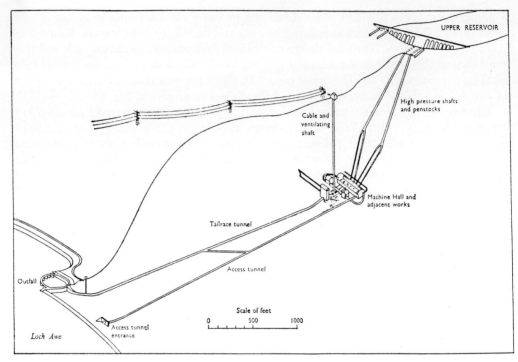

FIGURE 48   Cruachan pumped storage project: general layout

the power station diagonally. This posed very awkward and totally unexpected problems which necessitated a rather different and more complex mode of excavation than
had been planned and the erection of supplementary support. The method used for
excavating the machine hall is shown in Fig. 49 and Plate 26.

As early as 1962, the Board reported that 'the nature and the scale of the work are
such that it will require great concentration of effort if the project is to be finished on
time'.[79] But it was. Contracts had already been placed with Boving and English Electric
for the four generating sets. These companies, each of whom were responsible for two
sets, in turn sub-contracted the work to the Clydebank firms of John Brown Ltd. and
Harland and Wolff, respectively.[80] Meanwhile, progress on the civil engineering works
continued to be kept within the very tight timetable laid down by the Board, despite
all manner of unforeseen difficulties,[81] especially in the fabrication, erection and welding
of the steel tunnel linings needed to resist the great hydraulic pressure which would be
encountered. In the machine hall, excavation was completed early in 1964. Thereafter,
the contractors—Edmund Nuttall, Sons & Co.—concentrated on the concrete work
required for the provision of foundations for the plant and machinery and on the
accommodation required for the switchgear, transformers and control gear. The outfall
works at the Loch Awe end of the tailrace tunnel were exceptionally awkward. This
was because of the difficulties experienced in driving a cofferdam down to the steeply

237

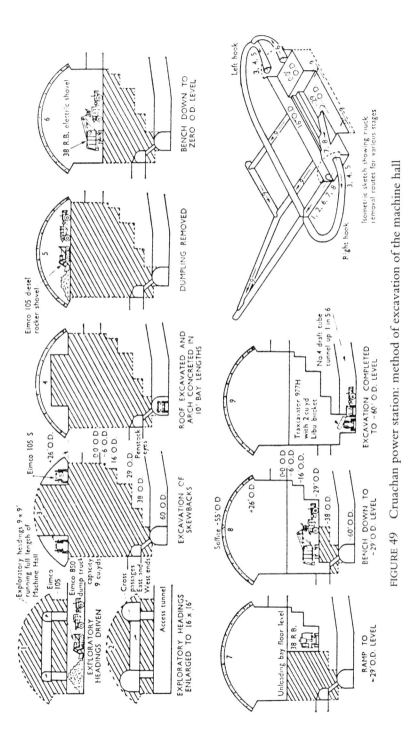

FIGURE 49   Cruachan power station: method of excavation of the machine hall

PLATE 26   Cruachan Power Station

inclined bedrock of the Loch, which was covered by an overburden of mixed gravel and boulders. The task was complicated by the sheer extent of the outfall works necessitated by the fine screens that had to be provided to prevent the entry of salmon smolts into the tailrace tunnel![82] A plan of the outfall is shown in Figure 47. The works can clearly be seen in Plate 27.

The delivery of plant to the site kept pace with the preparation of the foundation work. As with earlier schemes, many bridges on the delivery routes had had to be strengthened beforehand but, even so, several items such as rotors and stators had to be dismantled at the manufacturers' works and reassembled on site. This procedure also had to be adopted with the two main transformers. Built by Ferrantis, this was the first time that transformers had been transported in sections. This involved both special design features and the provision of extraordinary arrangements to put the components together under controlled conditions in special chambers built to accommodate them. For example, the insulation resistance of the transformers had to be safeguarded by assembling them inside lightweight plastic tents into which dustfree air was blown to prevent the entrance of dust or moisture. In the last twelve months of construction there were no fewer than 21 principal civil, mechanical and electrical contractors on the site, together with their numerous sub-contractors.[83] Their work, always arduous and frequently hazardous, had to be properly co-ordinated within a restricted working area and in circumstances of extreme pressure for 24 hours a day. The planning of this intense activity was carried out at meetings chaired by representatives of the Hydro Board attended by their consulting civil and mechanical and electrical engineers (James Williamson & Partners and Merz & McLellan), and it says much for the morale and energy of the workmen, the supervisory staff, and the contractors and engineers, that not only were programme revisions accepted constructively, and recurring difficulties (even crises) surmounted, but the works were completed more or less on time, and at only 8 per cent above the cost—£35 per kW—estimated some seven years earlier.

Of course, there were teething troubles.[84] The commissioning programme was delayed because of an accident to the concreting plant in the final stages, and damage was sustained to both No.1 and No.4 machines during early testing, but perhaps this was only to be expected in a project which incorporated so many entirely new features. Although HM the Queen inaugurated the scheme in October 1965, full generated output was not obtained from the first two sets until January 1966. Thereafter, a number of accidents—one involving the breakage of a number of shearing bolts which caused extensive damage to the guide vanes and runners—followed by repairs and modifications, postponed full working until 1967, when it was apparent that the efficiency of the plant was close to the expected figure, thus confirming that the overall design efficiency of 75 per cent for the scheme, including the transmission lines, had been achieved. Cruachan's subsequent contribution to the Scottish system during a typical winter week of 1969 is shown in Figure 50.

(ii) *Foyers*[85]

Cruachan had been planned and instigated before the momentous findings of the Public Inquiry into Fada-Fionn had been published. Because the conception of Cruachan had

PLATE 27   Aerial view of Cruachan project

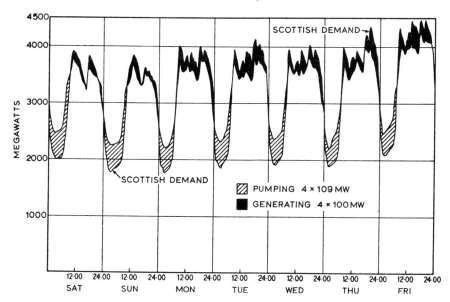

FIGURE 50   Operation of Cruachan pumped storage station

taken place many years before the Secretary of State for Scotland had been called upon to decide the fate of conventional hydro electric schemes, the successful completion of the Awe Scheme provided an uncertain guide to the attitude that the Scottish Office and the Treasury might take towards further pumped storage projects. The Board could have had little confidence that the Secretary of State's earlier hint that there was additional scope for such developments was more than simply an emollient to soothe their hurt. It may have been nothing more than a manifestation of the politician's perpetual quest to avoid reducing his options.

The first test came when the two Scottish Electricity Boards accepted a recommendation of their Joint Planning Committee that the completion of the Hunterston nuclear power station should be followed by a 300 MW pumped storage project. For this purpose, it was proposed to redevelop the catchment area of the British Aluminium Company's pioneering hydro-electric scheme at Foyers which had been taken over by the Hydro Board in 1967, the year in which the aluminium smelter was closed. Foyers was envisaged in Fulton's time as the possible site of a conventional scheme of about 60 mW. K R Vernon, Fulton's successor, saw that Foyers possessed great potential for pumped storage. Vernon's experience as a principal spokesman for the Board at the Fada-Fionn Inquiry, where he had been in the witness box for two whole days, had convinced him that scope for the promotion of conventional hydro was severely limited. Moreover, his background of system planning on mixed power systems (before coming to the Board in 1956 he had been with the British Electricity Authority and, briefly, the South of Scotland Electricity Board), and as the engineer responsible for the later stages of the construction of Cruachan, had made Vernon an enthusiast for pumped storage, which he saw not only as a means of exploiting the remaining sites available to the Board but as the most effective method of complementing large thermal units. Following intensive engineering and design studies, the Foyers Scheme—Construction Scheme No 40—was published in 1968. The Scheme would exploit the head of 589 feet between the existing reservoir of Loch Mhor and Loch Ness, but the flow to the upper reservoir would be increased by diversion aqueducts designed to capture the waters of the River Fechlin and the River E (see Fig. 51). It was the possibility of cheaply expanding the catchment area from 30 to 80 square miles and the existence of 'ready-made' upper and lower reservoirs which compensated for the relatively poor head: distance ratio of the site, which was only 1 : 18 (500-600 feet of head between the upper and lower reservoirs, which were about 10,000 feet apart).[86] Thus Foyers, like Cruachan, would not be a 'pure' pumped storage project, but a sort of hybrid, since about 25 per cent of its planned annual output (400 GWh) was likely to come from the run off of the natural and diverted catchments which together would help to feed the Loch Mhor reservoir.

At this early stage the estimated cost of such a project was put at £10.6 million (£35.2 per kW installed), of which £26.2 per kW would be attributable to pumped storage. Since the current cost of a thermal station of similar capacity would then have been about £50 per kW installed, it was apparent that a pumped storage scheme at Foyers would provide a most economical method of meeting the increased demand for electricity expected in the mid-1970s. The Scheme was confirmed by the Secretary of State in February 1969 (five objections having been withdrawn following negotiations), laid before Parliament in accordance with the statutory procedure, and formally approved in April.

The locations of the main elements in the scheme were determined by the geology and topography of the area, much of which lay in the shatter zone of the Great Glen Fault.[87] There was only one area of sufficiently high ground for the site of the surge shaft. Once this had been decided, the route of the low pressure tunnel from the upper reservoir, Loch Mhor, to the surge shaft had to be planned. The 'difficult' nature of the heavily fractured rock between Loch Mohr and the surge shaft made it impossible to employ a direct route, but it was believed that if the line of the tunnel was slightly bent it could be driven through Foyers granite without too great an increase in its length. Glen Liath—which lay between the surge shaft and Loch Mohr—constituted another problem. Should the low pressure system run *under* this valley either in the tunnel or in a buried pipeline, or should the system be carried *over* the valley floor in a surface pipeline? The latter method was adopted. The poor quality of the rock in the vicinity of Glen Liath made a tunnel impracticable, and since this made a section of pipeline unavoidable, this might as well run across the valley floor rather than beneath it, for this alternative would greatly facilitate the driving of the 9,400 feet low pressure tunnel from two easily accessible intermediate faces. The *location* of the power station and the high pressure system was more easily decided. Because of the *generally* faulted nature of the rock running parallel to Loch Ness, there was little point in chosing anything but the shortest possible route (see Fig. 52).

facing page
FIGURE 51   The Foyers scheme

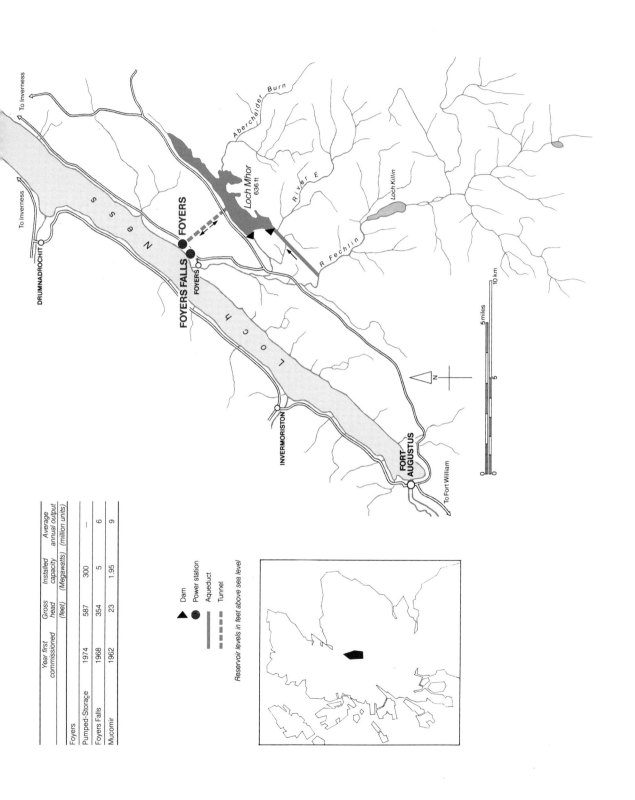

	Year first commissioned	Gross head (feet)	Installed capacity (Megawatts)	Average annual output (million units)
Foyers				
Pumped-Storage	1974	587	300	—
Foyers Falls	1968	354	5	6
Mucomir	1962	23	1.95	9

▲ Dam

● Power station

▬▬ Aqueduct

▬ ▬ Tunnel

Reservoir levels in feet above sea level

244

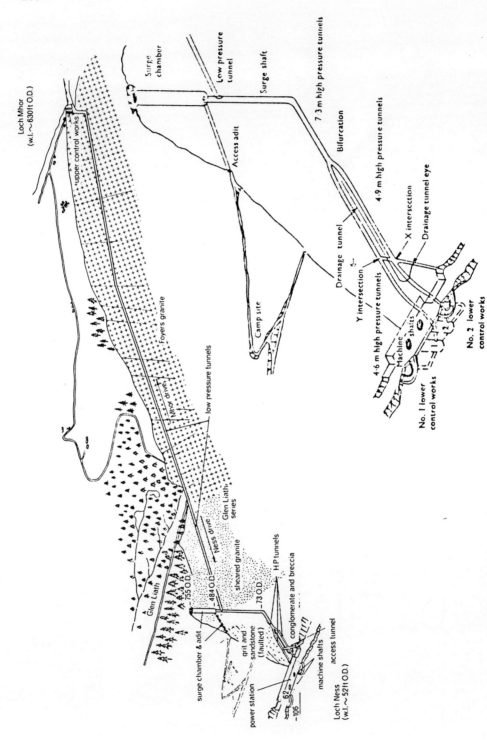

FIGURE 52   Foyers scheme: longitudinal sketches showing the low pressure tunnel system, the surge chamber and the high pressure tunnels

There remained the problem of deciding the nature and arrangement of the power station. Several possibilities were considered. The first, an underground machine hall close to the bottom of the surge shaft, was ruled out because the poor quality of the rock in the area would have made the construction of an access tunnel highly problematic. The second, a surface power station beside the loch, was rejected on amenity and economic grounds. The scenic quality of the whole area would have been gravely impaired during and after construction, and the cost of this arrangement would have been higher than the alternatives. The third possibility—the one finally adopted—was to build a power station on the shore of Loch Ness with two separate 165 feet shafts for the machines, connected to the surge chamber by a 24 feet diameter shaft and high pressure tunnel, and twin steel-lined tunnels (see Figs. 53 and 54).

In November 1969 the contractors moved on to the site to begin preliminary works, building new roads and reconstructing existing roads and tracks to make them suitable for heavy traffic. Although many difficulties were encountered, the majority of them were not entirely unexpected, and steady progress was made, generally in accordance with the planned timetable. There was one early problem that had not been anticipated: the contractors for the low pressure tunnel system between the surge shaft and Loch Mhor and the upper control works, Duncan Logan Construction Ltd., went into liquidation after only six months on the site. A contract for the completion of the works was awarded to Edmund Nuttall Ltd in May 1970, giving them both the main civil engineering contracts, for they had already won the contract for the lower control works, the power station, the high pressure tunnel and the surge facilities. The total value of these contracts was about £7 million. The order for supplying the two 150MW reversible pump-turbine motor generator sets, worth nearly £2 million, had been placed with Boving & Co., who had sub-contracted some of the work to John Brown (Engineering) Ltd. Clydebank.

By the summer of 1972, driving of all the tunnels and shafts between Loch Mhor

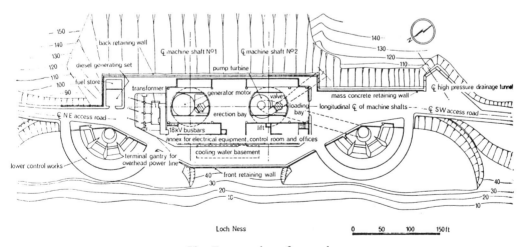

FIGURE 53   Foyers: plan of powerhouse area

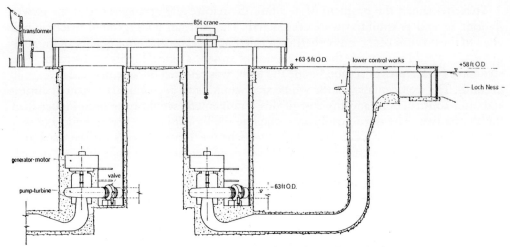

FIGURE 54   Foyers: section through machine shafts

and the power station had been completed and lining them with concrete was well under way. A feature of the design was the use of considerable lengths of steel lining for much of the high pressure system and a 19 feet diameter pipeline to convey the low pressure pipeline across Glen Liath. Because of transport difficulties it was decided to fabricate the steel linings and the pipeline on the site, and a large working area between the old British Aluminium Company's factory and the mouth of the River Foyers was prepared, using rock spoil from the tunnel excavations. On this site was erected a trimming shop where the steel plates—which had been brought by road from the old Colvilles' Motherwell works of the British Steel Corporation—were cut to size; a 1,200 ton former for bending the plates; a welding shop and a 45 ton Goliath crane to permit ease of movement of the 15 and 16 feet diameter pipes. Ten per cent of the circumferential welds were X-ray tested and the remainder were checked ultrasonically.

A notable achievement during 1972 was the lining of the surge chamber with concrete. Nearly 300 feet high, with a finished diameter of 61 feet, this was a formidable task, yet it was completed in 21 days of round-the-clock working, using a hydraulically operated continuously climbing shutter. During the same year a start was made on diverting the River Fechlin into the upper reservoir to add 65 million units of electricity to the existing natural run off; and, following a public inquiry into objections to the routing of part of the 275kV transmission line from Foyers, the Board agreed to place its first 3000 feet underground.

Numerous difficulties were encountered as the work proceeded, the majority of them stemming from the 'unusual ground conditions'. Initially, it proved to be almost impossible to drive the sheet piles of the cofferdam required to permit the construction of the upper control works at Loch Mhor. Only after considerable experimentation—and more than three months of double-shift working—was the contractor able to evolve a satisfactory method of driving the piles through what proved to be compact silt and sand containing tightly packed cobbles. There were many falls of rock and the danger of a major collapse at the vital intersection of the access tunnel and the high pressure tunnels adjacent to the power station; and flooding caused lengthy delays and expensive remedial action in sinking and sealing the southern, No.2 machine shaft. Despite these severe problems, which caused the reprogramming of much of the work, the first of the 150MW machine sets was completed by the Spring of 1974; the second, shortly after. Commissioning problems were relatively few—though heavy leakage suddenly developed, after load rejection tests had been undertaken, from a section of the low pressure conduit at the point where it crossed Glen Liath—and the Board's second pumped storage scheme was brought into service, smoothly and within a few months of the original timetable, later in the year.[88] The scale of the works are indicated by the sheer size of the machine sets, each one of which weighs 900 tons, the rotating parts alone accounting for 300 tons. When generating at full load, the two turbines pass water into Loch Ness at the rate of nearly 200 tons per second. When pumping at full power they are capable of lifting 160 tons of water per second from Loch Ness up to Loch Mhor, yet from the initiation of offloading as a pump to full load generation takes but 3 minutes, and from spinning in air to full load generating, only 80 seconds. Moreover, the power station is semi-automatic and remotely controlled by radio link from the group control centre, at this time sixteen miles away at Fort Augustus.

The Foyers project, officially inaugurated by William Ross in April 1975, had been remarkably successful. Although the final cost, £20.2 million, was almost double that provisionally estimated in 1967, 60 per cent of this increase had been due to inflation, and much of the remainder was ascribable either to the very difficult ground conditions encountered in the shatter zone of the Great Glen Fault or to additional works and design modifications.[89] Yet it was the last of the Board's constructional schemes. Numerous detailed investigations and design studies have since been carried out. These have shown Craigroyston on the east side of Loch Lomond to be the most suitable site for the next large scale pumped storage development, but sixteen years after the first ground, aerial and hydrographic surveys of this area were conducted, this most promising of schemes remains but a dream, an unfulfilled hope among those who continue to believe, like their predecessors; that hydro electricity is 'a fully renewable, benign and proven source of indigenous power, with no waste products, no health hazards to its operators or the public and with many beneficial effects on the communities and amenities' of the North of Scotland.[90]

CHAPTER 8

Epilogue, 1975–1987

This study has attempted to trace the history of the development of hydro-electricity in the North of Scotland from its experimental and inauspicious beginnings in the late nineteenth century; through an era of private enterprise, which foundered on the rock of Parliamentary obstruction in the 1930s; to a period of remarkable activity under the auspicies of a publicly-owned body vitalised by a group of exceptionally talented and inspired engineers who enjoyed the unswerving encouragement and support of those appointed to control and guide them.

This last episode was, as Tom Johnston always meant it to be, an adventure, a great social and economic experiment. Not for nothing did he abandon a Parliamentary career at its apogee. With the help of a small group of friends and the engineers whom they appointed, Johnston was intent on reversing the effect of decades of Highland neglect. No matter that he failed to attain his most optimistic purposes; no matter that economists told him and his associates that the necessary capital investment would produce a bigger yield in other fields of endeavour elsewhere in the United Kingdom; no matter that the Board was initially vilified for disturbing the fish, despoiling the desolate grandeur of the glens, and submerging the grazing of the sheep and the stag— harnessing the latent power of the waters and making low cost energy available for the people of the Highlands was a laudable objective, and one that *was* attained.

Of course, it could not go on. Eventually, the cost of it all was added up, and with that peculiar political arithmetic that ultimately transforms hopes and aspirations into arid symbols in a cost-benefit analysis, further conventional hydro and, a little later, pumped storage schemes were halted. The Board, still possessed of an inherited momentum, persisted but the Craigroyston scheme, prepared after an intensive series of environmental studies that MacColl would have marvelled at,[1] was never formally submitted for approval; and other possibilities, including several potentially valuable small and relatively inexpensive run-of-river schemes,[2] were rejected by the Secretary of State. The days when a plausible plan was given approval because it would save coal, would provide employment, would lend a proper balance to the system, were gone. The fact is that the increasing scale and technical efficiency of thermal and nuclear stations made the justification of harnessing the power from the remaining, less economic schemes almost impossible.

In conjunction with the rise in the cost of capital to heights undreamed of in the 1950s,[3] with the discovery and exploitation of the oil of the North sea, and with growing mastery of nuclear energy,[4] the case for further heavy investment in hydro schemes could not be sustained. And when the steeply rising growth of demand for electricity suddenly faltered in the 1970s, and experienced a reverse in the early 1980s—for the first time in the Board's history—the schemes so optimistically presented to the Mackenzie Committee in 1961 as 'additional projects—considered economic', could no longer honestly be so described (see Fig. 55 and Appendix Table 28).

In retrospect, some careful and disinterested observers have questioned whether much of the huge programme of capital investment should ever have been sanctioned. Lea, for example, pointed out in 1969 that 'the application of the pumped storage technique ... has rendered invalid all previous estimates of available hydro-power reserves in the Highlands ... If [this technique] had been sufficiently advanced 20 years ago, many of the present hydro-electric power schemes would never have been built in their present conventional form, and much of the £305 million spent by the Hydro-electric Board would have been differently invested'.[5] Indeed, Angus Fulton himself admitted as much in 1964.[6] But the fact is that with the then known technology, the Board's hydro schemes *did* make sense. A scheme such as Shin provided power where it was wanted, in the far North, for local distribution. Those who believe Aberdeen to be the next train stop after Edinburgh, just round the corner, as it were, and even some of those

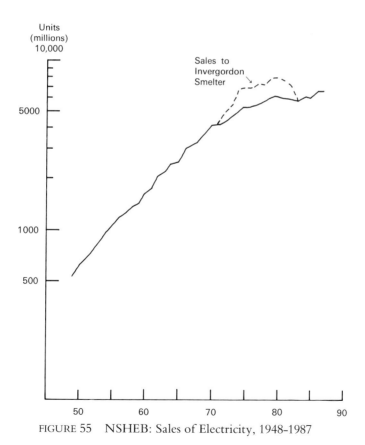

FIGURE 55   NSHEB: Sales of Electricity, 1948-1987

debating the merits of the Board's constructional schemes at Westminster, forget the great distances involved in the Board's area. They fail to understand the problems (and costs) involved in the long-distance transmission of electricity in a sometimes bitterly hostile environment, and its subsequent distribution to a widely scattered community. At the time of its promotion and execution, Shin (and the scheme is used merely for exemplification) was more than adequately justified. And it should be remembered too that although the Board may have invested over £300 million by 1970, no less than 35 per cent was required for transmission and distribution, an investment not greatly in excess of what would have been required however the rural areas were to be provided with electrical energy.[7]

To say that the Board's constructional programme should never have been sanctioned because of the inevitability of its technological obsolescence is much like arguing that the creation of the British railway network was an unmitigated waste of resources because its promoters should have foreseen the coming of the motor car. The fact is that the value of the majority of the Board's schemes, especially Cruachan and Foyers, have certainly been increased rather than diminished by the technological advances of the last twenty years.[8] Their ability to meet peak load demands enhances the ability of the Scottish mixed *system* rapidly to respond to load fluctuations. Their capital cost may have been high but their running costs are low and have been little influenced by the inflation of the past fifteen years.[9] Inevitably, with ageing, maintenance costs have grown slightly, but compared with the fuel and running costs of thermal stations these are diminutive. The Board's hydro schemes do produce energy very inexpensively and it is questionable whether without hydro development the electrification of the Highlands would have taken place as rapidly or as completely as it did.[10] Sir Christopher Hinton had been correct when in 1958 he predicted, 'In 20, 30 and 50 years hence people ... will say how tremendously fortunate it was that this water power development took place when it did.'[11]

Thus, with the cessation of new hydro schemes, it has been the Board's responsibility to employ its assets effectively. There is no doubt that this has been achieved. After an exhaustive inquiry in 1985, the Monopolies and Mergers Commission found that the Board 'does its job well. It strikes an appropriate balance between its requirement to supply electricity efficiently and economically and its environmental and social obligations. Managers whom we met impressed us with their knowledge, experience and dedication. They show a willingness to use new technology to improve efficiency and to experiment with new methods while not losing their understanding of, and sense of identification with, the environment in which they work'.[12]

The author of a study such as this can hardly help but become sympathetic towards his subject. As this alchemy takes place, he loses some part of his objectivity, feeling criticism almost as much as the officials involved and experiencing a certain pride when praiseworthy achievements are recognised. Nevertheless, the favourable verdict of the Monopolies and Mergers Commission *does* seem to be warranted. In the last two decades, the Board has come to terms with the abrupt termination of its original *raison d'etre*. Under the chairmanship of a succession of men devoted to the principles that inspire the Board, and helped by the part-time members who see their major rôle as explaining these principles to the public and of judging the performance of the executive,

Mr K R Vernon, sometime the Board's Chief Electrical and Mechanical Engineer (1964-66), and for the last twenty years the Board's Chief Executive (See Appendix 2), has transformed the orientation of the Board. Once a crusading body, perhaps too little touched by economic realities, the Board's continued survival has been ensured by Mr Vernon, who has turned the organisation—which, unlike other area boards in the electricity supply industry (other than the South of Scotland Electricity Board), is responsible for the generation, as well as transmission, distribution and sales of electricity—into a balanced, fully integrated, electricity board.

This transformation did not take place overnight. Perhaps the first major step took place as early as 1965 when new arrangements for the exchange of power and the operation of generating plant were agreed between the Board and the South of Scotland Electricity Board. The need for change had been influenced by the growth in loads in the Districts of both Boards with the concomitant introduction of large thermal stations and pumped storage on a large scale. The use of these large new plants involved considerable interchange of power between the systems of the two Boards, varying in quantity and direction at different times of the day and from year to year. The object of the arrangements was to operate the generating plants, consisting as they did of a mixture of conventional hydro, pumped storage and thermal plants, owned by each Board in a manner designed to provide electrical power in the most economical way, and to collaborate in the joint planning of future generating plant operation and interchange of power for the benefit of Scotland as a whole.[13]

This collaboration was continued with increasing amicability, and the understanding between the two Boards was undoubtedly enhanced when Mr C L C Allan, sometime the North Board's Chief Electrical and Mechnical Engineer (May 1954–December 1963), succeeded Sir Norman Elliott as Chairman of the South of Scotland Electricity Board in 1967. Mr Allan possessed intimate knowledge of the North of Scotland and was consequently better able than any of his predecessors to appreciate what problems his counterpart on the North Board, Mr K R Vernon, had to contend with. By the mid-1970s the operation of the Board's mainland power stations had become closely integrated with those of the South of Scotland Electricity Board; electricity supply in Scotland had become firmly based on a single merit order of power stations, and the generation function—planning, operation and financing—had become subject to comprehensive arrangements under the Joint Generating Account.

An illustration of how this resulted in mutually beneficial interchanges in power may be seen by the statistics presented in Appendix Table 30. These figures show, for example, that from *exporting* over 500 million units to the South Board in 1970-71, when both rainfall and run off in the Board's area were well above average and the hydro stations produced 3,441 million units (or 73 per cent of the requirements of the Board's system), within six years the Board was *importing* over 5,000 million units from the South Board. By 1976-77, the Carolina Port 'B' oil-fired thermal station at Dundee, opened ten years earlier with a capacity of 120,000 kW, had moved down the merit order. Coal supplies had become cheaper than oil and the production of thermal power was concentrated at the most efficient coal-fired stations operated by the South Board at Longannet and Cockenzie. In conjunction with a below average run off into the Board's reservoirs and relatively low hydro production, the Board's *net* import of energy from the South Board reached a record high level. Yet this *net* figure conceals extremely valuable exports of power to the South Board at times of peak load, much of it generated at the pumped storage stations of Cruachan and Foyers.

Ten years later, in the mid–1980s, following the commissioning of the Peterhead thermal station in May 1981, the Board had moved into surplus again. By burning gas which would otherwise have been uselessly flared off by the oil companies operating in the North Sea, in 1984–85 Peterhead produced nearly 7,000 million units of electricity— or more than double the Board's output of conventional hydro power.[14] In the following year, the opening of the petro-chemical plant at Mossmorran in Fife brought this supply of fuel to an end, and Peterhead reverted to its rôle of providing security of supply in the north-east of Scotland and a strategic reserve for the Scottish system as a whole. The result was that from being a net exporter for a period of three years, the North Board once again became a net importer, though the Board's pumped storage instal-lations continued to be used to maintain flexibility and to help minimise the overall operating costs of the Scottish system.

The point to emphasise is that by the 1970s, there *was* a coherent *Scottish* system of electrical generation and distribution. Conventional hydro continues to play an impor-tant rôle in that system, and if its relative overall contribution to the total system requirements has declined (especially with the growth of nuclear generation at Chap-elcross, Hunterston A and B, Dounreay and Torness), the power generated is cheap, cannot be held to be responsible for any pollution of the environment, and provides an invaluable element of flexibility in responding to peak loads.[15] The heavy investments of the past have more than justified themselves.

And what of the other objectives of the Board? Attempts to attract industry to the Highlands never flagged. Mr J C N Baillie, the chief commercial engineer, was indefatigable in publicising the industrial potential of the area, offering technical assist-ance and collaborating with the Local Authorities. He was undoubtedly successful in attracting some investment in light engineering, but it is probable that his efforts would have been more productive had he been able to offer special discount tariffs to bulk users. To this the Board would never agree. Had they wanted to—which is doubtful— there were statutory impediments to such a policy, for the legislation of 1943 prohibited them from practicing price discrimination. Even when special arrangements were made in 1969 to supply the British Aluminium Company's 100,000-ton smelter at Invergordon, the principles on which the terms of the power contract were drawn up, and which were authorised by the Government, were designed to safeguard the interests of the ordinary electricity consumers.[16] It was expected that the smelter would take a continuous load approaching 200MW from the Board's high voltage grid system. The Invergordon smelter came into operation in 1971, just as the Board's sales experienced a marked fall from their previous compound rate of growth of about 10 per cent per annum (see Fig. 55 and Appendix Table 29). For the next ten years, the British Aluminium Co. was the Board's largest individual consumer, responsible for about a quarter of all sales in the North of Scotland, but the special agreement between the Board and the Company was terminated at the end of 1981, following British Alu-minium's decision to close the smelter. Whether this disappointing outcome could have been avoided has been the subject of much controversy. Suffice it to say that the

Board maintained to the last that it would have been 'inequitable for its half-million other consumers to have [had] to carry any burden in respect of cheap power to the Invergordon smelter by means of high electricity tariffs'.[17]

In other ways too the Board has held fast to its original principles. Hopes of developing new forms of electrical generation have never been entirely abandoned. Not-withstanding earlier failures, in December 1980, a small 22kW aerogenerator was installed on South Ronaldsay, Orkney, to obtain further data on wind energy, and in the following year the Secretary of State for Energy announced a £6m. project for wind generation development consisting of a 250kW aerogenerator and subsequently a 3MW aerogenerator, both to be erected at Burgar Hill, Orkney. The Board have participated in this development in co-operation with the Wind Energy Group both by a financial commitment and by project management and, at the same time, they have continued research into a small aerogenerator suitable for providing heating and lighting to premises isolated from the public supply network. They have collaborated in studies to determine the economic feasibility of an oscillating water column device for wave power generation. Even the possibility of using peat in the generation of electricity has been resuscitated, with detailed investigations into the cost of peat har-vesting being resumed in 1982.[18]

But above all, the Board continued with its policy of uneconomic rural development, until by 1981 perhaps only 500 potential cosumers on the mainland and the islands remained unconnected. At punishing expense—partly offset by a European Regional Development Fund grant which reimbursed 30 per cent of the expenditure—the Board persevered, until in 1984 it inaugurated what was believed to be its final five year programme. Nearly half a century after the Cooper Committee Report, almost *every* potential consumer has been given a supply of electricity. However economically irrational this may have been, nothing could better demonstrate the Board's acute sense of social responsibility.

And all this has been done with a sensitive regard to environmental, scenic and amenity factors. Far from deterring visitors from the Highlands, the very availability of electrical power has greatly assisted and encouraged the valuable tourist trade. And, as in 1945 Tom Lawrie predicted they would,[19] many thousands visit the Board's major works each year to marvel at 'the hollow mountain' of Cruachan and the dam and fish ladder at Pitlochry. At Pitlochry, the number of visitors—like the number of fish many of them come to see—were checked by an electronic counter in 1973, when there was no less than 300,000. Since then the annual number of visitors to Pitlochry dam has risen to about half a million, almost a third of whom tour the permanent exhibition on the site. The Visitor's Centre Exhibition of Cruachan regularly attracts about 50,000 people a year.

Let us conclude where the North of Scotland Hydro Electric Board began, with the Government. The oldest of the existing nationalised industries, the Board was a creation of the State, and as such responsible to Parliament. Yet in those debates devoted to its activities and functions, the Board were invariably criticised—albeit by only a handful of MPs—for acting in a way which suggested they possessed a degree of autonomy which, its political enemies asserted, Parliament never intended to bestow upon them. It is true that such debates were infrequent, arising in a somewhat haphazard way usually when an aggrieved MP chose to move a Prayer for the annulment of a Constructional Scheme or when the Board sought to increase its borrowing powers; but if the Parliament at Westminster interested itself directly in the affairs of the Board only at irregular intervals, the Board was always conscious of the over-riding powers of the Secretary of State for Scotland.[20]

The statutory provisions which have governed the Secretary of State's relationship with the Hydro Board give the Scottish Office four key powers over the Board.[21] Firstly, there is the power of appointment. The Secretary of State appoints the Chairman and members of the Board, and he can also appoint the Deputy Chairman. As James Laing has observed, 'the importance of this power of appointment is difficult to analyse. It certainly colours the day-to-day relationship between the executive board members and the sponsoring department. The periodic appointment of non-executive board members also provides an opportunity for the Secretary of State to influence the general direction in which the Board is going or to strengthen any areas in which he considers the Board's performance could be strengthened.'[22]

It is hardly surprising that Mr Laing, an Under Secretary in the Scottish Office, found it 'difficult to offer examples in this sensitive area', but it is plausible that when Tom Johnston retired in 1959, the Scottish Office believed that in replacing him with Lord Strathclyde, sometime joint parliamentary under-secretary of state for Scotland (1945 and 1951-5) and Minister of State for the Scottish Office (1955-58), they were appointing one of their junior ministers who would adopt a more neutral and concilliatory posture towards the planned merger between the two Scottish Boards than Johnston had done.[23] In the event, Lord Strathclyde proved to be as powerful an advocate of the Hydro Board's independence as his predecessor, an attitude which could not entirely have been anticipated from his earlier contributions, as Commander Thomas Galbraith, to debates devoted to the Board and its activities. It is possible that the change in the opinions of Lord Strathclyde exemplifies similar transformations in the views of others appointed to the Board. In its part-time appointments, the Scottish Office patently attempted to ensure a reasonable political balance and to secure representation of those whose views were known to be not entirely sympathetic towards the Board's policies and objectives. This policy, it was believed, might curb the Board's exuberence and place some restraint upon the more adventurous of Tom Johnston's plans. Yet membership of the Board seems to have had the effect of converting several of those who had hitherto evinced a distrust of its purposes, or even a downright hostility towards its objectives, into its most fervent supporters. This appears to have been the case, for example, with Provost (later Sir) George McGlashan and Major P Hunter Gordon. This phenomenon tended to reduce the moderating influence of the Scottish Office. The 'power of appointment' did not always work in the way that had been intended.[24]

Be that as it may, there was and is no ambiguity about the other key powers possessed by the Secretary of State. He has the power to control the Board's borrowing, though his decisions are subject to Treasury approval in this vital matter; he has the power to control investment; and his consent is necessary for the construction of new schemes and individual generating stations.

In the course of this study we have encountered many examples of the Secretary of State's exercise of these powers and of the many other powers and compulsions possessed by the Government over the Board and over the nationalised industries in general. Sometimes these mechanisms have been seen to be somewhat crude. The virtual cessation of the Board's conventional hydro programme in the 1960s is largely to be explained by the Treasury's insistence on a very high real rate of return on such investments; but the more recent demand by the Government for the formulation of a Corporate plan and the implementation of procedures for monitoring progress towards its achievement are measures that are both rational and wise.[25] It is all very different from the time when Edward MacColl could say that 'the Treasury has given me £100m and I am going to spend it before they take it away';[26] but in the first decade of its existence how many could have imagined that the assets of the North of Scotland Hydro–Electric Board might eventually be sold to the private interests[27] whose motives had been regarded with such suspicion and distrust in those far off days?

APPENDIX 1

A simple guide to certain civil, electrical and economic questions involved in hydro-electrical developments

Mainly Civil

1   Rainfall, River Gauging and Run-off

Before a potential hydro scheme can even be contemplated, the engineer has to collect and analyse certain basic hydrographic and topographic data. Unless these are satisfctory, further progress is impossible. The scarcity and unreliability of existing hydrological information constituted a major problem to the Scottish pioneers of hydro-electricity. Of course, reasonable accurate figures of monthly and annual rainfall were available, but these figures were mainly of precipitation in populated areas; of those parts of Scotland that promised to be the sites of hydro development, the data were notoriously inadequate, even non-existent.[1] The Snell Committee, reporting in 1913 on the nation's water power resources had to admit that its *estimates* had been made possible only by the 'voluntary work of rainfall observers' whose efforts 'should be encourated and developed'.[2] Yet twenty-five years later, the 'Report on the Water Power Resources of Scotland', produced by a panel of experts at the request of the Hilleary Committee, had to take 'the average annual rainfall ..., as far as possible from the figures given in *British Rainfall*, 1935, published by the Meteorological Office', and these, 'owing to the lack of observing stations ... [had simply] been estimated from the results in surrounding districts'.[3]

For the hydraulic engineer such figures could be misleading, even dangerous.[4] Certainly, they were not conducive to the accurate assessment of economic potential. The problem was compounded by the fact that information about river flows—data of equal importance for the formulation of a hydro scheme—had to 'be deduced indirectly from rainfall' and the long-term isohyetal curves prepared by the Meteorological Office, so limited was river flow recording in Scotland.[5] As late as the mid-1940s, what little river gauging had been done in Scotland was confined to an organisation known as River Flow Records, whose moving spirit was a Captain McLean. Although he had established gauging posts on several of the river courses in Scotland, including the Ness and the Aberdeenshire Dee, this was pitifully inadequate to meet the needs of the engineer. For many rivers, it was impossible to construct flow duration curves.[6] Yet their importance cannot be over-emphasised:

> Flow characteristics vary from stream to stream and from river to river, depending on the nature of the ground, its slope, the overlying burden in the form of peat, moss, clay and sand, the amount of forestation, and the extent to which rock is exposed .... On a typical Highland river the summer flow may fall to perhaps one-fifteenth of the average flow, and a flood may be as much as 300 times the dry-weather flow. Should the river run through one or more lochs these figures may be substantially modified, depending on the size of the lochs relative to the extent of the catchment area .... [Furthermore], in Scotland generally the average rate of flow in the winter months is about double that of the summer months.[7] (See Fig. 56).

Without direct and continuous measurements of river flow, there conditions created

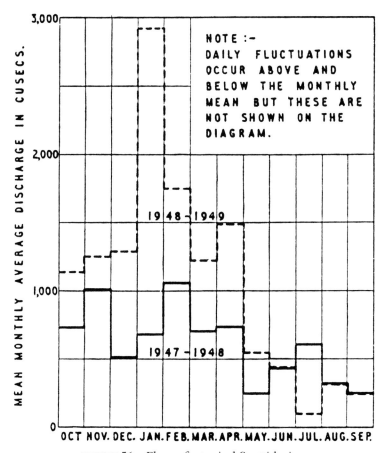

FIGURE 56   Flow of a typical Scottish river

considerable difficulty for the hydro engineer who sought to plan large schemes demanding heavy capital investment. It was not as if he could rectify years of neglect by extrapolating from figures intensively collected over a short period. The appropriate degree of accuracy demanded periods of observation of between thirty to thirty-five years.[8]

All this meant that the engineer could not be *sure* of the quantity of water available to him. He had no precise knowledge of the 'run-off'—that is, the amount of water actually leaving the area under consideration by its rivers and streams—and had to be content with whatever records were available plus the few measurements of discharge he was able to take himself during a comparatively short period. By combining these measurements with (potentially misleading) rainfall figures he had to estimate the probable maximum and minimum monthly and annual run-off.

These figures are important because they profoundly influence the design of many features of a hydro scheme.[9] For example, it will be seen that although in Scotland the demand for electricity and run-off follow a similar *pattern* throughout the year,[10] very substantial deviations from the average are experienced, especially in individual catchment areas. Consequently, if specific schemes are to fulfil their allotted share of power generation, there is a need for reservoirs sufficient to store substantial quantities of water ranging from 20 per cent to 60 per cent of a year's rainfall,[11] the aim being that over an interconnected system there is enough storage generally to even out seasonal variations[12] and, even more important, to provide *firm power*, that is, power that is available when it is required.

2   The Dam: Location and Height

But where is this storage to be provided?[13] The engineer will seek a natural basis, with a stream or river running through it, which can be closed by building a dam across its outlet. The obvious place to look for such a configuration is among mountains or hills. If the engineer is fortunate enough to be able to choose between a number of alternative sites which meet his technical criteria—the ascertainment of which almost invariably involves borings and sub-surface investigations—his choice will be determined by two further factors: the head of water available and the cost of developing the competing sites.

The 'head' may be defined as the vertical difference in level between the water being stored and that of the water after passing through the turbines which will convert the potential energy of that water into electrical power. Water a hundred feet high may be said to be capable of doing twice as much work as a similar quantity of water fifty feet high. 'This is expressed in the equation $P = Q \times H$ (power potential equals quantity of water multiplied by head). Placing a reservoir higher up in relation to its power station increases the amount of power that can be produced, *provided* that by so doing the quantity of water flowing into the reservoir is not drastically reduced; and provided it can be connected to the power station by a tunnel or pipeline'.[14] Even then the engineer will try to avoid a lengthy horizontal distance between the reservoir and the power station because of the capital cost of tunnels and pipelines, and the loss of energy caused by friction between the flowing water and the tunnel lining or the walls of the pipeline. In effect, the engineer looks for the shortest distance between reservoir and power station, and these are to be found where conditions permit steep descents.

The determination of the optimum reservoir site demands many detailed technical and economic calculations. Some may be relatively straightforward; others are made infinitely more complicated by inadequate knowledge of, for example, the run-off at high altitudes, the future costs of labour and constructional materials, the amount of compensation (in cash or in water) that might be demanded by landowners whose lands will be inundated by the reservoir or whose fishing rights are affected. Patently, statistical calculations will sometimes have to be subordinated to the experience and judgment of the engineer.

But one factor *is* susceptible to more accurate estimate: the determination of the height of the dam. Given even a rudimentary knowledge of run–off, it should be possible to build the dam high enough to contain *all* the water that might be expected to flow into it over a given period. However, such a dam would create a reservoir that would be full only for a relatively short time at irregular and widely-spaced intervals—say a week or two every ten years: only a very small amount of extra power would have been created at the expense of a very large addition to the cost of construction. After estimating the load factor[15] for the associated power station and making allowances for anticipated variations of water supply, the engineer adopts a compromise dictated by the result of calculations which show what extra power output can be expected for each foot added to the height of the dam. 'From these figures it is possible to determine the economic height to which the dam should be built; and it will probably emerge that at this height a good deal of water will be wasted at times of maximum flood, because it will not be worth while to build the dam high enough to hold it'.[16]

3   The Choice of Scheme

Although no two hydro-electric schemes are exactly alike, those with which this study is concerned may be divided into four main types: those without water storage; those which rely upon a dam to provide both storage and head; those using mountains or steep hills to develop heads many times greater than the height of the highest dam; and those employing pumped storage.

Those schemes which do not depend upon the storage of water are usually called run-of-river schemes, for the obvious reason that they utilise the potential power of the vast quantities of water to be found in the lower valleys of many rivers on their way to the sea. Their construction usually involves the building of a barrage or weir across the river, preferably where it is constrained by a relatively narrow gorge, and incorporating turbines into the weir. The head may be very small—though it can sometimes be slightly enlarged by rock excavation on the downstream side of the barrage—but this is compensated for by the sheer quantity of water passing through the turbines. The relevant equation, it will be remembered, is $P = Q \times H$. A diagrammatic representation of a run-of-river scheme is shown in Fig. 57. It should be noted that the

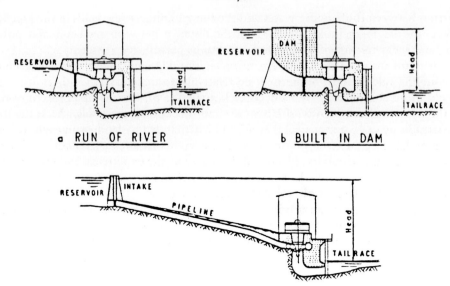

FIGURE 57   Diagrammatic examples of low head type of hydro–electric schemes

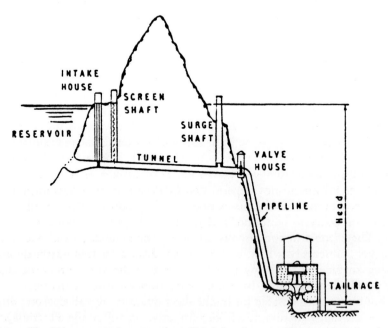

FIGURE 58   Diagrammatic examples of high head type of hydro–electric scheme

level of power output that can be *guaranteed* by a run-of-river scheme is limited to what can be produced by the minimum flow of the river.

The majority of Scottish rivers are relatively small and, as we have seen, characterised by great variability of flow. Conditions seldom favour what might be termed 'pure' run-of-river schemes and they are rare. Achanalt station on the River Bran is a good example. Nevertheless, there are a number of schemes which differ from them only to a minor degree. These involve the construction of a dam which as well as providing some storage also houses the turbines. Where they are similar to run-of-river projects is that they have a low head and derive their power from massive quantities of water. The power station and dam at Aigas is of this type. A further variation of the low head type of hydro-electric scheme is when the water from a reservoir, invariably created or supplemented by a dam, is carried by pipeline or canal a short distance downstream from the dam to capitalise upon a natural, if relatively slight, declivity in the river bed.

The third type of scheme , illustrated in Fig. 58, is most important in Scotland. Its distinctive feature is a pressure tunnel which draws water from a high-level reservoir and feeds it into a pipeline high above the power station. Ideally, this pipeline should be nearly vertical, but natural conditions rarely permit more than a very steep slope. This type of scheme usually exploits the power potential inherent in the differing water levels of adjacent lochs, each with its own catchment area. By damming the outlet to the higher loch, and leading the water through the mountains to a power station located on the side of the lower loch, a head can often be obtained much greater than would be possible by simply damming the higher loch and feeding the water directly to a power station. Sometimes, where the upper level loch is a large natural lake, it is possible to dispense with a dam altogether and simply draw the water from a tunnel driven into the bottom of the loch. Of course, the major cost incurred in this type of scheme is that of driving and lining the tunnel, often of considerable length and complexity.

Finally, there are pumped storage schemes. Although the economics of such schemes are complex, their mode of operation is quite simple. Their rationale resides in the difficulty of storing electrical energy in worthwhile quantities so that it is ready 'on tap' when required. One way of overcoming this problem is 'to use the energy generated by surplus plant capacity at night and at weekends to pump water from a low level reservoir or loch to a high level reservoir or loch in which the water is impounded and from which it can later be released to generate electricity at times of high demand'.[17] The technical requirements for pumped storage are four. First, a site that will provide a high head between upper and lower reservoirs, the horizontal distance between which should be relatively short (to minimise the capital cost of tunnels and pipes). Second, the lower reservoir must be of sufficient capacity to allow for the considerable flow of water required during the pumping and generation cycle without causing significant variations in the water level. Third, the storage plant must be linked with other plants which can supply the energy for pumping at off-peak periods. Fourth, the demand of the electricity systems of which the scheme is a part must be such that the peak energy which the pumped storage scheme produces can be absorbed. It may be noted that in addition to the capital cost of such schemes, what may be called their 'real' cost of operation lies in the loss of efficiency which occurs in transforming electrical power into hydraulic power and back again into electricity. This may amount to about 25 per cent.

In other words, for every 4 units of electricity used in pumping the water upwards the output is but 3 units. It will be appreciated that there has to be very real economic advantages to justify this use of energy.

4   *The Choice of Plant*

The most important item of plant with which this study is concerned is the turbine.[18] Essentially, modern turbines are direct descendents of the old water wheel: they are of the 'impulse' and 'reaction' types, and they are better illustrated than described. Of the impulse type, that most used in Scotland is the Pelton turbine (see Fig. 59). This design incorporates a wheel around the periphery of which are a series of cup-shaped buckets. Against these buckets one or more high-velocity jets of water are directed through a nozzle. Even the efficiency of the early Pelton wheel, devised in the late 1880s, was over 80 per cent and this has since been raised to over 90 per cent. The power output of the Pelton turbine depends on the velocity of the jet which in turn is dependent upon the head of water available. Although Peltons are smooth-running and extremely adaptable, they are particularly well suited to schemes where the operating head is high, that is

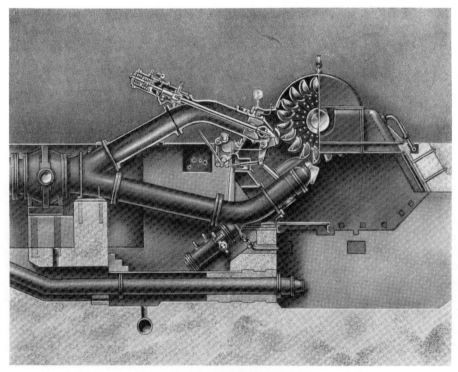

FIGURE 59   The Pelton turbine

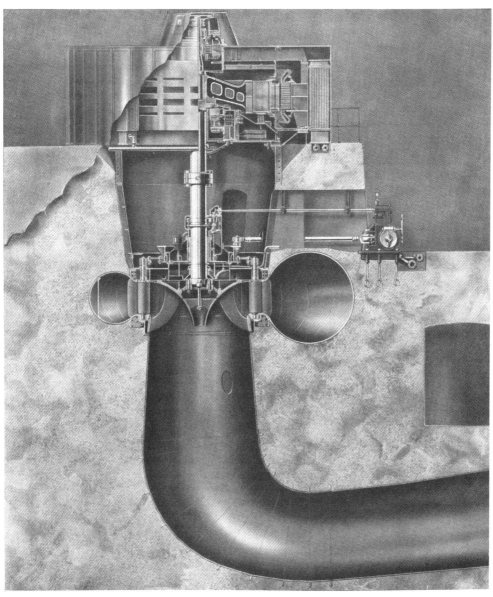

FIGURE 60   The Francis turbo–alternator

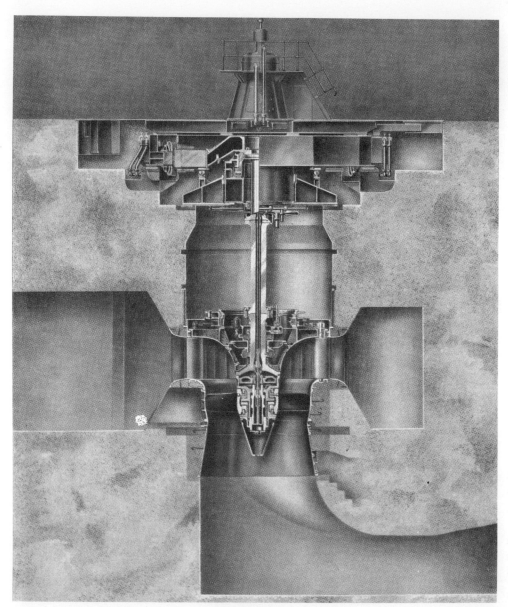

FIGURE 61 The Kaplan turbo–alternator

800 feet and over. For lower heads, their speed becomes rather slow and relatively uneconomic for electrical generation.

The most popular of the pressure or reaction group is the Francis turbine (see Fig. 60). It employs an arrangement of curved vanes in two sets. The outer one is stationary and its moveable inlet guide vanes direct the water on to the second set, the runner, which is free to rotate. Because the water approaches the turbine from a spiral steel casing shaped like a huge snail shell, a smooth and continuous flow is produced. The Francis turbine can operate on a wide range of heads, but it is most commonly used for those between a hundred and 1,500 feet. Its speed is easy to govern for widely fluctuating loads, but its highest efficiency—well over 90 per cent—is achieved only over the limited range of output for which it has specifically been designed.

The Kaplan, or propellor turbine (see Fig. 61)—again a reaction type—does not suffer from this disadvantage. In this design, the flow of water is parallel to the axis of the machine, which has blades shaped rather like those of a ship's propellor. Because the runner can be 'feathered', being automatically adjusted by a servo-mechanism, the Kaplan maintains a high efficiency over a wider range of head and load than the Francis, and this justifies its higher cost where heads are low and variable.

Two final points may be made: first, both Francis and Kaplan turbines share the same shaft as the electrical generators they serve, the two linked machines, the turbine and the generator, comprising one 'set'; second, although all types of turbines are constantly being improved, they had reached a very high level of efficiency even as early as 1920.

Mainly Economic[19]

5   The Nature of the Demand for Electricity: The Problem of Peak Load

Electricity cannot be stored in any worthwhile quantities. It has, therefore, to be produced and supplied exactly as and when the demand arises.[20] Consumers' requirements vary throughout the day, the week, the month and the year. In a typical system, demand is at its lowest around 4 a.m. but about breakfast time rises rapidly to reach a plateau which is essentially maintained throughout the morning. There follows a significant decline. This is reversed in the late afternoon to reach a new and short-lived peak which rapidly moderates as the industrial and commercial load falls off. The steepest daily decline occurs after 10 p.m. to a value corresponding to all-night heating and lighting and factories on night-shft. The magnitude of these daily variations— though not their basic pattern—is profoundly affected by seasonal factors: additional lighting and heating requirements in winter result in winter peaks being considerably higher than those experienced during the summer. Typical demand curves are shown in Fig. 62, though it will be appreciated that because demand is weather sensitive their precise level involves a random element.

These fluctuations in demand constitute the principal operational problem of the electricity supplier. Because statutory regulations impose upon suppliers the duty of satisfying the *actual* demand, whatever it may be, at any time throughout the year,

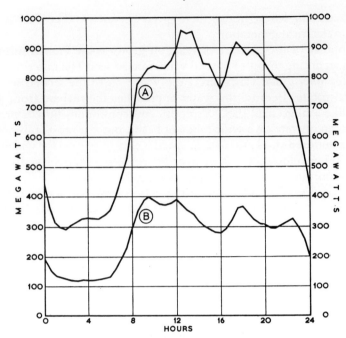

Ⓐ DAY OF MAXIMUM DEMAND – THURSDAY 4 · JAN · 1968
Ⓑ TYPICAL SUMMER WEEKDAY – TUESDAY 18 · JULY · 1967

FIGURE 62   Examples of summer and winter daily load curves

sufficient generating plant has to be installed to meet the peak winter load (and to provide a margin for breakdown), despite the fact that for much of the time a large proportion of this plant will be idle.[21] Plant required to meet the extreme peaks may run for only two or three hours a day even in the winter, and during the summer may not run at all. Conversely, there is a certain minimum demand, the base load, that obtains throughout the 24 hours, winter or summer, and the plant required to meet this load can be run continuously day in, day out. Consequently, the most modern and efficient plant is used for this purpose.

6   The Different Characteristics of Thermal and Hydro Generation

The amount of capital investment in the electrical industry is determined, then, by the maximum demand, whether this be satisfied by thermal or by hydro plant. However, these two methods of power generation have very different operating characteristics. Fluctuating demand causes greater problems for thermal stations, whether the heat for their boilers comes from coal, oil, gas or nuclear energy, than for water-power plants.

It takes anything up to 8 hours to heat up a boiler and steam turbine from cold to the point where they are operating at load. To accelerate this process may cause thermal stresses and the risk of dangerous distortion, which can wreck the equipment. If a steam station is to work on a ten hour basis, as it might if regularly called upon simply to meet day time demands between, say, 8 a.m. and 6 p.m., the only practical procedure is to bank the boilers during the off-load period (in this example, 6 p.m. to 8 a.m. on the following day). Sometimes the turbines are kept running light, usually at reduced speed. Keeping the generators on standby involves burning fuel for the sole purpose of keeping the plant hot and ready to take load when required. Even then the response may be sluggish.[22] Conversely, a swift drop in demand involves wasting steam, and hence fuel, because the process is not instantaneously reversible. Briefly, steam-raising plant cannot quickly be switched on and off. This means that high efficiency steam power stations are much more suitable for base load than they are for day load. For meeting short period peak loads, such as are encountered at around 6 p.m. on a winter's evening, they are at their greatest economic disadvantage.

By contrast, hydro-electric schemes are much more flexible. Water-driven turbines do not have to contend with thermal problems and to start them requires little more than opening the valves—or "turning on the taps"—which allow water to flow through the turbines. It is possible for a hydro-electric generating set to be put on full load within a few minutes of an increase in demand arising. It, can, moreover, equally swiftly be shut down. Clearly, water power is ideally suited to meet peak loads, for it is immediately available and there are no standby losses. But hydro systems are not without their own peculiar technical disadvantages. Except in times of prolonged industrial dispute, fuel for steam driven stations is usually readily available. By contrast, the 'fuel' for hydro-electric stations, rainfall, flunctuates during the course of the year. Although it is highly convenient that in Scotland run-off and demand for electricity follow a similar annual pattern (see Fig. 63) this does not preclude occasional droughts

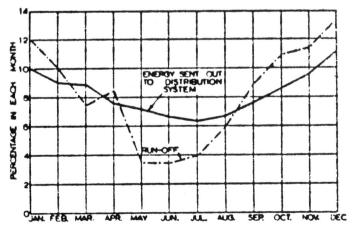

FIGURE 63   Comparison of the variation of load and the variation of run-off

or periods when the rainfall drops well below the customary averages for months on end. This means, in effect, that hydro systems are liable to unpredictable shortages of 'fuel'. The result can be a marked reduction in output, and it is to avoid such a consequence that so much effort and expense are devoted to ensuring that hydro schemes are provided with appropriate storage facilities in the form of reservoirs.

Scottish rivers, especially when regulated by dams, are characterised by a certain minimum flow that can be relied upon, and plant can be installed of a capacity appropriate to this flow. This plant can work continuously and supply a base load; it is capable of generating so many 'firm' units of power. Installed capacity beyond this point can operate only if the flow of water is sufficient: it will generate 'secondary' as compared with 'firm' power. Of course, it is possible to increase the 'firm' power capacity of a catchment area by building storage reservoirs which retain water until it is required. Indeed, the natural run-off into the reservoir may be supplemented by civil engineering works which divert the headwaters of streams that would otherwise 'run to waste' into adjoining, but unexploited catchment areas. It is at this point that economic factors have to be considered, for it is necessary to resolve the question: how much storage is it worthwhile building for the increase in firm capacity that it affords? The answer is of particular importance in the Scottish context because Scottish hydro schemes are predominantly of the storage type. The shape of the curve in Fig. 64 shows that a very high degree of water utilisation can be obtained only at the cost of a very high percentage of storage. It will seldom be economical to squeeze out, as it were, every possible unit of power: a point is usually reached when the provision of additional storage, normally at considerable expense, has progressively less value in improving the firm output from a scheme.[23]

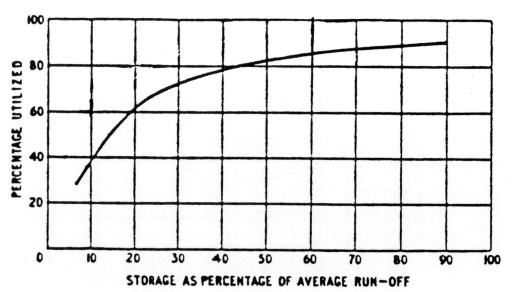

FIGURE 64   The relationship between water utilised and the amount of storage provided

7   Thermal or Hydro?

So far, we have simply compared some of the operating characteristics of thermal and hydro generation. This approach should not be construed as meaning that an organisation created to supply electricity must chose one *or* the other. Indeed, it should be clear that thermal and hydro-electric plant are essentially complementary and that electricity will be produced most efficiently in a mixed system; one in which a proportion of the base load might be produced by run-of-river hydro schemes, the rest of the base load by thermal plant, and the peak load by hydro schemes that involve storage. A possible representation of this situation is presented in Fig. 65 which shows what is known as an annual load-duration curve with the various types of generating capacity fitted into the area delineated by the curve.[24]

But, of course, what is technically ideal may be neither physically possible nor economically sensible. For example, given the amount and distribution of rainfall in conjunction with the land forms in England, it will be obvious that the scope for hydro development is extremely limited compared with the opportunities inherent in the Scottish Highlands with their mountains and heavy rainfall. If to these contrasting

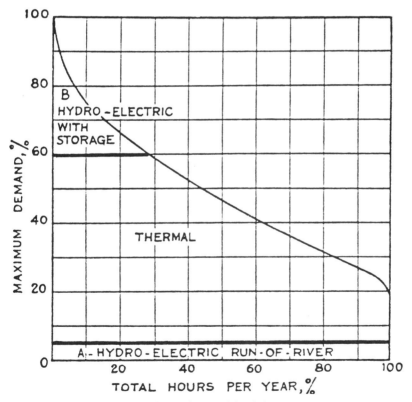

FIGURE 65   Idealised annual load duration curve

characteristics be added the differing availability and cost of coal in the two areas, England's concentration on steam generation is readily explicable. It would not be an exaggeration to say that in Great Britain only Scotland can aspire to a mixed system that even approaches the ideal theoretical model.[25]

Exactly what proportions of the total demand for electricity will be provided by thermal power and by hydro power is (or should be) determined by their relative costs. Given an existing system that includes thermal and hydro generation, if expected *future* demands (which are themselves difficult to forecast accurately) can most economically be met by the output of thermal stations,[26] there can be no *economic* justification for further investment in hydro stations. Similarly, if future demand can best—that is, most economically—be met by additional investment in hydro plant, then hydro development should be preferred, even to the exclusion of further investment in thermal generation. In practice, of course, additional demand for electricity is *likely* to be met by contributions from both types of power generation in such a way that costs per unit of output are minimised, but to establish the best investment programme for an electricity generating and supply system is exceptionally difficult.[27]

8   The Relative Costs of Thermal and Hydro Power

The capital cost of a hydro scheme is very much higher than that of a steam station of similar capacity. That is, the expenditure upon the construction of the main storage works (dams and reservoirs) and associated aqueducts, and on the tunnels, pipelines, control gates and their operating mechanisms, that form the major components of a typical hydro scheme is usually much greater than that incurred by providing the structural features peculiar to a thermal station: tall chimneys, jetties, railway sidings for fuel supplies, fuel-handling plant and arrangements for the circulation of the cooling water. This may be illustrated by the following table:[28]

Table 19: *Capital Cost of Different Types of Generation, per Kilowatt Installed, late 1950s*

Type of Generation	kW Installed	Cost per kW
Hydro	22,000	£140
Coal-fired 'A'	30,000	75
Coal-fired 'B'	200,000	50
Nuclear	315,000	174

But although the capital cost per installed kilowatt of hydro electric schemes may be, say, three times of that of comparable conventional steam stations, this higher capital cost is offset by several major factors. First and foremost, there is no fuel cost. Second, the total operating charges, which comprise mainly salaries and wages for generation and maintenance, and oil and stores, are extremely low when considered as a running cost per unit. It has been estimated that they do not exceed 10–15 per cent of the works cost per unit generated from coal. Maintenance and repair costs are also much lower for water power than for steam plant. Third, the life of a hydro electric station and the capital charges are spread out over a correspondingly longer period. Although there is no universally accepted figure for the effective life spans of the different capital components of thermal and hydro schemes, the following table gives the various amortisation periods employed in the late 1950s:

Table 20: *Topical Amortization Periods of the major capital components of thermal stations and hydro schemes* (in years)[29]

Civil Engineering Structures	
(a) Dams, tunnels and canals	80
(b) Power houses	40
Steel	
Pipeline, penstocks and surge shafts	35
Plant	
(a) Mechanical	25
(b) Electrical	25

The fourth factor that is said to offset the mich higher capital cost of hydro is that whereas 70 per cent of the generating costs of a steam station—fuel, staff and maintenance—are subject to inflation, the corresponding figure for a hydro-electric development does not amount to much more than 10 per cent.

The Chairmen and Chief Officers of the North of Scotland Hydro-Electric Board, 1943-1987

Lord Airlie	*Chairman*, 1943-46	1943-1946
A E MacColl	Deputy Chairman and Chief Executive Officer, 1943-1951	1943-1951
Thomas Lawrie	Secretary, 1943-1948; General Manager, 1948-1955	1943-1955
W D D Fenton	Commercial Engineer, 1943-1948; Secretary and Commercial Engineer, 1948-1954	1943-1954
A N Ferrier	Accountant, 1943-1948; Chief Accountant, 1948-1965; Chief Financial Officer, 1965-1968	1943-1968
A A Fulton	Hydraulic Engineer, 1943-1948; Chief Hydraulic and Civil Engineer, 1948-1955; General Manager, 1955-1966	1943-1966
W Guthrie	Electrical Engineer, 1943-1947	1943-1947
Thomas Johnston	*Chairman*, 1946-1959	1946-1959
J J Cargill	Chief Mechanical and Electrical Engineer, 1948-1954	1948-1954
C L C Allan	Chief Electrical and Mechanical Engineer, 1954-1963	1954-1963
H W Simpson	Secretary, 1955-1961; Secretary and Solicitor, 1961-1971	1955-1971
J C N Baillie	Chief Commercial Engineer, 1955-1965; Chief Commercial Officer, 1965-1974	1955-1974
P L Aitken	Chief Hydraulic Engineer, 1955-1978; Chief Hydro-Electric Development Engineer 1978-1980	1955-1980
L H Dickerson	Chief Civil Engineer, 1955-1970	1955-1970
Lord Strathclyde	*Chairman*, 1959-1967	1959-1967
K R Vernon	Chief Electrical and Mechanical Engineer, 1964-1966; General Manager and Chief Engineer, 1966-1968; General Manager, 1968-1972; Deputy Chairman and General Manager, 1973-1974; Deputy Chairman and Chief Executive, 1974-	1964-
Tom Fraser	*Chairman*, 1967-1973	1967-1973
D J Miller	Deputy Chief Engineer, 1966-1968; Chief Engineer, 1968-1973	1966-1973

J W Farquhar	Chief Financial Officer, 1968-1972	1968-1972
W M M Harrison	Chief Personnel Officer, 1968-1985	1968-1985
Frank Johnson	Chief Civil Engineer, 1970-	1970-
D A S MacLaren	Secretary and Solicitor, 1971-1977	1971-1977
I A Gordon	Chief Financial Officer, 1972-1975	1972-1975
Sir Douglas Haddow	*Chairman*, 1973-1978	1973-1978
A T L Murray	Chief Engineer, 1974-	1974-
F W Daniel	Chief Commercial Officer, 1974-1979	1974-1979
A D Stewart	Chief Financial Officer, 1975-1985; Financial Director, 1985-	1975-
J E M Watts	Secretary, 1977-	1977-
R J Jackson	Chief Planning Officer, 1978-1985; Personnel Director, 1985-	1978-
Lord Kirkhill	*Chairman*, 1979-1982	1979-1982
M C Whitfield	Chief Commercial Officer, 1979-1984	1979-1984
Michael Joughin	*Chairman*, 1983-	1983-
A A Robertson	Computing and Services Controller, 1983-	1983-
J M Chatwin	Chief Commercial Officer, 1984-1985; Commercial Director, 1985-1987	1984-1987
K H Jackson	Commercial Director, 1987-	1987-

Source: NSHEB: *Annual Reports and Accounts.*

APPENDIX 3

Members of the Board of the North of Scotland Hydro-Electric Board, 1943–1987

Neil S Beaton	1943–1954
(Sir) Hugh MacKenzie, Deputy Chairman, 1951–59	1943–1959
(Sir) Duncan Watson	1943–1947
(Sir) John M Erskine, Deputy Chairman, 1960–61	1948–1961
(Sir) George McGlashan	1948–1961
Lord Provost A Powrie	1948–1949
G R McIntosh	1949–1957
E S Harrison	1951–1954
W Leonard	1951–1956
A I Mackenzie, Deputy Chairman, 1961–1970	1951–1970
Provost A Macrea	1956–1964
I A Duncan Millar, Deputy Chairman, 1970–1972	1956–1972
Lord Provost William Hughes (Lord Hughes of Hawkhill)	1957–1964
John Jardine	1958–1960
Lt.Col. Robert Neilson	1960
Major P Hunter Gordon	1960–1965
Councillor (Lord Provost) Norman Hogg	1961–1972
Lord Macdonald	1962–1970
A A Fulton*	1962–1966
(Sir) Norman R Elliot	1965–1967
Baillie Mrs Agnes S Holway	1965–1970
David L Urquhart	1966–1968
C L C Allan	1967–1973
Lord Tayside	1968–1971
Col. H A C Mackenzie	1970–1975
K R Vernon*, Deputy Chairman, 1973–	1970–
Councillor Angus Wallace	1971–1976
D D S Craib	1971–1979
S L Henderson	1972–1975
Councillor Ian S Campbell	1973–1981
W Kemp	1973–1980
F Tombs	1974–1977
Councillor Agnes G Keay	1976–1981
C A MacLeod	1976–1984
D F Hardie	1977–1983

D R Berridge	1977-1982
Mrs C A M Davis	1980-
G W Worthington	1981-1983
M G N Walker	1982-
Rear Admiral D A Dunbar-Nasmith	1982-1985
D J Miller	1982-
A T H Tulloch	1984-
C S Macphie	1984-
D F Myles	1985-
G Barrie	1985-

★ Full time members.
Source: NSHEB: *Annual Reports and Accounts*.

APPENDIX 4

Statistical Tables

TABLE 21   *NSHEB: Growth of Capacity and Output, 1949–1970*

	Kilowatts Installed			Million Units Generated		
	Conventional Hydro	Total	$\frac{\text{Hydro}}{\text{Total}}$ %	Conventional Hydro	Total	$\frac{\text{Hydro}}{\text{Total}}$ %
1949	86,915	250,970	34.6	322★	710	45.5
1950	284,750	452,970	62.9	522	878	59.5
1951	367,500	538,576	68.2	702	1,081	64.9
1952	391,225	559,602	69.9	889	1,237	71.9
1953	398,665	567,322	70.3	914	1,333	68.6
1954	431,385	594,372	72.6	1,183	1,566	75.5
1955	558,795	704,042	79.4	840†	1,432	58.7
1956	660,310	807,969	81.7	1,282	1,744	73.5
1957	729,326	911,390	80.0	1,624	1,913	84.9
1958	813,066	995,462	81.7	1,683	2,043	82.4
1959	866,472	1,047,248	82.7	1,836	2,196	83.6
1960	875,012	1,052,584	83.2	2,096	2,435	86.1
1961	884,512	1,062,084	83.3	2,726	2,909	93.7
1962	957,662	1,134,194	84.4	2,681	2,829	92.6
1963	1,046,708	1,221,869	85.7	2,210‡	2,612	84.6
31 March 1965§	1,047,058	1,227,379	85.3	2,819	3,141	89.7
31 March 1966	1,047,058	1,349,279	77.6	2,989	3,534	84.6
31 March 1967	1,047,058	1,769,479#	59.2	3,214	4,550¶	70.6
31 March 1968	1,047,058	1,867,425★★	56.1	3,225	4,722††	68.3
31 March 1969	1,051,863	1,814,888★★	58.0	2,248	3,487‡‡	64.5
31 March 1970	1,051,973	1,815,648★★	57.9	2,586	3,873§§	66.8

★ Output in 1949 almost entirely from Grampian Co.'s pre-war Rannoch and Tummel Schemes.
† Year of drought.
‡ Annual run off only 80.3 per cent of long-term average.
§ Period of 15 months.
# Includes 300,000 kW pumped storage.
¶ Includes −14 million units (Generated, 171m; pumped 185m) for pumped storage.
★★ Includes 400,000 kW pumped storage.
†† Includes −95 million units (Generated, 452m; pumped, 547m) for pumped storage.
‡‡ Includes −129 million units (Generated, 483m; pumped, 612m) for pumped storage.
§§ Includes −184 million units (Generated, 683m; pumped 867m) for pumped storage.

Source: NSHEB, *Annual Reports and Accounts.*

TABLE 22   *Major Transmission Schemes, 1951-61*

Scheme	Completion Date	Circuit Miles 132kV Line	Approved Scheme Estimated £000s	Approximate Final Cost £000s
(a) *Approved and Completed*				
Sloy-Glasgow (5)	1951	138.8	910.0	1,167.6
Tummel-Garry-Bonnybridge (9)	1957	141.2	1,650.0	1,220.4
Fannich-Boat of Garten (10)	1955	116.2	800.0	997.1
Keith-Aberdeen (11)	1951	46.1	689.0	773.7
Tummel-Inveruglas (17)	1952	50.8	498.0	441.2
Boat of Garten-Aberdeen (52)	1953	128.0	698.0	554.8
Garry-Moriston (63)	1956	37.5	930.0	670.9
Breadalbane (66)	1958	16.2	865.0	949.9
Fort Augustus-Glentruin (67)	1954	50.4	450.0	408.8
Shin-Caithness (72)	1958	140.6	1,702.0	1,231.0
Kintore/Aberdeen and Sub-stations	1959	49.1	795.6	840.5
Nairn/Elgin/Keith and Sub-stations	1961	78.4	674.3	624.8
Others	1951-61	487.0	7,710.5	7,034.9
Total		1,480.3	16,781.8	16,915.5

Scheme	Year of Approval	Circuit Miles 132kV Line	Approved Scheme Estimated £000s	Approximate Final Cost £000s
(b) *Approved but not yet completed*				
Clachan-Carradale & Sub-stations	1955	131	1,374.2	—
Charleston-Glenagnes & Sub-stations	1957	5	694.0	—
Kintore-Tealing & Sub-stations	1958	317	3,456.0	—
Others	1956-59	76	1,910.8	—
Total		529	7,435.0	
(c) *Under promotion but not yet approved*				
3 Schemes	—	126	3,678.0	—

Source: NSHEB, Evidence for Mackenzie Committee, Tables II(i)T, II(ii)T, dated 10th May 1961.

TABLE 23 *Farms and Crofts connected to the Board's Systems*

Year	FARMS			CROFTS			FARMS & CROFTS		
	Number connected during year	Cumulative total of connections	Total Number and Percentage connected	Number connected during year	Cumulative total of connections	Total Number and Percentage connected	Number connected during year	Cumulative total of connections	Total Number and Percentage connected
Connected at 1 April 1948		1,400	19,300 / 7.3		550	2,180 / 2.5		1,950	41,100 / 4.7
1948/49	494	1,894	9.8	401	951	4.4	895	2,845	6.9
1949/50	589	2,483	12.9	1,300	2,251	10.3	1,889	4,734	11.5
1950/51	763	3,246	16.8	1,119	3,370	15.5	1,882	6,616	16.1
1951/52	1,034	4,280	22.2	1,620	4,990	22.9	2,654	9,270	22.6
1952/53	1,025	5,305	27.5	2,001	6,991	32.1	3,026	12,296	30.0
1953/54	1,208	6,513	33.7	2,015	9,006	41.3	3,223	15,519	37.8
1954/55	1,680	8,193	42.5	1,479	10,485	48.1	3,159	18,678	45.4
1955/56	1,453	9,646	50.0	1,050	11,535	52.9	2,503	21,181	51.5
1956/57	1,285	10,931	56.6	720	12,255	56.2	2,005	23,186	56.4
1957/58	1,128	12,059	62.5	793	13,048	59.9	1,921	25,107	61.1
1958/59	1,084	13,143	68.1	238	13,286	60.9	1,322	26,429	64.3
1959/60	1,250	14,393	19,200* / 75.0	328	13,614	19,759* / 68.9	1,578	28,007	38,959* / 71.9
1960/61	1,017	15,410	80.3	2,459	16,073	81.3	3,476	31,483	80.8
1961/62	489	15,899	82.8	104	16,177	81.9	593	32,076	82.3
1962/63	397	16,296	84.9	48	16,115	82.1	445	32,521	83.5
1963/64	678	16,974	88.4	9	16,234	82.2	687	33,208	85.2
1964/65	441	17,415	19,008 / 91.6	94	16,328	19,339 / 84.4	535	33,743	38,347 / 88.0
1965/66	339	17,754	19,008 / 93.4	109	16,437	19,193 / 85.6	448	34,191	38,201 / 89.5
1966/67	346	18,100	95.2	31	16,468	85.8	377	34,568	90.5
1967/68	192	18,292	96.2	89	16,557	86.3	281	34,849	91.2
1968/69	2	18,294	96.2	97	16,654	86.8	99	34,948	91.5
1969/70	38	18,332	96.4	316	16,970	88.4	354	35,302	92.4
1970/71	47	18,379	96.7	125	17,095	89.1	172	35,474	92.9
1971/72†	56	18,435	97.0	67	17,162	89.4	123	35,597	93.2

* Numbers corrected after agreement with the Crofters Commission.
† Last year for which details of connections to crofts are given.
Source: NSHEB, *Annual Reports.*

TABLE 24   *NSHEB: Diesel Areas, capital commitments and average capital cost of connecting consumers, estimated 1952*

Diesel Area	Number of consumers connected or to be connected under current programmes	Cost per consumer £	Potential consumers not yet provided for	
			No.	%age
Arran	1,032	116	200	16
Shetland	1,403	204	3,047	68
Orkney	2,633	158	2,517	49
Lewis	4,996	134	1,100	18
Caithness	1,968	338	800	29
Islay	902	226	98	10
Total Diesel Areas	12,934	182	7,762	38
cf Hydro and steam areas	85,286	129	81,818	49

Source: NSHEB, Finance and General Purposes Committee, Minute 296, 7 March 1952.

TABLE 25   *Provision of Supply to the 14,420 Uneconomic Premises in Board's Area, 1961**

I	Estimate of total extra generating capacity required			Estimated Consumption
	Premises to be supplied from Highland Grid		10,815	21,000kW
	Premises in Diesel areas		3,605	5,900kW
		Total	14,420	26,900kW

II	Areas within Highland Grid System	
	Estimated cost of connection	£5,407,500
	Deduct contribution by consumers	675,937
	Net cost of connections	4,731,563
	Annual revenue needed to avoid loss†	946,313
	Estimated annual revenue	350,000
	Estimated annual deficiency	596,313

III	Diesel Areas	
	Estimated cost of connection	£1,802,500
	Deduct contributions by consumers	180,000
	Net cost of connections	1,622,500
	Annual charges to cover interest, sinking fund, repairs and maintenance	162,250
	Annual revenue‡	Nil
	Extra generation losses on very small islands	90,000
	Estimated annual deficiency	252,250

IV	Total estimated annual losses	£ 848,563

Notes: * A small addition was made to the 13,758 unconnected premises revealed by the investigations of the area managers (Table 16).

† In mainland grid areas, the annual revenue needed to avoid loss was taken as 20 per cent of the outlay incurred in providing the supply lines, the accepted practice in the electricity supply industry.

‡ In Diesel areas, no revenue from consumers has been allowed for because experience indicated that in these areas the revenue received barely met the cost of generation.

Source: NSHEB, *Sundry Papers for Mackenzie Committee*, HEB M5(4), in G/5, Part 2, and HEB M7(6), in G/5, Part 3.

TABLE 26 *Grampian and Highland Regions: Population and Employment Statistics, 1931–1971*

Employment in	1931 Grampian	1931 Highland	1951 Grampian	1951 Highland	1961 Grampian	1961 Highland	1971 Grampian	1971 Highland
(1) Agriculture, Forestry & Fishing	45,793	37,095	36,184	24,506	30,930	17,350	21,500	11,500
(3) Food, Drink & Tobacco	10,850	5,049	9,980	2,209	8,800	1,180	15,820	2,840
(9) Electrical Engineering	365	139	177	43	580	60	800	220
(13) Textiles	5,997	2,116	4,749	2,390	4,460	2,520	4,420	2,230
(18) Paper, printing & publishing	5,067	284	4,993	291	5,900	340	6,090	1,340
(20) Construction	7,881	5,317	12,321	13,305	12,180	10,110	14,400	10,690
(21) Gas, Electricity & Water	1,001	217	1,746	670	2,000	1,070	1,910	910
(22) Transport & Communication	13,112	8,603	14,820	8,414	13,030	7,950	10,310	7,000
(23) Distributive trades	30,627	10,068	26,011	9,258	29,300	12,450	25,200	10,690
(25) Professional & Scientific	10,731	5,309	14,779	6,619	19,740	11,210	25,910	12,890
(26) Miscellaneous services	23,973	12,973	18,992	10,145	18,940	10,490	20,170	12,940
Total Employed	188,346	101,902	181,234	87,048	177,090	87,100	180,800	89,660
Total Population	436,014	238,456	453,777	231,144	442,971	226,981	441,090	234,240

Notes: (i) Counties in Grampian region: Aberdeen, Banff, Kincardineshire, Moray (Elgin); and in the Highland region: Caithness, Inverness, Nairn, Orkney and Shetland, Ross and Cromarty, Sutherland.

(ii) Full details of the classification of the employment data are provided by Lee. The numbers in brackets refer to those industrial orders of particular importance in the North of Scotland.

Source: C H Lee, *British Regional Employment Statistics, 1841–1971* (Cambridge, C.U.P., 1979).

TABLE 27   *Sales of Electricity to Different Classes of Consumers, 1949-1962, in millions of units*

	1949	1950	1951	1952	1953	1954	1955	1956	1957	1958	1959	1960	1961	1962
Units sold in Board's area														
Domestic and Crofts	206	228	226	293	323	366	421	472	506	570	618	699	804	965
Farm	15	20	28	38	44	60	70	89	97	114	118	131	143	161
Commercial	102	117	132	144	155	186	204	232	244	275	287	327	368	420
Industrial	163	200	218	230	267	268	287	307	324	340	369	407	421	464
Public Lighting	6	6	7	8	10	10	11	11	13	14	16	17	19	20
Traction	19	16	14	14	12	12	11	7	2	1	—	—	—	—
Units used in construction of hydro electric schemes	27	19	16	20	35	41	57	50	45	35	13	21	27	28
Total	538	606	681	747	846	943	1,061	1,168	1,231	1,349	1,421	1,602	1,782	2,058
Units sold to South of Scotland Board	56	136	235	308	304	390	184	362	466	463	550	565	780	572
Total Units Sold	594	742	916	1,051	1,150	1,333	1,245	1,530	1,697	1,812	1,971	2,167	2,562	2,630

Source: NSHEB, *Annual Reports*, 1950-1962.

TABLE 28   *Sales of Electricity: some comparative statistics, 1948-1962*

(a) *Share of total sales to major sectors (% ages)*

	Domestic and Farms			Farms		Industrial		
	GB	HB	SB	HB	SB	GB	HB	SB
1948	35	n.d.	—	n.d.	—	49	n.d.	—
1949	34	41	—	3	—	50	27	—
1950	33	41	—	3	—	50	27	—
1951	34	43	—	4	—	50	32	—
1952	32	44	—	5	—	50	31	—
1953	32	43	—	5	—	50	32	—
1954	31	45	—	6	—	51	28	—
1955	31	46	31	7	2	51	27	53
1956	32	48	32	8	2	51	26	52
1957	32	49	32	8	2	51	26	51
1958	34	51	34	8	2	49	25	48
1959	34	52	35	8	2	49	26	46
1960	34	52	36	8	2	49	25	45
1961	36	53	40	8	2	47	24	42
1962	39	55	40★	8	2	44	23	41★

★ Estimated.

Source: Great Britain, calculated from L Hannah, *Engineers, Managers and Politicians*, p.292; NSHEB, calculated from data in Table 27; South of Scotland Electricity Board, calculated from data in Mackenzie Committee Report, Table II, p.17.

(b) *Comparison between cost of electricity per unit in the Board's area and in the areas of the Area Boards, 1953-1954*

Area Board	PENCE PER UNIT SOLD							
	Domestic Premises d.	Farms d.	Commercial Premises d.	Total Domestic, Farms and Commercial d.	Industrial d.	Public Lighting d.	Traction d.	Total (Excluding inter-Board sales) d.
London	1.657	1.860	2.174	1.879	1.703	1.383	1.413	1.814
South Eastern	1.571	1.635	2.036	1.687	1.317	1.712	1.328	1.573
Southern	1.667	1.425	1.867	1.717	1.391	1.582	1.228	1.593
South Western	1.706	1.448	2.162	1.828	1.390	1.664	—	1.677
Eastern	1.550	1.695	1.851	1.622	1.371	1.883	1.263	1.521
East Midlands	1.465	1.419	1.798	1.546	1.083	1.196	1.038	1.283
Midlands	1.391	1.337	1.750	1.500	1.113	1.214	1.105	1.269
South Wales	1.665	1.399	1.727	1.679	0.901	1.214	1.049	1.064
Merseyside and North Wales	1.563	1.322	1.755	1.618	1.124	1.137	1.135	1.336
Yorkshire	1.361	1.553	1.699	1.463	0.970	1.331	0.976	1.137
North Eastern	1.616	1.372	1.930	1.713	1.056	1.569	1.066	1.272
North Western	1.431	1.342	1.947	1.592	1.117	1.193	0.911	1.296
South East Scotland	1.441	1.400	1.860	1.584	1.148	1.431	1.036	1.368
South West Scotland	1.415	1.550	1.635	1.489	1.209	1.226	—	1.331
TOTAL	1.532	1.467	1.913	1.646	1.146	1.393	1.146	1.381
Hydro-Electric Board	1.597	1.484	1.924	1.684	1.400	1.926	1.202	1.583

Source: NSHEB, Agenda Papers for Board Meeting of 20 October 1954.

TABLE 29   *NSHEB: Sales of Electricity in Board's Area to Different Classes of Consumers, 1963-1987* (in millions of units)

Year ending 31 March	1964	1965	1966	1967	1968	1969	1970	1971	1972	1973
Domestic and Crofts	1,128	1,269	1,482	1,577	1,786	1,969	2,177	2,306	2,409	2,612
Farm	173	182	203	203	205	212	219	217	217	227
Commercial	501	530	591	620	671	746	819	852	907	973
Industrial	508	563	601	629	658	786	847	728	1,327	1,711
Public Lighting	22	24	25	26	30	35	35	39	40	42
Total	2,332	2,568	2,901	3,055	3,351	3,747	4,097	4,142	4,900	5,565
Invergordon Smelter (inc. in 'Industrial')	—	—	—	—	—	—	—	—	611	898

Year ending 31 March	1974	1975	1976	1977	1978	1979	1980	1981	1982	1983
Domestic	2.851	2,987	2,811	2,964	2,994	3,174	3,128	3,023	3,034	2,899
Farm	229	236	218	221	248	248	241	234	230	223
Commercial	972	1,067	1,090	1,194	1,293	1,377	1,442	1,416	1,450	1,464
Industrial	2,532	2,508	2,790	2,791	2,578	2,901	3,041	2,947	2,354	1,223
Public Lighting	44	50	51	55	53	56	57	67	70	74
Total	6,628	6,848	6,960	7,225	7,166	7,756	7,909	7,687	7,138	5,883
Invergordon Smelter (inc. in 'Industrial)	1,626	1,502	1,787	1,671	1,477	1,707	1,850	1,765	1,234	nil

Year ending 31 March	1984	1985	1986	1987
Domestic	3,003	2,975	3,191	3,204
Farm	221	215	237	242
Commercial	1,537	1,573	1,635	1,668
Industrial	1,246	1,282	1,363	1,386
Public Lighting	76	76	79	80
Total	6,083	6,121	6,505	6,580

Source: NSHEB, *Annual Reports and Accounts.*

TABLE 30 *NSHEB: Total System Requirements, 1970–1987* (millions of units)

Year ending 31 March	Generated by NSHEB						Total (T)	Net Import/Export with SSEB	Purchases from UKAEA & Others	Total System Requirements (T.S.R.)	C.H. / T.S.R. %	T / T.S.R. %
	Conventional Hydro (CH)	As % of T	Pumped Storage	Steam	Diesel	Gas Turbines						
1971	3,441	66	−155	1,808	129	—	5,223	−526	45	4,742	74	110
1972	2,346	60	−171	1,583	142	—	3,900	1,520	49	5,469	43	71
1973	2,561	58	−91	1,787	159	—	4,416	1,773	43	6,232	41	71
1974	3,197	63	−27	1,742	181	—	5,093	2,127	35	7,255	44	70
1975	2,899	64	−41	1,499	198	—	4,555	2,927	20	7,502	39	61
1976	2,730	84	−140	425	219	—	3,234	4,528	26	7,788	35	42
1977	2,379	89	−217	268	235	—	2,665	5,069	159	7,893	30	34
1978	2,881	89	−97	176	266	—	3,226	4,492	208	7,926	36	41
1979	2,777	86	−98	244	310	—	3,233	5,037	270	8,540	33	38
1980	3,103	90	−106	116	320	4	3,437	5,168	100	8,705	36	40
1981	3,234	85	−41	282	300	20	3,795	4,517	156	8,468	38	45
1982	3,099	87	−2	137	303	24	3,561	4,128	214	7,903	39	45
1983	3,651	54	−37	2,908	257	22	6,801	−252	81	6,630	55	103
1984	3,263	43	−86	4,200	246	1	7,624	−933	152	6,843	48	111
1985	2,493	26	−58	6,916	249	2	9,602	−3,239	642	7,005	36	137
1986	3,179	91	−33	94	264	1	3,505	3,002	895	7,402	43	47
1987	3,369	66	44	1,421	268	7	5,109	1,504	851	7,464	45	68

Source: NSHEB, *Annual Reports and Accounts.*

TABLE 31   *NSHEB: Installed Generation Capacity, 1971-1987* (in Megawatts)

	Conventional Hydro	Pumped Storage	Steam	Diesel	Gas Turbines	Total Installed
1971	1,052	400	316	62	—	1,830
1972	1,052	400	307	62	—	1,821
1973	1,052	400	307	73	—	1,832
1974	1,052	400	307	84	—	1,843
1975	1,052	700	307	91	—	2,150
1976	1,052	700	307	101	—	2,160
1977	1,052	700	307	117	—	2,176
1978	1,052	700	240	117	—	2,109
1979	1,052	700	240	121	3	2,116
1980	1,052	700	240	121	3	2,116
1981	1,052	700	240	120	13	2,125
1982	1,052	700	660	126	13	2,551
1983	1,052	700	1,260	126	35	3,173
1984	1;058	700	1,260	126	35	3,179
1985	1,062	700	1,320	142	35	3,259
1986	1,062	700	1,320	142	35	3,259
1987	1,064	700	1,320	142	35	3,262

Source: NSHEB, *Annual Reports and Accounts.*

TABLE 32   NSHEB: *Gross Capital Investment, 1968-1987*

During Year ending 31 March	Capital Investment during year (£m)					Gross Capital Investment (£m) at end of year		
	Total	On Hydro-Electric Generation	On Steam Generation	On Transmission	On Distribution	Total	On Hydro-Electric Generation	On Steam Generation
1968	7.6	1.0	0.1	1.0	4.8	312.9	186.8	14.9
1969	7.7	0.6	0.0	1.6	4.7	320.6	187.4	15.0
1970	8.2	1.7	0.0	1.4	4.7	328.8	189.1	15.0
1971	11.3	2.7	0.2	1.9	5.4	340.1	191.9	15.2
1972	14.4	4.0	0.4	2.6	5.5	354.5	195.9	15.6
1973	16.1	4.5	0.5	3.5	6.0	370.6	200.3	16.1
1974	16.9	3.4	2.8	2.5	6.4	387.4	203.8	18.9
1975	32.2	3.7	15.0	2.8	9.0	419.6	207.4	33.9
1976	70.1	1.2	48.4	5.7	12.9	489.7	208.6	82.3
1977	77.2	0.3	55.5	7.4	11.4	556.9	208.9	137.9
1978	63.5	0.4	37.9	12.4	10.5	630.3	209.3	175.8
1979	47.6	0.1	26.4	7.2	10.5	677.9	209.4	202.2
1980	42.7	0.3	20.2	2.4	14.1	720.6	209.7	222.4
1981*	38.3	1.2	10.2	2.3	14.4	758.6	210.9	232.6
1982	29.1	1.1	3.9	2.9	15.7	787.7	212.0	236.5
1983	38.4	1.8	2.7	4.0	18.1	826.1	213.8	239.2
1984	44.5	2.3†	2.1	3.2	25.5	870.6	216.1	241.3
1985	38.3	2.6†	0.5	2.7	24.7	908.9	218.7	241.6
1986	44.5	5.6†	0.4	4.8	30.5	953.4	224.3	242.0
1987	54.7	12.1†		3.9	33.7	1008.1	—	

Notes: ★ As from 31 March 1980, the Board adopted a new accounting policy and the figures given in the last three columns for 1981 and subsequent years do *not* appear in the Accounts. They have been reconstructed and presented here simply for the purposes of comparison with earlier years.
†Includes an unspecified amount for wind-power generation.

Source: NSHEB, *Annual Reports and Accounts.*

TABLE 33   *NSHEB: Number of Employees, 1968–87*

As 31 March	No. of Employees	million units sold per employee★
1968	3,993	0.839
1969	3,860	0.970
1970	3,863	1.061
1971	3,832	1.081
1972	3,641	1.178
1973	3,588	1.300
1974	3,673	1.362
1975	3,745	1.428
1976	3,808	1.358
1977	3,796	1.463
1978	3,910	1.455
1979	4,059	1.490
1980	4,146	1.461
1981	4,115	1.435
1982	4,005	1.474
1983	3,920	1.501
1984	3,840	1.584
1985	3,830	1.600
1986	3,767	1.727
1987	3,795	1.734

★ Excludes sales to Invergordon Smelter, 1972–1982.
Source: NSHEB, *Annual Reports and Accounts*.

Notes

CHAPTER 1

1   Such misconceptions have been commented on by, for example, William Wilson, in the 'Discussion' of the paper by A S Valentine and E M Bergstrom. 'Hydro-Electric Development in Great Britain, with special reference to the Works of the Grampian Electricity Supply Co.', *Journal of the Institution of Electrical Engineers*, Vol.76 (1935), p.164; J K Hunter & R W Mountain, 'Hydro-Electric Development: Some Economic Aspects', *Journal of the Institution of Civil Engineers*, Vol.19 (1942), p.135; W Sutcliffe in the 'Discussion' of the paper by A E MacColl, 'Hydro-Electric Development in Scotland', *Transactions of the Institution of Engineers and Shipbuilders in Scotland*, Vol.89 (1946), p.480. It seems almost unnecessary to add that among those most guilty of propagating these misleading ideas have been the politicians.
2   In the 'Discussion' of Hunter and Mountain, *op.cit.*, p.168.

CHAPTER 2

1   George Hill, *Tunnel and Dam—the Story of the Galloway Hydros* (Glasgow: South of Scotland Electricity Board, 1984), p.2. The earliest public supply of hydro-electric power was in 1881, when the streets of Godalming, in Surrey, were illuminated by electricity from a generator provided by a water wheel in the River Way. K H Lea, 'Hydro-Electric Power Generation in the Highlands of Scotland', *Transactions and Papers of the Institute of British Geographers*, Publication No.46 (1969), p.155; and see A Page, 'Electricity Supply in Great Britain', *Journal of the Institution of Electrical Engineers*, Vol.66 (1927), p.1.
2   Hill, *op.cit.*, pp.3-4; details of the generating equipment are given by D G Tucker, 'Hydro-Electricity for Public Supply in Britain, 1881-1894', *Industrial Archaeological Review*, Vol.1, No.2 (1977), p.133. The Gunther turbine was of the Girard type. See also W Murray Morrison, 'Aluminium and Highland Water Power', *Journal of the Institute of Metals*, Vol.LXV (1939), p.22.
3   R B Anderson, 'The Development of Electricity Supplies in the North of Scotland', typescript of an Address to the Scottish Centre of the Institution of Electrical Engineers, delivered at Edinburgh 4 October, and Glasgow 5 October 1960, pp.1,3. An abstract of this Address is printed in the *Proceedings of the Institution of Electrical Engineers*, Vol.108, Part A (1961), pp.30-2. The non-statutory undertaking established by the monks of St Benedict's Abbey continued to supply Fort Augustus until 1951, when the North of Scotland Hydro-Electric Board took over the responsibilities and replaced the overhead cable network. Anderson, 'Address', p.1.

4   'Electric Lighting by Water power at Fort William', *The Electrical Engineer*, Vol.19, 5 March 1897, pp.294-5. An interesting feature of the Fort William Scheme was the use of storage batteries or 'accumulators' to augment the electricity supply when the load exceeded the capacity of the turbines. I owe this reference to Tucker, *op.cit.*, p.163.

5   Hill, *op.cit.*, pp.5-7.

6   Lea, *op.cit.*, p.155; Anderson, *Proceedings Inst. Elect. Engineers*, p.31. When this scheme was taken over by the North of Scotland Hydro-Electric Board, the engineers reported that it was the only system they had encountered in which they poles were held up by the overhead lines! (Communication from Mr I A Duncan Millar).

7   Lea, *op.cit.*, p.156. With the exception of the Ravens (Ben Wyvis) scheme, all the systems provided Direct Current. Anderson, *typescript*, opposite p.4.

8   This entire section is heavily dependent upon W Murray Morrison's Autumn Lecture to the Institute of Metals in 1939, published under the title 'Aluminium and Highland Water Power' in the *Journal of the Institute of Metals*, Vol.LXV (1939), pp.17-36. Morrison was the first engineer to be appointed to the British Aluminium Company in January 1895. Subsequently, he became the company's Deputy Chairman and Managing Director. Additional data was obtained from Lea, *op.cit.*, pp.156-8; David Turnock, *The New Scotland* (Newton Abbot: David & Charles, 1979), pp.93-7; *Encyclopaedia Britannica*, 11th edn (1910-1911), Vol.1, pp.767-72; T A L Paton and J Guthrie Brown, *Power from Water*, p.76; and various numbers of the *Investors' Review*, 1895-1908. The early development of the aluminium industry in Britain has been clearly surveyed by T G L Hopkins, 'The Development and Location of the Aluminium Industry in the United Kingdom' (unpublished B Litt thesis, University of Oxford, 1957), pp.1-44.

9   See Louis Stott, *The Waterfalls of Scotland* (Aberdeen: Aberdeen University Press, 1987), pp.79-81.

10 Initially the surplus power was leased to the Acetylene Illuminating Co. for this purpose; not until 1899 did the British Aluminium Company itself produce calcium carbide. Morrison, *op.cit.*, p.23.

11 In its early years, the British Aluminium Co's management was repeatedly criticised by the *Investors' Review* for its pricing policy; its inability to combat foreign competition; and its unrealistically heavy capitalisation. On 29 July 1899, the *Review* commented acidly that 'Possibly the company might do better if it sold cheaper, but anyhow an undertaking which has worked such havoc around the Falls of Foyers is not deserving of sympathy.' By 1908, the company was being congratulated upon its possession of a fine business, the profits of which were expected to be enhanced as a result of the formation of a selling ring of aluminium manufacturers. *Ibid.*, 25 April, 1908.

12 At the end of 1907 the British Aluminium Company held 50,052 shares, valued at nearly half a million pounds, in the Loch Leven Water and Electric Power Co. The two companies were merged by a Transfer Act obtained in 1910. Morrison, *op.cit.*, p.26.

13 The civil engineering works are described by Alfred H Roberts, 'The Loch Leven Water-Power Works', *Minutes of the Proceedings of the Institute of Civil Engineers*, CLXXXVII (1911-12), pp.28-73, and the hydro-electric plant by Frederic Bolton Sonnenschein, 'The Hydro-Electric Plant in the British Aluminium Company's Factory at Kinlochleven', in the same source, pp.74-84.

14 These pipes, which were lapped welded, were purchased from a Silesian firm. No British firm had enough experience to make them. Mr C S Meik, in the 'Discussion' of the papers by Roberts and Sonnenschein, *loc.cit.*, pp.88-9.

15 Paton and Brown, *op.cit.*, p.80.

16 Patrick MacGill, *Children of the Dead End* (London: Herbert Jenkins, 1914). A Summary

of the book in the context of MacGill's other works is provided by James E Handley, *The Navvy in Scotland* (Cork University Press, 1970), pp.349-62.

17   For the story of the Woodhead Tunnel, see Terry Coleman, *The Railway Navvies* (London: Hutchinson, 1965), pp.115-138; for the Caledonian Canal, see Handley, *op.cit.*, pp.55-63.

18   MacGill, *op.cit.*, pp.213, 219.

19   *Investors' Review*, Vol.XXI, p.575, 25th April, 1908. The total capital expenditure involved in the Kinlochleven Scheme was later agreed to be £620,359. *Court of Session Cases*, 1937, p.571.

20   Morrison, *op.cit.*, pp.27-8; *Balfour Beatty, 1909-1984: A 75th Anniversary Brochure*, p.6; *Court of Session Cases*, 1937, p.569.

21   The plan entailed the construction of two dams: one at the northern end of Loch Treig, and the other some distance downstream of Loch Laggan. Loch Treig was to serve as the main storage reservoir, water from its own catchment area being supplemented by that conveyed by tunnel from Loch Laggan. From Loch Treig the waters were to be taken by a tunnel seven miles long, beginning at the south-western end of the Loch and emerging at the new power houses at Kinlochleven. William T Halcrow, 'The Lochaber Water-Power Scheme', *Minutes of the Proceedings of the Institution of Civil Engineers*, Vol.231 (1930-31), Part I, p.31.

22   There were seven rain gauges on or adjoining the catchment area at the time when the scheme was before Parliament, records being available over periods ranging from two to 45 years. After 1918 the British Aluminium Company established additional rain-gauges distributed over the catchment area. Rainfall records of the Summit of Ben Nevis recorded an average of 161 inches per annum, the minimum and maximum falls recorded over a 19 year period being 108 and 240 inches. The wettest month had 48.3 inches and the maximum for one day was 7.3 inches. Halcrow, *op.cit.*, p.36.

23   This involved the diversion of the Loch Laggan outlet from the River Spean to Loch Treig. Initially this tunnel was to be four miles long since the original site for the dam across the River Spean was $1\frac{1}{4}$ miles upstream from the site selected by Mr C S Meik, Halcrow's partner, in 1921. The alteration was approved by Supplementary Act in 1930. Halcrow, 'The Lochaber Scheme', p.91.

24   In addition to the sources cited in note 8, the account of the Lochaber scheme rests upon W T Halcrow, 'The Lochaber Water-Power Scheme', *op.cit.*, pp.31-63, and the ensuing discussion and correspondence, pp.64-103; Alan Graeme, 'The Lochaber Power Scheme', *The Scots Magazine*, New Series, XI, No.6 (September, 1929), *frontispiece* and pp.401-404; *Balfour Beatty: 75th Anniversary Brochure* (1984), pp.12-17; Patrick Howat, *The Lochaber Narrow Gauge Railway* (Birchencliffe, Huddersfield: The Narrow Gauge Railway Society, 1980).

25   The choice of materials for lining the tunnel was complicated by the knowledge, derived from experience of Kinlochleven, that the acids in the mountain waters attacked the surface of concrete exposed to them. Following exhaustive tests, it was decided to use Portland cement concrete for the lining and *ciment fondu* for the bottom, or invert, of the tunnel, these being the most resistant materials permitted by the available budget. Halcrow, *op.cit.*, p.38, and see W T Halcrow, G B Brook and R Preston, 'The Corrosive Attack of Moorland Water on Concrete', *Transactions of the Institution of Water Engineers*, Vol 33, p.187.

26   For example, the arch dam at No.6 stream was 137 feet in length and 38 feet at its maximum height. Halcrow, 'The Lochaber Water-Power Scheme', p.41.

27   The authoritative account of the building and operation of the Lochaber Railway is that by Patrick Howat, *op.cit.*

28   Because the liquid oxygen was evaporating all the time the charges were being loaded,

the process necessitated following a very strict time table, conformity to which could not always be attained because the men were relatively untrained. Although the use of LOX was abandoned, its potential re-introduction served as a very useful bargaining counter in negotiations designed to secure reductions in the price of gelignite. I am grateful to Mr D M Balfour for this information.

29   Howat, *op.cit.*, p.23.
30   Halcrow, 'Lochaber Scheme', p.61.
31   W Murray Morrison in the discussion of Halcrow, *ibid*, p.68.
32   The most useful account of the second stage of the Lochaber Scheme is that by A H Naylor, 'The Second-Stage Development of the Lochaber Water-Power Scheme' in the *Journal of the Institution of Civil Engineers*, Vol. V (1936-37), pp.3-48, with a discussion, pp.49-88. An interesting issue discussed by Naylor was the reason for choosing a gravity as opposed to an arch dam at Laggan, *ibid.*, pp.8-9.
33   Because the main tunnel was a pressure tunnel, the entire scheme produced a single pressure system with an unbroken head of approximately 800 feet. The static head, being dependent upon the level of Loch Treig, could vary from 819 feet down to 695 feet (the minimum permitted level), a range of 124 feet.
34   Howat, *op.cit.*, p.29.
35   W Murray Morrison, 'Aluminium and Highland Water Power', p.32, reported that by 1939 the three Highland schemes had involved the purchase of 100,000 acres of land.
36   Halcrow, 'The Lochaber Scheme', p.33, cf W Murray Morrison in the subsequent discussion, p.68.
37   Though this had not inhibited—perhaps even encouraged— detailed comparative speculations by a number of those present at the meeting. See the observations made by Professor S M Dixon, Dr Lowe-Brown and Mr W N McClean. *Ibid.*, pp.79, 81, 84-5.
38   Paton and Guthrie Brown, *op.cit.*, p.86.
39   Lea, *op.cit.*, p.158, adversely compares the capital cost of Lochaber with contemporary schemes in Norway and Canada. The Isle Maligne power Station in Canada, designed, like Lochaber, solely for aluminium production, and opened in 1926, had an installed capacity of 360 MW, four times that of Lochaber, and a capital cost of less than £20 per kW installed. It is not without relevance that the British Aluminium Co. pioneered the production of aluminium in Norway in the first decade of the twentieth century. See Morrison, 'Aluminium and Highland Water Power', p.27.
40   Anderson, *op.cit.*, typescript, p.13. Being refused permission to raise or lower, 'or otherwise affect' the natural level of Loch Ericht meant that the promoters were restricted to storage between winter and summer levels.
41   *Ibid.*, p.14.
42   See Appendix 1, p.256.
43   For Beaumont Pease, as he was called, see M W Kirby, *Men of Business and Politics: The Rise and Fall of the Quaker Pease Dynasty of North-east England, 1700-1943* (London: Allen & Unwin, 1984), pp.121-2, and the *Dictionary of Business Biography*, Vol.4, 594-5.
44   Anderson, *op.cit.*, p.17; A S Valentine & E M Bergstrom, 'Hydro-electric Development in Great Britain, with special reference to the works of the Grampian Electricity Supply Co.', *Journal of the Institution of Electrical Engineers*, Vo.76 (1935), p.132.
45   *Balfour Beatty*, p.1, and see Leslie Hannah, 'George Balfour', in *Dictionary of Business Biography*, Vol. 1, pp.125-7. The following three paragraphs draw heavily on these two sources. Additional details were provided by Anderson, *op.cit.*, typescript.
46   *Balfour Beatty*, p.1.
47   Leslie Hannah, *Electricity Before Nationalisation*, pp.130, 378; Valentine & Bergstrom, *op.cit.*,

p.132; Anderson, *op.cit.*, typescript, p.17; *Balfour Beatty*, p.11. See also Report of the [Cooper] Committee on Hydro-Electric Development in Scotland, Cmd. 6406 (1942), p.7. The Grampian Co. began to *distribute* electricity in various districts of its area in 1926. Initially, this electricty was purchased in bulk from the Scottish Central Electric Power Co., a source that was later augmented by taking over the Arbroath Electric Light and Power Co. and installing a new steam plant in the Arbroath generating station. The details are given by Anderson, *op.cit.*, typescript, pp.15-6.

48 A S Valentine & E M Bergstrom, *op.cit.*, p.132. The following account of the Grampian scheme is based on this source; a series of five articles in successive weekly issues of *The Engineer*, the first of which is dated 7 August 1931 (Rannoch Development); 6 and 13 July 1934 (Tummel Development); and a publication by the Scottish Power Company, *The Hydro-Electric Power Works of the Grampian Electricity Supply Company* (undated, c.1935).

49 Except where the route crossed the River Ericht and the water from the dam had to be carried across the river by means of a riveted steel pipe nearly 11 feet in diameter, approximately half way between the River Ericht and the Surge shaft. The Mheugaidh stream was diverted into the tunnel through a vertical shaft.

50 The clearest description of the Tummel Development is that in *The Engineer*, 6 and 13 July 1934.

51 The tunnel between Loch Seilich and Loch Cuaich was driven from both ends and a perfect junction was effected on 1 August 1940. See *The Times*, 2 August 1940.

52 Report of the [Cooper] Committee on Hydro-Electric Development in Scotland, Cmd. 6406 (1942), pp.7-8.

53 This is Lea's conclusion, *op.cit.*, p.159.

54 See above, pp.3-4.

55 Quoted by Anderson, *op.cit.*, transcript, p.10, on which source this paragraph is largely based.

56 The Scottish Economic Committee [the Hilleary Committee], *The Highlands and Islands of Scotland* (1938), pp.134-5.

57 N C Bridge, in the discussion of a paper on 'Hydro-Electric Development in Scotland', by A E MacColl, delivered on 9 April 1946. *Tractions of the Institution of Engineers and Shipbuilders in Scotland*, Vol.89 (1946), p.47.

58 The purpose of this company was to concentrate the engineering experience and financial powers of its members in the investigation, exploitation, development and execution of comprehensive engineering works. By promoting the Falls of Clyde scheme, the Power and Traction Co. hoped to provide work for its associated companies, particularly for the English Electric Co. and Sir William Arrol; to demonstrate to the engineering world the ability of British manufacturers to design and construct hydro-electric works; and to secure the not inconsiderable commission of one per cent of the value of the contracts placed. George Hill, *Tunnel and Dam—the Story of the Galloway Hydros* (South of Scotland Electricity Board, 1984), p.13.

59 Norrie Fraser, 'The Man and the Mission', in Norrie Fraser (ed), *Sir Edward MacColl: A Maker of Modern Scotland* (Edinburgh: Stanley Press, 1956), p.3, on which source this and the following two paragraphs are largely based. Additional details were provided by Valentine and Bergstrom, *op.cit.*, pp.129-30; W T Halcrow, 'Scottish Hydro-electric Stations'; *The Engineer*, 14 September, 1934, p.289; and Paton and Brown, *op.cit.*, pp.34,83.

60 This figure has been calculated from data given by Paton and Brown, *op.cit.*, p.200.

61 Paton and Brown, *op.cit.*, p.83. cf the statement made by Lord Hamilton of Dalzell to the House of Lords in 1943, 127 *H.L.Deb.*, 5th Series, 9 June 1943, col.966. See below, p.48.

62 MS 'Report on the Water Power Resources of Scotland', undated, c.1937, p.17. The cost

per kilowatt installed of the Falls of Clyde Scheme was £27.2. The copy of this report in the archives of the North of Scotland Hydro-Electric Board is the personal copy of Sir Edward MacColl; it is almost certain that it was prepared for the Hilleary Committee (See below, p.52) and formed the basis for Chapter 13 of the Hilleary Committee's report on *The Highlands and Islands of Scotland* (1938).

63   The significance of the Galloway scheme is such that it not only attracted much contemporary analysis but has been accorded pivotal importance in the development of hydro-electricity in this country. The standard work is that by George Hill, *Tunnel and Dam—the Story of the Galloway Hydros* (South of Scotland Electricity Board, 1984), based upon his thesis for the degree of PhD of the University of Strathclyde, 1984. See also William Hudson and John Kenneth Hunter, 'The Galloway Hydro-Electric Development, with special reference to the Constructional Works', *Journal of the Institute of Civil Engineers*, Vol.8 (1937-38), pp.323-75; William Hawthorne and Frederick Herbert Williams, 'The Galloway Hydro-Electric Development, with special reference to the Mechanical and Electrical Plant', *Journal of the Institute of Civil Engineers*, Vol.8 (1937-38), pp.376-406; R W Mountain, 'The Galloway Hydro-Electric Development, with special reference to its Interconnection with the Grid', *Journal of the Institute of Civil Engineers*, Vol.8 (1937-38), pp.407-422; Paton and Brown, *op.cit.*, pp.90-98; *Engineering*, Vol.138 (1934, Part 2), Vol.142 (1936, Part 2); *The Engineer*, Vol.158 (1934, Part 2), Vol.162 (1936, Part 2).

64   Paton and Brown, *op.cit.*, p.90.

65   See above, p.3.

66   Hill, *op.cit.*, pp.7-10.

67   *Ibid.*, p.12. For William McLellan and the firm of Merz and McLellan, see Hannah, *Electricity before Nationalisation*, *passim*, and John Rowland, *Progress in Power: The Contribution of Charles Merz and his associates to sixty years of electrical development, 1899-1959* (London: privately published by Newman Neame for Merz and McLellan, 1960).

68   Hill, *op.cit.*, p.13.

69   These are clearly set out by Hill, *op.cit.*, pp.13-26.

70   Quoted by Paton & Brown, *op.cit.*, p.91.

71   There appears to be universal agreement that James Williamson, the chief engineer to Sir Alexander Gibb and Partners, possessed a brilliance amounting to genius in planning hydro schemes. He would work initially from ordnance maps, then stride the hills with but little equipment to position dams, tunnels and surge shafts with uncanny accuracy. Back in his office, he covered his plans with calculations of storage, run-off and load factor before sending out his teams of young engineers—'Gibb's Light Horse'—to survey the chosen sites, surveys which rarely showed the need for more than minor changes. James Williamson later established his own consultancy. I am indebted to Mr I A Duncan Millar, sometime a member of Sir Alexander Gibb & Partners, for this information. See also Paton and Brown, *op.cit.*, p.160.

72   Paton and Brown, *op.cit.*, p.94.

73   Hill, *op.cit.*, p.29; Hudson and Hunter, *op.cit.*, p.355.

74   Hudson & Hunter, *op.cit.*, p.353.

75   Paton & Brown, *op.cit.*, p.95.

76   Hill, *op.cit.*, p.31.

77   *Ibid.*, p.44.

78   *Ibid.*, p.45; Hannah, *Electricity before Nationalisation*, p.130. The total installed capacity of the Galloway power stations was 102,000 kW. For the years 1937-41, the actual annual output averaged 208 million units at a percentage load factor of 23.4.

79   Hill, *op.cit.*, pp.24-6.

80   *Ibid.*, p.26.

81   Norrie Fraser, *op.cit.*, p.5.

82   For the debates on these bills, see the Fifth series of *House of Commons Debates*, Vols.310, cols.517-70 (18 March 1936); 321, cols. 1237-98 (10 March 1937); and 334, cols. 422-84 (6 April 1938). Hereafter cited simply by the year, volume number and column number.

83   *HC Deb.*, 1937, 321, col.1296.

84   *HC Deb.*, 1938, 334, col.439.

85   *HC Deb.*, 1938, 334, col.479.

86   *HC Deb.*, 1937, 321, col.1275.

87   *Ibid.*, cols.1288-89.

88   *HC Deb.*, 1938, 334, col.444.

89   *HC Deb.*, 1936, 310, cols.528,540.

90   *HC Deb*, 1937, 321, cols.1276-7.

91   *HC Deb.*, 1938, 334, cols.465-6.

92   *HC Deb.*, 1938, 334, cols.468, 470. cf. Mr J J Davidson, member for Maryhill, 'the promoters of the undertaking are not setting up an industry in the North of Scotland merely for the purpose of producing carbide or providing electricity. They are setting up their industry there to provide ... profits ....' *Ibid.*, 321, col.1268.

93   *HC Deb.*, 1936, 310, col.526. Instead, one member acidly implied, of clearing away the debris and sewage which the Town of Inverness was too mean to dispose of properly. *Ibid.*, col.562. A point taken up by James Maxton in 1938 (*HC Deb.*, 1938, 334, cols.475-76). Sir Malcolm returned to his charge repeatedly, e.g. *HC Deb.*, 1937, 321, cols.1244-46; 1938, 334, cols.422-5.

94   *H C Deb.*, 1937, 321, cols.1283-4.

95   *HC Deb.*, 1937, 321, cols 1239-40.

96   As *Engineering*, 13 December, 1929, p.778, pointed out, other witnesses affirmed that 'most of the land affected is not open to this migratory class of the population'. Or, as James Maxton was to say of a similar argument used against the Caledonian Power Bill., 'If I tried to get into [that area] I would be chased by gamekeepers'. 334 *HC Deb.*, 5th series, col.474.

97   *Engineering*, 13 December 1929, p.778. The rejection of the bill was criticised by this influential journal as being 'a heavy blow to the policy inherent in the national scheme of electrical reorganisation. At the present time, a number of towns in the district desire a supply of electricity, and were willing to obtain that supply from the Grampian Company. In all probability they will now apply for permission to erect their own plant, and it is a little difficult to see how that permission can be refused. There will, therefore, be an unnecessary multiplication of small power stations'.

98   See 374 *HC Deb*, 5th series, September-November 1941, cols.207-71. During the course of the debate, Major Neven-Spence, member for Orkney and Zetland, and Chairman of the Joint Parliamentary Commission which had examined the bill in Edinburgh in April 1941, explained that 'when the Private Legislation Procedure (Scottish) Act was passed in 1936 it was then considered that Scotland had got hold of something—a rather valuable concession, almost a little bit of Home Rule, because it ensured that Scottish private legislation would be heard by a Commission or Committee of Scottish Members sitting in Scotland'. As far as Major Neven-Spence knew, 'every Order [thus] examined ... and approved ... has subsequently been confirmed by Parliament', and he believed that if the Grampian Electricity Supply bill was rejected, 'a very serious blow [would] be struck at the confidence felt in this kind of procedure'. (col.217). Later in the debate, Tom Johnston explained the procedure under the 1936 Act more fully (cols.233-35).

99   *Ibid.*, col.207.

100 *Ibid.*, cols. 208-213. Sir George Courthope reinforced Keeling's argument on amenities by describing the 'disgusting' state of Loch Laggan which 'instead of being beautiful sheets of water, is stretches of unsightly evil-smelling mud' (cols.252-53), and David Kirkwood described the desolation of Kinlochleven (cols.263-64).

101 *Ibid.*, col.237.

102 *Ibid.*, col.249.

103 *Ibid.*, cols.255-56

CHAPTER 3

1   374 *H.C.Deb.*, 5th series (1940-41), cols.237-38, 259, 233-34.

2   For example, Hamish McKinven, 'Water Power and the Bomb', *Scotsman*, 27 February 1987.

3   Even then he could not be sure. The debate on the Grampian Electricity Supply Order Confirmation Bill took place on 10 September, 1941, when Johnston's 'Council of State' had yet to meet and there was no guarantee that even when it did there would be agreement concerning his plan for hydro development. The careful wording of his reply to Mr Henderson Stewart is significant: 'I do not want to be pushed too far, or to say that a scheme will be presented. I do suggest, however, that it is unsafe to assume that Parliament will delay its decision until the post-war period'. 374 *H.C.Deb.*, 5s. (1940-41), col.237.

4   Thomas Johnston, *Memories* (London: Collins, 1952), p.148. Professor R H Campbell has recently attempted an assessment of the work of this 'Council of State': 'The Committee of Ex-Secretaries of State for Scotland and Industrial Policy, 1941-45', *Scottish Industrial History*, Vol.2, Nos.2 & 3 (1979), pp.1-10.

5   Lord Alness had served as Secretary for Scotland from December 1916 to November 1922 before the office became a full secretaryship of state in 1926. The tenure of office of the other members of the Council were Sinclair (later lst Viscount Thurso), August 1931-October 1932; Elliot, November 1936-May 1938; Colville (later Lord Clydesmuir), May 1938-May 1940; Ernest Brown, May 1940-February 1941.

6   Minutes of the Scottish Council on Post-War Problems, first meeting, 29 September, 1941, section 1 (Scottish Record Office, Scottish Home and Health Department: HH 50/166). It will be noticed that the Minutes refer to the 'Scottish Council on Post-War Problems', although Johnston's autobiography says 'we were officially designated The Scottish Advisory Council of ex-Secretaries'. He adds that 'the Press had cottoned on to the label Council of State, and Council of State we remained' (*Memories*, p.149). The membership and functions of the Council were explained to the House of Commons in responses to a 'private notice' question by Mr Erskine Hill. Here it was referred to as the 'Advisory Council on post-war planning in Scotland'. 374 *H.C. Deb.*, 5 s. (1940-41), cols 304-7. See also George Pottinger, *The Secretaries of State for Scotland, 1926-76* (Edinburgh: Scottish Academic Press, 1979), pp.91-2.

7   Minutes of the Scottish Council on Post War Problems, 29 September, 1941. Sections 3,4. As President of the Board of Trade, Sir Andrew Duncan had an official responsibility for electricity, but his authority on this subject was derived from his earlier experience as the first chairman of the Central Electricity Board, a post he held from 1927 to 1935. For Duncan, see Hannah, *Electricity before Nationalisation*, especially pp.102, 337.

8   Papers concerning the composition of the Cooper Committee are contained in Scottish Record Office, DD 11/18. On Weir, see Hannah, *Electricity before Nationalisation*, *passim*,

particularly pp.90-100; W J Reader, *Architect of Air Power: the Life of the First Viscount Weir of Eastwood, 1877-1959* (London: Collins, 1968), particularly pp.310-11; *The Dictionary of Scottish Business Biography* (edited by A Slaven and Sydney Checkland), Vol.1, pp.197-200; and the Weir Papers (Churchill College, Cambridge, archives collection), class 22/10.

9   *Report of the [Cooper] Committee on Hydro-Electric Development in Scotland*, Cmd. 6406 (1942), para 1. Hereinafter referred to as *Cooper Committee*.

10   T M C [Lord Cooper] to Tom Johnston, 11 September 1941. SRO, DD 11/18. There is no evidence to suggest that Lord Cooper had examined the much more systematic and detailed, typewritten 'Report on the Water Power Resources of Scotland with special reference to Potential Developments in the Scottish Highlands', on which Chapter 13 of the Hilleary Report ('Water Power in the Highlands') had apparently been based (See below p.52). In 1936, in the absence of the Secretary of State, who was indisposed, Cooper had presented to the House of Commons the views of the Scottish Office on the first Caledonian Power Bill. During the course of the debate, he had twice affirmed his belief 'that the West Highland area is practically the only, if not the only, source of water power now left for development in this country'. 310 *H.C.Deb.*, 5 s (1936), cols. 546, 547.

11   See the exhaustive examination of each major point of the Hilleary Report contained in SRO DD 11/18, and R W Mountain, 'Central Electricity Board to Hydro Board', in Norrie Fraser, ed., *Sir Edward MacColl*, p.20.

12   387 *H.C.Deb.*, 5th series (1942-43), col.181.

13   *Cooper Committee*, paragraphs 5-14.

14   *Ibid.*, paragraph 26.

15   *Ibid.*, paragraph 63. In answering the question 'By what authority or body should future developments be undertaken?', a Joint Memorandum prepared by the Electricity Commissioners and the Central Electricity Board for the Cooper Committee stated that *for the area of the North and West of the Caledonian Canal*, 'it is suggested that a small *ad hoc* Authority whose members should be apopointed, not elected, and possibly vested with some powers for the promotion of local industries as well as for the supply of electricity, would provide a ...satisfactory solution ....' (p.14). A copy of this memorandum is included among the papers in SRO 11/19.

16   *Cooper Committee*, paragraph 69.

17   *Ibid.*, paragraph 85.

18   *Ibid.*, paragraph 87.

19   Notes of a meeting between the Secretary of State and representatives of the Association of County Councils and the Convention of Royal Burghs, 20 November 1942. SRO DD 11/20. Johnston prefaced his remarks by emphasising the secrecy of the discussions as the Report 'had not yet been made available to Parliament'. Emphasis supplied.

20   (Draft) 'Memorandum by the Secretary of State for Scotland for the Lord President's Committee', paragraph 4. The memorandum is among the papers in SRO DD 11/20; it is undated but, from its position, would appear to have been prepared about December, 1942.

21   This is apparent from the debate in the House of Lords, 127 *H.L. Deb.*, 5th series (1942-43), cols.953, 973, 977. The articles in *Forward*—the independent Labour journal which Johnston founded in 1906 and edited—were later assembled and published under the title of *Our Scots Noble Families* (Glasgow, 1913 and 1926). See Johnston, *Memories*, pp.32, 35. Pottinger affirms that 'there were credible reports that Johnston eventually tried to buy up all the extant volumes with a view to suppressing them'. *The Secretaries of State for Scotland*, p.87.

22   A J Aglen to D Milne, 30 October 1942. SRO DD 11/20. Emphasis supplied.

23   See W J Reader, *Architect of Air Power.*, p.312; T Johnston, *Memories*, pp. 149-50, 174-76.

24   387 *H.C.Deb.*, 5th series, 24 February 1943, cols.180-261.

25   127 *H.L. Deb.*, 5th series, 9 June 1943, col.947.
26   Reader, *Lord Weir*, p.313.
27   SRO, DD 11/20.
28   387 *H.C.Deb.*, 24 February 1943, cols.232–241. The Amendment is from col.232, and other substantial quotations from cols. 235-36. 238-39, 240.
29   *Ibid.*, col.247.
30   *Ibid.*, col.198. Major Neven-Spence, member for Orkney and Zetland, emphasised that 'One cannot overload an undertaking by carrying electricity to very isolated houses, farms, and communities ... there will be many places which have not an earthly hope of getting any electricity out of any Grid scheme' (col.231), and Mr J S C Reid, Lord Cooper's successor as Lord Advocate, in replying to the debate, said that people must not think 'that everyone, irrespective of where he is, will get an early supply' (col.257).
31   *Ibid.*, col.202. This point was taken up by others. Mr Sloan, member for South Ayrshire, for example, asked 'Is there any guarantee of any kind that there is to be any industrial development in the Highlands?' (col.222).
32   127 *H.L.Deb.*, 9 June 1943, col.955.
33   *Ibid.*, cols.973-76. Lord Brocket, who was in general agreement with the tenor of Lord Airlie's argument, wanted the Secretary of State 'to set up a much wider Commission, which might be called the Highland Commission, which would go into not only hydro-electric questions but matters affecting agriculture, fishing, the tourist industry and even sport' (col.980).
34   A point made specifically by Lord Alness, *Ibid.*, col.951, and Lord Saltoun (col.976).

CHAPTER 4

1   6 & 7 Geo. 6. Chapter 32 [5 August 1943].
2   The DoE file EL 32, part 15, 'Appointments to Electricity Boards: NSHEB' has been destroyed. Leslie Hannah, 'Rough Draft of Scottish Section', prepared for *Engineers, Managers and Politicians*, commissioned by the Electricity Council on behalf of the Central Electricity Generating Board, the Area Boards in England and Wales and the two Scottish Electricity Boards, p.11, note 3. Hereinafter cited: Hannah, 'Rough Draft'.
3   See above, p.48.
4   127 *H.L.Deb.*, 9 June 1943, col.974.
5   See The Earl of Airlie's 'Foreword' to Norrie Fraser (ed), *Sir Edward MacColl*.
6   See above, pp.24-5.
7   J Henderson, 'The Central Electricity Board', in Norrie Fraser (ed), *Sir Edward MacColl*, on which source the following five photographs are largely based.
8   For example, MacColl devised the apparently simple but effective solution to insulator flashover by the regular washing of insulators. This method of overcoming the problem had been suggested by the observation that the fault never seemed to occur on tension sets which were held in position vertically, and so were cleaned by rainfall, but was confined to suspension strings of insulators which were held horizontally, and thus tended to get far more dirty.
9   The abortive Loch Sloy pumped storage scheme was described by MacColl in a paper to the Institution of Engineers and Shipbuilders in Scotland in 1946. See A E MacColl, 'Hydro-Electric Development in Scotland', *Transactions of the Institution of Engineers and Shipbuilders in Scotland*, Vol.89 (1946), p.462. It is touched upon by Henderson, 'The

Central Electricity Board', p.35; Leslie Hannah, 'Rough Draft', p.14; and W T Halcrow, 'Water Power and its Applications to the Production of Metals', pp.166. Mr Leslie Dickerson believes that MacColl had confidential discussions with George Balfour and Sir Andrew MacTaggart about Balfour, Beatty & Co.'s possible involvement in such a scheme.

10   Henderson, 'The Central Electricity Board', p.15.

11   R W Mountain, 'Central Electricity Board to Hydro Board', in Norrie Fraser (ed), *Sir Edward MacColl*, p.20.

12   See above, p.39 and note 10 to Chapter 3.

13   See, for example, R W Mountain, 'Central Electricity Board to Hydro Board', *loc.cit.* p.20; Hannah, 'Rough Draft', p.14.

14   The first representative of the Central Electricity Board on the North of Scotland Hydro-Electric Board was Walter Whigham, a director of the Bank of England. Whigham had to resign soon after appointment because of ill-health. His place was taken by Sir Duncan Watson. A Scot, Watson was a trained engineer who had made his fortune in an electrical contracting business in London before becoming chairman of the Electricity Committee and Conservative mayor of Marylebone. He was knighted for his work as founder chairman of the London Joint Electricity Authority. Hannah, *Electricity before National-isation*, p.103.

15   Lord Airlie, in proposing a toast at the bi-centenary of the British Linen Bank in 1946, expressed his belief that Scotland should have more freedom to direct its own domestic affairs. See Charles A Malcolm, *The History of the British Linen Bank* (Edinburgh: privately printed for the Bank, 1950), p.159.

16   387 *H.C.Deb.*, 24 February 1943, cols 183-84. For Hugh Beaton, see James Kinloch and John Butt, *History of the Scottish Co-operative Wholesale Society Limited* (Glasgow: S.C.W.S., 1981), *passim.*, but especially p.31.

17   Interviews with Mr L H Dickerson, Mr C L C Allan and Mr H W Simpson, September 1986.

18   *Who's Who*, 1976.

19   Sir Charles Westlake, in a posthumous tribute to Thomas Lawrie, *Proceedings of the Institute of Electrical Engineers.*, vol.103, Pt A (June, 1956), p.220.

20   *Electrical Review*, 19 August 1955, p.349; *The Engineer*. Vol.200 (1955), p.248.

21   Interviews with L H Dickerson and Mr H W Simpson, September 1986.

22   NSHEB *Minutes*, 4 October 1943. J R Beard's deputy on the panal and the partner primarily responsible for Merz & McLellan's work for the board, was T G N Haldane. John Rowland, *Progress in Power*, p.101.

23   The duties, responsibilities and remuneration of the members of the Panel of Technical Advisers were formalised in a series of agreements entered into during the summer of 1944. It is apparent from a file ('F/1 Consulting Engineers') among the records of the North of Scotland Hydro-Electric Board that in drawing up the contracts, Thomas Lawrie consulted similar agreements for which he had been responsible in his capacity as secretary to the Galloway Water Power Company. The indespensibility of the Panel has been emphasised by H W Simpson. Interview, September, 1986.

24   The original members of the Amenity Committee were Colonel the Hon. Ian Campbell (chairman), John Bowan, Robert Hurd, Lady MacGregor of MacGregor and Dr I H Ma-civer; and of the Fisheries Committee, Colonel Sir Donald W Cameron of Lochiel (chair-man), Colonel the Hon Ian Campbell, William Malloch, P J Robinson, and F H Williams.

25   W L Calderwood possessed an encyclopaedic knowledge of the habits of the salmon and experience of fish passes in many parts of the world. He had been retained as adviser to the Galloway Scheme. See, for example, Hudson & Hunter, 'The Galloway Hydro-

Electric Development ...', p.351. Dr John Berry had been Research Officer and latterly Director of a Research Station of University College, Southampton. His thesis for the degree of PhD awarded by St Andrews University was 'The Fresh Water Development of *Salmo-Salar*'. He is a Fellow of the Royal Society of Edinburgh.

26 ˒ J Guthrie Brown, 'The Bonny Fechter' in Norrie Fraser (ed), *Sir Edward MacColl*, p.25.

27 See the Hydro-Electric Development (Scotland) Act, 1943, section 4(i).

28 North of Scotland Hydro-Electric Board, *Development Scheme*, p.8, Notes 1 and 2. Emphasis supplied.

29 J Guthrie Brown, *op.cit.*, p.25.

30 Hannah, *Electricity before Nationalisation.*, p.332. This and the following paragraph is based on this invaluable source, pp.329-340.

31 *Ibid.*, p.340.

32 'War Cabinet, Reconstruction Committee, Future of Electricity: Memorandum by the Secretary of State for Scotland (R.44)', undated but apparently 3 February 1944. SRO DD 11/15. It should be noted that under the Act of 1922, the Grampian Electricity Supply Company had an extensive area of development and distribution in Perthshire and Inverness-shire.

33 Gwilym Lloyd-George to Thomas Johnston, 12 February 1944. SRO DD 11/15.

34 Draft letter, dated 16 February 1944, from Tom Johnston to Gwilym Lloyd-George. SRO DD 11/15. The italics are in the original.

35 Gwilym Lloyd-George to Tom Johnston, 22 April 1944. SRO DD 11/15.

36 (Draft) letter, undated, but apparently *c.* 10 May 1944 (SRO DD 11/15). This letter is accompanied by some parts of a correspondence between C C Cunningham, St Andrew's House, Edinburgh, and A G Aglen, Scottish Home Department, London, in which the two civil servants discuss the best wording and tactics for the Secretary of State to adopt. The letters betray a deep-rooted suspicion of the Ministry of Fuel and Power and emphasise 'the enormity of Lloyd-George's proposals'.

37 The advantages of the site were carefully set out by the Dean of the Faculty (pp.59-60) and explained by MacColl (pp. 155ff), Williamson (pp.243-44), and Fulton (p.533). *Public Inquiry into Constructional Scheme No.1* held in December 1944 and January 1945. A full transcript of the Inquiry is among the records of the North of Scotland Hydro-Electric Board. This source will hereinafter be referred to as *Public Inquiry (Sloy)*. The advantages were summarised in the Commemorative Booklet issued by the North of Scotland Hydro-Electric Board on the occasion of the opening of the Loch Sloy Scheme on 18 October 1950, p.21. Hereinafter, *Commemorative Booklet (Sloy)*.

38 E MacColl, evidence before the *Public Inquiry (Sloy)*, p.160.

39 See above, p.51.

40 That a variant of it was considered is apparent from MacColl's address to the Institution of Engineers and Shipbuilders in Scotland. MacColl, 'Hydro-Electric Development in Scotland' (1946), pp.462-3.

41 W D D Fenton, '*Pro Patria Mori*', in Norrie Fraser (ed), *Sir Edward MacColl*, p.34.

42 The three projects included in Constructional Scheme No.1 were number 11 (Sloy), 49 (tributaries of Loch Nevis and Loch Morâr), and 60 (River Udalain) in the Development Scheme.

43 Scottish Home Department, *North of Scotland Hydro-Electric Board. Constructional Scheme No.1: Explanatory Memorandum*, Cmd. 6596 (1945), paragraph 13. Hereinafter cited as *Sloy Explanatory Memorandum*.

44 The Amenity Committee reserved the right to be consulted on the nature and appearance of every permanent structure—the power station, dam, dwelling houses and the like—

which would be required; and the Fishery Committee on the provision of compensation water in connection with the projects at Loch Morar and Loch Alsh.

45 J Guthrie Brown, 'The Bonny Fechter', p.26.

46 *Sloy Explanatory Memorandum*, 'Report of Public Inquiry', paragraphs 2,7.

47 *Public Inquiry (Sloy)*, pp.2–45; *Sloy Explanatory Memorandum*, 'Report of Public Inquiry', paragraphs 3,4,9.

48 The Dean of Faculty remained unruffled even when it was discovered that the Chairman had never been given a copy of the Board's Development Plan. To Mr Cameron's observation that 'I am told that it is such a rare document that no copy is available for me', he responded 'We have the *rara avis* caged here if you wish to see it'. *Public Inquiry (Sloy)*, p.52.

49 Guthrie Brown later referred to the months of preparation by the Board to get the scheme through. Guthrie Brown, 'The Bonny Fechter', p.26.

50 *Sloy Explanatory Memorandum*, 'Report of Public Inquiry', paragraph 8. Mr Cameron was specifically requested by Mr Hill Watson to state in his Report that he had been stopped from developing this line of argument.

51 *Ibid.*, paragraph 36.

52 *Public Inquiry (Sloy)*, pp.591, 597.

53 *Sloy Explanatory Memorandum*, 'Report of Public Inquiry', paragraph 50. Mr Cameron also believed it was significant that 'it was only on 19 September 1944, almost three months *after* the publication of Constructional Scheme No.1. that the County Council resolved "to acquire Loch Sloy".' *Ibid*, paragraph 44. Dunbarton County Council maintained their opposition, and seemed intent on forcing a debate on the scheme in Parliament. However, at the last moment, they accepted the offer of a small water supply from Sloy; this was taken up in the 1960s.

54 Tummel Garry was project No.25 in the Development Scheme and Gairloch, project No.74. Project No.74 involved the impounding of the waters of Loch Bad-an-Sgalaig, Dubh Loch, Am Feur-loch and the River Kerry and tributary streams by means of a dam across the River Kerry, and the generation of electricity at a power station on the north bank of the River Kerry. The total power installed was expected to have an ultimate capacity of 3,000 kW.

55 The details of the Tummel Garry project were discussed at considerable length throughout the course of the Public Inquiry. The clearest statement of the function of the Pitlochry reservoir was given by James Williamson. *Public Inquiry into Constructional Scheme No.2*, pp.244–5. Hereinafter cited *Public Inquiry (Tummel-Garry)*. The scheme was, of course, summarised in Scottish Home Department, *North of Scotland Hydro-Electric Board, Constructional Scheme No.2: Explanatory Memorandum*, Cmd.6660 (1945), pp.2, 7–8. Hereinafter cited *Tummel-Garry Explanatory Memorandum*.

56 *Tummel-Garry Explanatory Memorandum*, p.8, paragraph 5; and see Paton and Guthrie Brown, *op.cit.*, p.87.

57 The foregoing data were given in the Public Inquiry and are conveniently summarised in the subsequent Report, which constitutes part of the *Tummel-Garry Explanatory Memorandum*, pp.8–9, paragraphs 7–10.

58 Guthrie Brown, 'The Bonny Fechter', p.26.

59 Other recommendations relating to the concealment of pipe-lines, the disposal of spoil (Amenity Committee), and the amount of compensation water (Fisheries Committee) were accepted by the Board. These matters are summarised in the *Tummel-Garry Explanatory Memorandum*, pp.2–3, paragraph 5.

60 Tom Johnston, *Memories*, p.174.

61   *Public Inquiry (Tummel-Garry)*, p.6.
62   *Ibid.*, p.15.
63   *Ibid.*, pp.26-7.
64   Tom Johnston, *Memories*, p.178.
65   *Public Inquiry (Tummel-Garry)*, p.65.
66   *Ibid.*, p.75.
67   For example, Lord Airlie was apparently unaware that far from the Grampian Power Co. needing more power, they sold substantial quantities to the Central Electricity Board. *Ibid.*, pp.79 ff, 95.
68   *Ibid.*, pp.100-107.
69   *Ibid.*, p.59.
70   *Ibid.*, pp.125, 136, 148-50.
71   From the luncheon adjournment on the third day to the morning of the fifth day. *Ibid.*, pp.311-453.
72   *Ibid.*, p.416.
73   *Ibid.*, evidence of W L Calderwood, pp.512-65; and Dr John Berry, pp.565-612.
74   *Ibid.*, p.678-80.
75   *Ibid.*, p.785.
76   *Ibid.*, p.1000.
77   *Ibid.*, pp.1071-2. His calculations were based on the following estimates:

Cost of works:	£6,200,000	
Cost of transmission:	1,250,000	
	———————	
Total capital cost:	*c. £7.5 million*	
Gross revenue:	£ 567,000	
	———————	
Against which set charges	339,310	charges on works
	111,610	transmission costs
	30,000	contingencies
	———————	
Total charges	£ 480,920	
'Profit'	£ 86,080	
	———————	

78   *Ibid.*, p.1082.
79   *Ibid.*, p.1110.
80   *Ibid.*, pp.1117, 1119-20, 1123, 1126.
81   *Ibid.*, p.1129. Mr Thomson appeared for the Atholl Estates.
82   *Ibid.*, pp.1132, 1162, 1169, 1178, 1180, 1187.
83   *Tummel-Garry Explanatory Memorandum*, p.18, paragraph 63.
84   *Ibid.*, p.18, paragraph 61.
85   *Ibid.*, p.16, paragraph 49.
86   *Ibid.*, p.18, paragraph 60.
87   *Ibid.*, p.14, paragraph 38.
88   *Ibid.*, p.9, paragraph 11.
89   *H.C.Deb.*, 1945, 415, cols.2184-93.

90 *Ibid.*, cols.2193-201.
91 *Ibid.*, cols.2239-45.
92 *Ibid.*, cols.2233-9.
93 *Ibid.*, cols.2201-4.
94 *Ibid.*, cols.2221-4.
95 *House of Lords Debates*, Fifth series, Vol.137, cols.1171-1200 (22 November 1945); Vol.138, cols.207-55 (3 December 1945). Hereinafter cited *H.L.Deb.*, 1945, 137 and 138.
96 *H.L.Deb.*, 1945, 137, col.1188. Similar arguments were used by Lord Teviot (138, cols.213-4) Viscount Samuel (138, cols.227), and Lord Sempill (138, cols.228-31).
97 *H.L.Deb.*, 1945, 138, col. 247. Lord Westwood referred to Lord Cherwell's statement 'in this House ... that so far nuclear power fission shows no sign of producing atomic energy in any immediately useful form except low-grade heat; and he gave details to show that atomic energy might be a thing of the future, but it certainly was not of the immediate future'.
98 *H.L.Deb.*, 1945, 137, col.1191.
99 *H.L.Deb.*, 1945, 138, col.207. The words are those of Lord Lang of Lambeth, who until 1942 had been Archbishop of Canterbury.
100 *H.L.Deb*, 1945, 137, cols.1198-9.
101 *H.L.Deb.*, 1945, 138, cols.219-22. There was, Lord Rushcliffe asserted 'not a glen, river or waterfall in Scotland which is safe from ... the depredations of the Hydro-Electric Board and its technical advisers, all men, according to Lord Airlie, at the heads of their professions'.
102 *Ibid.*, cols.231-4.
103 North of Scotland Hydro-Electric Board Records: Duntelchaig File, 9/01/12, June 1944—April 1951. Hereinafter cited NSHEB: *Duntelchaig*.
104 *Ibid.*, Thomas Lawrie to Lord Airlie, 9 July 1945. Calderwood, who submitted his first *detailed* report to the Board in July 1945, 'could not but regard this project as unfortunate ... However in this case the proposals are not so bad as I thought they were'. W L. Calderwood to T Lawrie, 11 July 1945. When Calderwood had advised the Board that the original proposals to divert the Upper Findhorn would seriously damage the spawning, the scheme was immediately amended. NSHEB, Board Minutes 389, 27 June 1945.
105 The Duntelchaig file contains lists of all proprietors of lands and fishings to whom details of the scheme were sent in August 1945.
106 NSHEB: *Duntelchaig*, Memorandum on the Findhorn-Duntelchaig Scheme: 'Supply of Water to the Royal Burgh of Inverness', dated 21 November 1945. This memorandum contains copies of the major correspondence between the Board and the Town Clerk and precise estimates of the savings to the Council from the Board's proposals. 'These proposals for joint operation would save the Town Council about £104,000 on capital expenditure account and about £4,600 per annum on the operating costs and charges of the Water Department'.
107 NSHEB: *Duntelchaig*, Thomas Lawrie to Sir John Kennedy, the Electricity Commission, 16 July 1945.
108 NSHEB: *Duntelchaig*, It was freely acknowledged that a water supply partially drawn from the Findhorn and the Nairn and delivered at Loch Ashie would not be as pure as that derived solely from Loch Duntelchaig, but the Board did offer to meet the capital cost of the purification works (£69,000) and to meet half the annual operating costs of the works.
109 A full report of the special meeting of Inverness Town Council at which it was decided that the Council would 'proceed with [their] Provisional Order to obtain absolute control of [their] water supply from Loch Duntelchaig', was carried by *The Northern Chronicle*,

28 November 1945. During the course of the debate one speaker spoke of his abhorrence that the water of the Findhorn should pollute the water of Loch Duntelchaig', and Col E G Henderson referred to the Board's 'Hitlerish' way of doing business.

110 NSHEB: *Duntelchaig*. The expression used by Lawrie in his letter to the Electricity Commissioners, 1 July 1945.

111 NSHEB *Board Minute* 484(c), 18 December 1945; NSHEB, *Second Annual Report* (1945), p.8; NSHEB, 'Loch Duntelchaig', Memorandum, dated 15 February 1958, for the Board Meeting of 19 February 1958. It is noteworthy that Inverness Burgh did not carry out the works for which they obtained powers.

112 Johnston, *Memories*, p.178.

113 *Ibid*.

114 NSHEB, *Board Minutes*, 13 March 1946.

115 Lord Airlie's 'Foreword' to *Sir Edward MacColl*, Norrie Fraser (ed).

CHAPTER 5

1 Johnston, *Memories*, p.178. Johnston's *immediate* successor as Secretary of State for Scotland was the Sixth Earl of Rosebery. Lord Rosebery held office for only two months, when Joseph Westwood was appointed.

2 See above, pp.56-9.

3 Johnston, *Memories*, pp.174-5.

4 *Times*, 6 September 1965, p.10.

5 *Glasgow Herald*, 6 September 1965, p.3.

6 NSHEB, *Second Annual Report* (1945), p.6; NSHEB, Booklet issued at the Opening of the *Loch Sloy Hydro-Electric Scheme* by Her Majesty the Queen, 18 October 1950, p.10 (hereinafter cited NSHEB, *Sloy: Commemorative Booklet*); Panel of Technical Advisers to the North of Scotland Hydro-Electric Board: *Progress Report*, July 1945 (hereinafter cited *Progress Report*).

7 The predominant mica-schist rock on the site of the dam was unsuitable for concrete aggregate. Two alternative sources of good aggregate were located near the dam, one consisting of granite, situated at a high elevation about 3 miles north, and the other of grano-diorite (tonalite) in the Coiregrogain Valley about $1\frac{1}{2}$ miles south. Subsequent investigation revealed that the southerly site was preferable for exploitation, and the Board decided to open a quarry at Coiregrogain from which to supply crushed aggregate to all the contractors. *The Engineer*, Vol. CXC, 4 August, 1950; see also James Stevenson, 'The Construction of Loch Sloy Dam', *Proceedings of the Institution of Civil Engineers*, Vol.1, Part III, August 1952, pp.176-7; *Engineering* Vol.170, 7 July 1950, p.3. The account of the construction of Loch Sloy rests heavily on these three sources.

8 See Stevenson, *op.cit*., p.178, and the ensuing discussion of his paper which was presented to a meeting of the Works Construction Division of the Institution of Civil Engineers, 12 February, 1952, pp.211, 218.

9 The decision to erect cableways was taken by the Board and the use of this invaluable equipment was made available to the contractors free of charge. The cableways attracted much contemporary comment, and their mode of construction and operation were described in detail by *The Engineer*, *Engineering* and by James Stevenson, *op.cit*., pp.172-5.

10 A J Roberston, *The Bleak Mid-Winter: 1947* (Manchester: Manchester University Press, 1987).

11 All these shortages were discussed in detail by the Cabinet Investment Programmes Com-
    mittee in May 1948. The Board's labour problems were so serious that the Committee
    believed that 'the labour available might not be sufficient to make use of the [scarce] materials
    estimated to be required'. Not only was labour short, the wastage was exceptionally high—
    a 'turnover of 2,300 men had been necessary to secure an increase of 400 in one month'—
    and it was of indifferent quality. Allocations of steel in the early months of 1948 had fallen
    22 per cent below requirements and cement could be supplied only 'at the expense of
    other Scottish schemes'. 'Extract from Minutes of the Cabinet Investment Programmes
    Committee, 28 May 1948', among Agenda Papers for Board meeting of 9 June 1948.
12 Balfour, Beatty & Co. to James Williamson & Partners, 2 September 1948, among Agenda
    Papers for Board's meeting of 11 October 1948. Cf. pp.105-6.
13 To provide a typical example. On 31 March, 1947, J D Mitchell, the Chief Welfare Officer
    reported from the camp at Inveruglas that 'During the past few weeks we have had an
    influx of labour of an undesirable kind and several agitators have unfortunately undermined
    the standing of their own [Local Welfare] Committee. The climax came at a general
    Meeting of the men where a protest was made against the introduction of a meal-ticket
    system when two of the places on the Committee were filled ... by men who have since
    done little else except stir up trouble and complaints'. NSHEB: *Chief Welfare Officer's
    Report*, March 1947.
14 Johnston, *Memories*, p.179.
15 The problem of providing accommodation at the same rate as that of recruitment was still
    acute even as late as the summer of 1947. The problem was exacerbated by extensive storm
    damage in the dreadful winter of 1946-47.
16 See, for example, NSHEB, *Progress Report* for month ending 1 May 1947: Constructional
    Scheme No.1, Loch Sloy.
17 The clearest discussion of the relative technical and economic merits of the different types
    of dam which might have been adopted for Sloy is that by E J K Chapman and D Fraser
    Campbell, 'The Design and Economics of Massive Buttress Dams', *Fifth International Con-
    gress on Large Dams, held in Paris, 1955*, pp.277-99. See also *The Engineer*, 21 July 1950.
18 Sir Andrew MacTaggart in the discussion of Stevenson's paper, *loc.cit.*, p.206.
19 James Stevenson, replying to the discussion of his paper, *ibid.*, p.220.
20 The decision to scrap the original design and substitute pre-casting was subsequently to be
    praised as demonstrating an unusual degree of co-operation between the engineers and the
    contractors. J C Waddington, *ibid.*, p.212.
21 NSHEB: *Progress Report* (April 1947), p.2.
22 The impact of the necessary diversion on the timetable, and on the financial arrangements
    between the Board and the contractors, Edmund Nuttall, Sons & Co., are discussed in a
    letter, dated 12 April 1950, from Nuttalls to the consulting engineers, James Williamson &
    Partners, among the Board's Agenda Papers for the meeting of 10 May 1950.
23 Interview with Mr J Black, a foreman at Loch Sloy.
24 The journal *Engineering* devoted considerable space to the design, especially of the second
    bifurcation, which it found 'of interest, since geometrically it consists of splitting two cones
    which taper from 10ft to 7ft in diameter in mitre fashion'. *Loc cit.*, 21 July 1950, pp.49-50.
25 NSHEB: *Progress Report on Loch Sloy Project* (April 1947), p.3.
26 NSHEB: *Progress Report on Loch Sloy Project* (June 1947), p.1, *ibid* (August 1947), p.4.
27 *Ibid.* (September 1947), p.3.
28 *The English Electric Journal*, Vol.12, No.3, (June 1951), p.17, the source of much of the
    preceding two paragraphs.
29 The first generating set was put into commercial service on 6 March 1950, the others were

put into service on 20 July 1950, 30 November 1950 and 1 February 1951. *Ibid.*, p.18.

30   See above, p.60.

31   For the high-level tunnels, see James Williamson, in discussion of the paper by Angus Fulton. 'Civil Engineering Aspects of Hydro-Electric Development in Scotland', *Proceedings of the Institution of Civil Engineers*, Part I, Vol.1 (1952), p.284; NSHEB, *Sloy: Commemorative Booklet*, p.12; *The Engineer*, Vol. CXCl (22 June 1951); *Water Power*, Vol.2 (September-October 1950).

32   The source of this paragraph is an anonymous essay, probably prepared for a newspaper article, among the NSHEB papers relating to Loch Sloy.

33   T B Morrison, Chief Lands Officer, DOAS, in Norrie Fraser, *op.cit.*, p.54; the earlier quotation, concerning the electric light bulbs, is from W D D Fenton's contribution to the same symposium, p.35.

34   NSHEB, *Sloy Commemorative Booklet*, p.7. The author of the text is anonymous but the wording of the general introduction, from which the first quotation is taken, was undoubtedly inspired by Johnston; it is certainly in keeping with his 'Foreword' to the booklet (p.6).

35   See above, pp.63-4; *The Engineer*, 2 September 1955, pp.334-6; Paton and Brown, *op.cit.*, pp.130-2.

36   J Guthrie Brown, 'The Bonnie Fechter', in Norrie Fraser (ed), *op.cit.*, p.27.

37   *Engineering*, 1 December 1950, p.427. This information is from first of a series of four articles on 'The Tummel-Garry Scheme of the North of Scotland Hydro-Electric Board' in this periodical, December 1950.

38   Personal interview with Mr J Black; NSHEB, *Progress Report* (Civil Engineering), 20 June 1947—24 July 1947.

39   NSHEB, *Progress Report* (Civil Engineering), Tummel-Garry Project, 25 July 1947—21 August 1947. The quotation is from the 'General' section of the Report: details relating to individual contractors follow and give substance to the general observations. A detailed account of 'The Driving and Lining of the Clunie Tunnel on the Tummel-Garry Hydro-Electric Project' was presented to a meeting of the Works Construction Division of the Institution of Civil Engineers in February, 1950, by C F Grundy. This account, and the discussion which followed, sheds additional light on the reasons for the high labour turnover. At certain points the extremely hard quartzite encountered in the Clunie tunnel—its hardness on Moh's scale was about 7-8; on the same scale the hardness of a diamond is 10—necessitated drill charges at every 18 inches; the noise at the face was all but intolerable; tunnelling equipment was often unobtainable (some had a two-year delivery date); and there was a chronic shortage of skilled foremen. Grundy believed that 'no progress would be made [in solving the labour problem] until it was the practice to look upon the tunnel driver as a super-craftsman and to encourage suitable workmen to be trained and to stay in the craft and become really proud of their achievements' (p.39).

40   *Ibid.*, 19 September 1947—23 October 1947.

41   For the Control of Engagement Orders see, for example, Alec Cairncross, *Years of Recovery: British Economic Policy 1945-51* (London: Methuen, 1975), pp.305, 338, 397.

42   NSHEB: *Progress Report* (Civil Engineering), Tummel-Garry Project, 23 January 1948—19 February 1947.

43   NSHEB, 'Notes of a Meeting with Messrs Keir & Cawder and Representatives of the Italian Contracting Firm of Astaldi's on 12 January 1948', Agenda Papers for Board Meeting of 14 July 1948.

44   *Engineering*, 1 December 1950, p.426.

45   J Guthrie Brown, 'The Bonnie Fechter', in Norrie Fraser (ed), *op.cit.*, p.27.

46   See *The Engineer*, 2 September 1955, p.335, *Engineering*, 1 December 1950, p.426. In the

case of Pitlochry certain difficulties *were* experienced. The cofferdam works were kept low in order to reduce costs, and the provisions made to deal with floods proved to be inadequate. On four occasions the west cofferdam was overtopped and the workings were intentionally flooded to prevent a serious breach. The complications of using two-stage cofferdam methods are outlined by Fulton and Dickerson, 'Design and Constructional Features of Hydro-electric Dams built in Scotland since 1945', *Proceedings of the Institution of Civil Engineers*, Vol.29 (1964), pp.721,725.

47   The dimensions for the pools were governed by the necessity to keep turbulence to a minimum. They were obtained by experiment at the Imperial College of Science & Technology, London, by Professor C M White, and checked in a full-scale model before any passes were built. See A A Fulton, *op.cit.*, p.264; *The Engineer*, 1 December 1950, p.429.

48   See Johnston, *Memories*, p.184: 'On one Perthshire series of schemes alone, I am sure upon fish ladders and one thing after another, we must have spent nearly a quarter of a million sterling in ensuring that damage to salmon was avoided'. See also T Lawrie 'Highland Water Power—The Developments of the North of Scotland Hydro-Electric Board', *Proceedings of the Institution of Electrical Engineers*, Part A, Vol.103 (1956), pp.214-5; Paton & Brown, *op.cit.*, pp.64-5. Even the design of the intake to the Clunie Tunnel, about 200ft upstream of the dam, was affected by the needs of the salmon. The entrance had to be big enough, 114ft × 36ft, to reduce the velocity of the flow of water sufficiently to prevent small fish being held against the screens and killed. See *The Engineer*, 1 December 1950, p.429.

49   A detailed discussion of the Tummel-Garry drum gates can be found in *Engineering*, 1 December 1950, pp.427-29. Drum gates had previously been extensively employed on high dams in the United States. Their use on the comparatively low dams at Clunie and Pitlochry gave rise to special problems. It was the solution of these problems that was the reason for the experiments at Imperial College. See also Paton & Brown, *op.cit.*, pp.52-3.

50   J Guthrie Brown, in Norrie Fraser (ed), *op.cit.*, p.28.

51   For the construction of Clunie tunnel, see *Engineering*, 8 December 1950, pp.460-62; *The Engineer*, 10 and 17 March 1950.

52   For the genesis of the Clunie Memorial Arch, see Guthrie Brown, in Norrie Fraser (ed), *op.cit.*, p.30, and Paton & Brown, *op.cit.*, p.130.

53   NSHEB, *Annual Report and Statement of Accounts*, *1950*, p.10.

54   J Guthrie Brown, in Norrie Fraser (ed), *op.cit.*, p.29.

55   Lady Margaret MacColl, 'Last Word' in Norrie Fraser (ed), *op.cit.*, p.64.

56   J Guthrie Brown, in Norrie Fraser (ed), *op.cit.*, p.29.

57   A complete list of the consultants and architects employed by the Board in 1948 is included among the Agenda Papers for the Board Meeting of 8 September 1948.

58   NSHEB: Agenda Papers (Additional) for Board Meeting, 14 January 1948, Item 2.

59   Leslie Hannah, *Engineers, Managers and Politicians*, pp.1-2.

60   Sir Norman Chester, *The Nationalisation of British Industry* (London: HMSO, 1975), pp.428-9.

61   See above, pp.57-9.

62   T Johnston, *Memories*, p.180.

63   L Hannah, *Electricity before Nationalisation*, p.130. The relationship between the CEB and the infant Hydro-Board has been examined by the same author in his 'Rough Draft', pp.29-32, and the subsequent paragraph is derived largely from this source.

64   The CEB had agreed to pay a price above the cost of the cheapest new coal-fire station, but below that of some existing stations which they would otherwise have had to incorporate into the Central Scotland scheme and pay accordingly. CEB Minutes, 23/24/29 June 1927 (Hannah, 'Rough Draft', p.29, note 4; and see *Electricity Before Nationalisation*, pp.130, 378, note 63).

65 The Cooper Committee had recommended 'that the Central Electricity Board should pay for supplies to the grid a price not less than that paid by them for supplies from the most efficient steam stations in Scotland ... and at coal prices ruling in the Central Scotland District' (*Cooper Committee*, p.27, paragraph 63, (7)(b)).

66 The CEB complained that if hydro power were used to meet load growth the Cooper Committee formula would involve comparison with older and increasingly obsolescent plant in Scotland. From the viewpoint of the national economy it was argued that the price paid by the CEB should be determined with reference to more efficient modern plant. In fact, the price which the Hydro Board received from the sale of electricity to the CEB was defined as the 'cost of production of the *most* economical steam-generating station operated to the instructions of the CEB', and for the first few years of its existence this target station was the Ironbridge generating station owned by the West Midlands Joint Electricity Authority. See MacColl, 'Hydro-Electric Development in Scotland', p.457. Emphasis supplied. 'The Rules for ascertaining the price payable to the Central Electricity Board to the Board for electricity supplied in any year', are set down as the Fourth Schedule to the 1943 Act.

67 NSHEB, 'Enquiry into Point or Points of Delivery of Electricity by Hydro Board to Central Board', a bound volume of the papers relating to the case and on which the following paragraph is based. The specific references below, 68-73, relate to documents in this collection.

68 'The HEB Case', 10 January 1946, paragraphs 21,22,35.

69 'The CEB Case', 30 March 1946, paragraph 23. Later paragraphs 24-6, stated that the CEB was prepared to permit the Hydro Board to deliver some part of its supplies at 132kV 'at non-generating Grid points in substitution for delivery of three of the selected generating station points of connection'. These Grid points should be at Greenock, Port Dundas, and Motherwell. Delivery at lower voltage busbars would be at Braehead, Clyde's Mill, Bonnybridge, at 'a new station in the East', Portobello and Dundee.

70 It has to be said that Harold Hobson did make some concessions in a letter to Lord Airlie, dated 26 March 1946, but the general tenor of the negotiations which followed is summed up in an entry in the 'Brief Diary of events' in the case, dated 23 April 1945: 'The Hydro Board met Mr Hobson and Sir Johnstone Wright in Edinburgh to "discuss" Mr Hobson's proposals. There was no real discussion for on Mr Hobson's part it was "take it or leave it". For its part, the Board was almost equally adamant: Hobson's "offer" was subsequently withdrawn.'

71 The Hydro Board estimated that they would derive an annual profit of £268,000 from sales of electricity generated at Sloy and at Tummel-Garry. The annual cost of transmission of this power to the CEB would be £157,000 if their proposals were accepted and £252,000 if they gave in to the demands of the CEB, producing balances of £111,000 and only £16,000 respectively with which to finance uneconomic schemes. 'Hydro Board's Reply to Central Board's Case', paras 9-11.

72 'Summary of early negotiations and present position', 22 March 1946, para 12.

73 A E Marson, Secretary to the Electricity Commissioners, to the Secretary, North of Scotland Hydro-Electric Board, 25 April 1946.

74 For the Hydro Board's reception of the Determination by the Electricity Commissioners, see NSHEB *Minute* No.580, 8 May 1946; and for the CEB's reaction, Hannah, 'Rough Notes', p.32. Hannah observes (Note 1) that 'The Commissioners ... were old enemies of the CEB and friends of the NSHEB; the CEB's lawyers advised that the Commissioners had exceeded their powers; they certainly seem to have done their best for the NSHEB and hydro-electricity, though their past record was not one which inspires confidence in their

economic judgement'. For Tom Johnston's faith in the wisdom of the Electricity Commissioners, see *Memories*, p.181.

75   The Board's reply to this inquiry is interesting. Although it emphasises their desire to 'continue to administer the ... Act of 1943, in its present form', they made it plain that they would be prepared to take over the other undertakings in the North of Scotland and would not be averse to the whole of Scotland being treated as 'a single region, but the initiative in the matter might come from the Commissioners themselves or the Secretary of State'. NSHEB *Minutes* 486 (18 December 1945) and 496 (9 January 1946).

76   Johnston, *Memories*, p.180. Johnston adds, 'Mr Morrison ... though with greater native caution not broadcasting his conversion, left me in no doubt whatever but that we could count on his support'. Following his visit to Sloy, Morrison wrote to Tom Johnston that 'I can assure you that I shall always wish, insofar as I have a say in these matters, to see that proper regard is had, in Government plans, to the good work being done by the Hydro-Electric Board'. NSHEB, *Minute* No. 669 (16 October 1946).

77   Chester, *Nationalisation*, p.431, citing Cabinet Committee: Ministerial Committee on the Socialisation of Industries (46) 39, 9th Meeting.

78   *Ibid.*, p.432; and see Hannah, 'Rough Notes', p.34, from which it is clear that further meetings between Shinwell, Tom Johnston and other representatives of the Hydro Board took place.

79   Chester, *Nationalisation*, p.432, and see Johnston, *Memories*, p.181. It should be noted that distribution schemes had *only* to secure the approval of the Secretary of State.

80   The full list comprised: (i) *The Electricity Departments of the following local authorities*: Aberdeen, Buckie, Dundee, Inverness, Lossiemouth and Branderburgh, Oban and Perth; (ii) *Undertakings of the following companies*: Campbeltown and Mid-Argyll Electric Supply Co., Crieff Electric Supply Co.Ltd., Dunoon and District Electricity Supply Co.Ltd., Grampian Electricity Supply Co., Loch Leven Electricity Supply Co.Ltd., North of Scotland Electric Light and Power Co.Ltd., Peterhead Electricity Co.Ltd., Stornoway Electric Supply Co.Ltd., Thurso and District Electric Supply Co.Ltd.; (iii) *Holding Companies*: Scottish Power Co.Ltd. NSHEB, *Annual Report*, 1948, Appendix III, p.44.

81   NSHEB, *Annual Report*, 1948, pp.9-10 .

82   Johnston, *Memories*, p.180. For Lord Citrine, see Hannah, *Engineers, Managers and Politicians*, *passim*.

83   Hannah, *Engineers, Managers and Politicians*, p.151.

84   Johnston, *Memories*, p.181.

CHAPTER 6

1   NSHEB, *Annual Report and Accounts*, 1950, p.7.

2   Tom Lawrie, Secretary to the Board from its inception, had been appointed General Manager in 1948. Lawrie died, almost certainly from exhaustion, in 1955 and was succeeded by Angus Fulton, the Board's first hydraulic engineer. MacColl's *title* of Deputy Chairman and Chief Executive Officer was not reinstated until 1973. See Appendix 2.

3   Interview with Mr Peter Aitken, the Board's Chief Hydraulic Engineer from 1955 to 1980. In October 1948 Balfour Beatty & Co. informed the consulting engineers for the Fannich Project, Sir Alexander Gibb & Partners, that on this contract they were unable to pay their way, and that every week saw an increase in their deficit. They explained '... there is too much tunnelling in course of construction today in Scotland for the amount of labour available .... The result is tunnelling men go from job to job picking out the

best conditions they can obtain until necessity has raised the wages to a premium beyond what anyone would have visualised when tendering for the work'. Balfour Beatty & Co. to Sir Alexander Gibb & Partners, 4 October 1948, among Agenda Papers for Board meeting of 11 October 1948. It is noteworthy that the Board often complained that in obtaining supplies of such necessary materials as sand and gravel, they were confronted by 'rings' of contractors, all of whom quoted identical prices. For example, NSHEB, Finance and General Purposes Committee, Minute 353, 1 September 1952.

4   NSHEB, *Annual Report and Accounts*, 1958, p.1.

5   Those readers who require more details are directed to the source materials on which these accounts are based.

6   The schemes have been discussed collectively within generation groups in an order determined by the dates of the earliest scheme within each group.

7   Aspects of the Conon Valley development have been the subject of many articles in the technical press. The neatest summary of its major features is that by Paton and Brown, *op.cit.*, pp.132-5, and the Board's own publication, *Power from the Glens*, 2nd edn, pp.16-9. Much greater details of the Fannich Scheme can be found in *The Engineer*, Vol.191 (1951), pp.746-9, 780-3; *Engineering*, Vol.172 (1951), pp.64-8, 129-32; and *Water Power*, Vol.3 (1951). A useful article on the Glascarnoch-Luichart-Torr Achilty section is in *Water Power*, Vol.6 (1954), pp.113-16; and the most detailed study of the Orrin project is that by A G Gowers, 'Some Points of Interest in the Design and Construction of Orrin Dam, Ross-shire', *Proceedings of the Institution of Civil Engineers*, Vo.24 (1963). pp.449-72.

8   See above, p.13.

9   The six major contractors and their most important works were as follows: Reed and Mallik, Salisbury, for Luichart, Glascarnoch, and Vaich dams, and the Rannoch aqueduct; William Tawse, Torr Achilty dam and power station; A M Carmichael for Glascarnoch and Vaich tunnels; George Wimpey for Luichart tunnel; Duncan Logan, for Meig dam and Luichart power station; and J Campbell & Son, Inverness, for Glascarnoch (Mossford) power station.

10 The International Commission on Large Dams defines a dam in terms of its height from foundation level to crest. A large dam is one with a height of at least 50ft or 15 metres. J Guthrie Brown in the 'Discussion' of the paper by Gowers, *op.cit.*, *Proceedings of the Institution of Civil Engineers*, Vol.27 (1964), p.378.

11 This important point was made by Gowers, *op.cit.*, p.459, and emphasised in the 'Discussion' by Angus Fulton, *loc.cit.*, p.377.

12 A P Shrimpton (of Freeman, Fox & Partners) in the discussion of the paper by Gowers, *ibid.*, p.384.

13 Peter L Aitken, Leslie H Dickerson and William J M Menzies, 'Fish Passes and Screens on Water Power Works', *Proceedings of the Institution of Civil Engineers*, Vol.35 (1966), pp.34 ff. While Sir Alexander Gibb & Partners were grappling with the design of the fish ladder at Pitlochry, Borland, a keen salmon fisher, devoted much thought to the problems of getting salmon over the much higher dams being contemplated by the Board. He built a model of his pass at Kilmarnock, and Mr I A Duncan Millar, then resident engineer at Pitlochry, was commissioned to produce salmon parr of a certain sise to observe their behaviour when confronted by the pass—such was Borland's attention to detail that 'exactly similar young trout' were rejected for these experiments. I am indebted to Mr I A Duncan Miller for this information. The subsequent refinement of the design and its adaptation to different conditions are discussed by Aitken, Dickerson and Menzies, *op.cit.*

14 Gowers, *op.cit.*, p.462. See also the contributions to the discussion of the paper made by O Elsden and G A Bonnyman, both of Sir Alexander Gibb & Partners, *loc.cit.*, pp.381, 384.

15 *Water Power*, Vol.6 (1954), p.115.

16 Angus Fulton, in the Discussion of Gowers' paper, *Proceedings of the Institution of Civil Engineers*, Vol.27 (1964), p.377.

17 NSHEB, *Annual Report*, 1946, p.7. This account of the Affric Scheme is based largely on the Board's *Annual Reports*, 1946-52; *Engineering*, Vol.174 (1952), pp.457-60, 489-93, 553-5; *The Engineer*, Vol.193 (1952), pp.490-2, 522-6, 554-6; G G Dillon, 'The Mullardoch-Fasnakyle-Affric Tunnels', *Proceedings of the Institution of Civil Engineers*; C M Roberts, 'Special Features of the Affric Hydro-Electric Scheme (Scotland)', *Proceedings of the Institution of Civil Engineers*, Part 1, Vol.2 (1953), pp.520-55, and the 'Discussion', pp.584-606, and 'Correspondence', pp.606-609; W Eastwood, G A Taylor and J Allen, 'Scale Model Experiments on High-Head Syphons and Vortex Chambers connected thereto', *Proceedings of the Institution of Civil Engineers*, Part 1, Vol.2 (1953), pp.556-84; and miscellaneous papers among the NSHEB archives, including *Power From the Glens*, 2nd edn, pp.20-3.

18 The details of such activity are contained in the *Progress Reports* submitted to the Board by the consulting civil engineers, Sir William Halcrow & Partners.

19 These cuts—and their impact on the Board's schemes—are discussed in a letter from Tom Johnston to the Secretary of State, a copy of which is among the Agenda Papers for the meeting of 11 January 1950: T Johnston to Arthur Woodburn, 21 December 1949.

20 The thickening and raising the height of Mullardoch Dam is duscussed in detail by Roberts, *op.cit.*, pp.541-55, from which source the quotation is taken (p.541). See also *Engineering*, Vol.74, p.459, and A A Fulton, 'Civil Engineering Aspects of Hydro-Electric Development in Scotland', p.273-4.

21 A vivid account of the construction of 'The Mullardoch-Fasnakyle-Affric Tunnels' was given to a meeting of the Works Construction Engineering Division of the Institution of Civil Engineers on 28 February 1950, by Edmund C Dillon. It is apparent that all of the labour difficulties encountered at Sloy and Tummel-Garry were repeated at Affric. One of the contributors to the discussion, George Ford, provided some remarkable figures on labour turnover. The contractors required a labour force of about 1,500—1,600 men; up to the end of December 1949, nearly 9,200 men had been enrolled. During the six months ending 31 December, 1949, 2,578 men and 2,516 boys had been taken on. 'There had been, therefore, a continuous wastage of about 20-30 per cent per month'. It was believed that mechanisation was one possible solution to the problem but because of the great scarcity of operators and mechanics to maintain and repair machines even 'complete mechanisation was of doubtful value' (p.32), and could continue to be so until schemes existed 'for the education of labour forces to allow proper usage and maintenances of large-scale and expensive equipment' (p.25).

22 Into this section are led two side stream intakes. They were of an original design, their final form having been evolved after extensive model tests by Professor J Allen at Aberdeen University. The main object of the design was to avoid injecting air into the tunnel which, *inter alia*, could interfere with the efficiency of the turbines because they would be supplied with an emulsion with a density less than that of water. The matter is discussed at length by Eastwood, Taylor and Allan, *op.cit.* See also *The Engineer*, Vol.193, pp.525-6.

23 But, as Angus Fulton observed in the discussion of Roberts' paper before the Institution of Civil Engineers (*loc.cit.*, p.586), if steel had been saved it had been done at the expense of cement, which was almost equally scarce.

24 *Engineering*, Vol.174, 17 October 1952, p.507; Paton and Brown, *op.cit.*, p.123. Tom Lawrie to Lord Lovat, 7 February 1955, among the Agenda Papers for the Board Meeting of 16 March 1955. See also *HC Deb*, 1958, 591, col.967.

25 *HC Deb*, 1958, 591, cols.946-76.

26   The Strathfarrar and Kilmorack Scheme is the subject of a two-part article in *Water Power*, Vol.16 (1964), pp.50-69, 95-106, and a Paper, 'Design Aspects of the Strathfarrar and Kilmorack Hydro-electric Scheme', by C M Roberts, E B Wilson and J G Wiltshire, in *Proceedings of the Institution of Civil Engineers*, Vol.30 (1965), pp.449-87.

27   Roberts *et.al.*, *op.cit.*, p.453. The use of gates was, in fact, dictated by the necessity of flood control. It was decided to make them automatic only after 'a world-wide enquiry, covering about 800 gates, which revealed that, although there was often reluctance to incorporate automatic devices, there was no report of such a device having failed to act when it should'. *Ibid.*, p.483. See also the subsequent 'Discussion', *Proceedings of the Institution of Civil Engineers*, Vo..35 (1966), p.125.

28   A Deriaz machine is similar to a Kaplan but has inclined blades. It is particularly suitable for the head range between the Kaplan and the Francis turbine. The Deriaz turbine is briefly discussed by Roberts *et al.*, *op.cit.*, pp.482-83, and more fully by P Deriaz, 'Comparative study of Kaplan and Deriaz turbines', *Electrica Review*, November 1959.

29   Indeed, the entire Strathfarrar and Kilmorack scheme is of the greatest interest to the civil engineer. See Roberts *et al.*, *op.cit.*, and the subsequent, 'Discussion' in *Proceedings of the Institution of Civil Engineers*, Vol.35 (1966), pp.120-44.

30   J Guthrie Brown, in 'Discussion' of Fulton and Dickerson's paper, 'Design and constructional features of hydro-electric dams built in Scotland since 1945', *Proceedings of the Institution of Civil Engineers*, Vol.33 (1966), p.454. See also the 'Discussion' of the paper by Roberts *et al.*, *loc.cit.*, p.126.

31   Roberts *et al.*, *op.cit.*, p.453. The valley was, in fact, described as being 'a symmetrical trapezoidal ... of Moine psammitic granulite with thin drift cover, with a theoretical dam chord/height ratio of 3.3/1'. The Board may also have been influenced by the success of the arch dam at Chliostair in Harris - the first structural arch dam built in Britain—which was engineered by Mr L H Dickerson and his staff. It is noteworthy that the Board's two hydro stations in Lewis (Gisla) and Harris (Chliostair) were built at the insistence of Tom Johnston to show that even the most remote parts of the Board's area had not been forgotten. These two schemes—both commissioned in 1960—were built against much advice that the money would be better spent elsewhere. I am indebted to Mr I A Duncan Millar for this information. See also Discussion of paper by Roberts *et al.*, *loc.cit.*, pp.122,134.

32   Roberts *et al.*, *op.cit.*, p.453.

33   'Discussion' of the paper by Roberts *et al.*, *loc.cit.*, see particularly paras.146, 150, 151, pp.136-7.

34   *Ibid.*, para.170, p.144.

35   A summary statement on the instrumentation of the Monar dam is provided by *Water Power*, Vol.16, 1964, p.55.

36   This brief account of the salient features of the Garry and Moriston developments is based on the NSHEB's Construction Scheme files and *Annual Reports*; a remarkably detailed series of six articles in *The Engineer*, Vol.202 (1956), pp.468-70, 503-5, 545-6, 577-9, 611-14, 647-9; *Water Power*, Vol.11 (1959), 204-11, 247-55; and C M Roberts, Edgar B Wilson, J H Thornton and H Headland, 'The Garry and Moriston Hydro-Electric Schemes', *Proceedings of the Institution of Civil Engineers*, Vol.11 (1958), pp.41-68.

37   See above, pp.31-3.

38   The influence of the provision for salmon on the design and construction of the Garry scheme is discussed by Roberts *et al* (1958), pp.56-7, on which this paragraph is based.

39   The Trieg dam of the Lochaber scheme is an early example of a rockfill dam and, according to Sir William Halcrow, it inspired many imitations overseas. Its use in Scotland was much more limited, partly because the prevalent rocks in the Highlands are schists, which are

generally laminar in structure, and which sometimes deteriorate due to weathering. Fishery interests too are antagonistic to rock-fill dams because the sluicing away of 'fines' during construction make a river temporarily unsuitable for fish. The site at Quoich was particularly suitable for a rockfill dam. The rock available—partly from a nearby quarry and partly (about 26 per cent) from tunnel spoil—was granulite and, as we have seen, special precautions were taken to settle out the rock flour, or fines. *The Engineer*, Vol.202 (1956), p.503.

40 As a further aid to secure good compaction, no material smaller than $\frac{3}{8}$in. was used in the construction.

41 The lengths and heights of Cruadloch north and south were, respectively, 450ft and 53ft and 280ft and 70ft.

42 *The Engineer*, Vol.202 (1956), p.611

43 Calculated from figures given by Roberts *et al*, *op.cit*., p.49. This paper gives details of the equipment required *on the Cluanie site* for the grinding of the slag (chemical analysis of which was made at each tapping of the furnaces at Clyde Iron), its subsequent use in the concrete mixers, and the distribution of the resulting product. MacColl's instigation of inquiries into the use of blast furnace slag is referred to in a memorandum on 'Cement Supplies', dated 24 November 1949, among the Agenda Papers for the Board Meeting of 16 November 1949.

44 Among the advantages said to be offered by underground power stations are

   (i) a greater freedom to make optimum use of head and ground conditions;
   (ii) the possibility of using short high-pressure intake shafts in rock;
   (iii) the elimination of tunnel lining except at points of weakness and at special junctions;
   (iv) simplified constructions in foundations, walls and crane runways;
   (v) protection from surface rock falls and floods;
   (vi) low maintenance costs.

   See Roberts *et al*, *op.cit*, p.58.

45 It is evident that in the design and lighting of underground power stations, the Board's engineers were influenced by contemporary Swedish practice. See 'Visit to Sweden' by A A Fulton and C L C Allan, Note for Agenda of Board Meeting of 21 October 1953.

46 Loch Shin is the largest of the Board's reservoirs. Flooding much of the top spawning grounds brought home to the Fishery experts that smolt escapment from long reservoirs closed by dams was very difficult. Smolts are largely current-borne, and when the major draw off through the intake tunnels to the turbines is partially impeded by screens, there is little to attract the smolts to the relatively small flow allowed down a fish pass. I am indebted to Mr I A Duncan Miller for this information.

47 NSHEB, *Annual Report*, 1960, p.5. Perhaps because of its straightforward design, its uneventful progress, and its relatively small scale, the Shin scheme attracted little attention in the technical press. Nor were there any aspects of the scheme sufficiently novel to warrant detailed examination by the Institution of Civil Engineers. The Shin scheme did not entirely escape public notice, however. In a debate on the Board's *Report and Accounts* in 1958, Sir David Robertson criticised the Board's inability to keep within its estimated costs: 'I believe the cause is unrestricted overtime, men working 12 hours a day, with time and a half on Saturday and double time on Sunday. I believe the publicans have benefited greatly from the work on the Shin scheme on which fantastic wages have been paid'. *H.C.Deb.*, 1958, 581, col.127.

48 The Breadalbane scheme, like the other schemes, has an extensive technical literature. Among the more important sources on which this account is based are: *The Engineer*,

Vol.206 (1958), pp.44-6, 84-9, 124-6, 164-5; *Water Power*, Vol.8 (1956), pp.8-16, Vol.11 (1959), pp.141-4; A A Fulton and W T Marshall, 'The Use of Fly Ash and similar materials in concrete', *Proceedings of the Institution of Civil Engineers*; Part 1, Vol.5 (1956), pp.714-30; and A C Allen, 'Features of Lednock dam, including the use of fly ash', *Proceedings of the Institution of Civil Engineers*, Vol.13 (1959), pp.179-96. The Board's own publications, especially the *Annual Reports* and *Power from the Glens*, 2nd edition, have also been useful.

49   *Water Power*, Vol.11 (1959), p.142. See also *The Engineer*, Vol.206, p.164: 'it is unlikely that any other large Pelton wheel will ever be installed in the Board's future schemes'.

50   In fact, the Trief process was employed at Breadalbane as well, but its use was confined to certain of the outlying aqueducts. *The Engineer*, Vol.206, p.84.

51   See Fulton & Marshall, *op.cit.*, pp.714-15, 727-8, and A C Allen, *op.cit.*, pp.186-95. From an economic viewpoint, it would clearly have been desirable to replace a larger proportion of cement by fly ash, but the experiments carried out by Prof. Marshall at Glasgow revealed that the loss of initial strength increased considerably when the replacement proportion rose from 20 per cent to 30 per cent. One very real problem was the variability of the fly ash. That this was much greater than expected was attributed to the fact that Braehead power station, the source of the fly ash, was compelled to use so many different coals during the period during which it was supplying fly ash to Lednock. During 1956, 103 varieties of Scottish coal were used in addition to coal imported from the United States. (Allen, pp.187-8, 194).

52   *The Engineer*, Vol.206, p.84.

53   It is interesting that, at the design stage, three alternatives to the buttress dam were considered. These were gravity, earth- and rock-fill types. Estimates of the buttress and earth-fill designs were so close that both were investigated in detail and the latter was included as an alternative in the tender documents; it attracted the second lowest bid. *Ibid.*, p.85.

54   See the observations of A C Allen in the 'Discussion' of A A Fulton, 'Civil Engineering aspects of hydro-electric developments in Scotland', *Proceedings of the Institution of Civil Engineers*, Part 1, Vol.1 (1952), pp.290-2.

55   The general rule for lifts using Portland cement concrete was 5ft. At Giorra, regular lifts of 10ft—using 20 per cent fly ash concrete (i.e. 20 per cent of the cement content was replaced by fly ash)—were used successfully. At Lawers, using blast furnace concrete, a final lift of 15ft was attempted. See Fulton & Dickerson, *op.cit.*, p.733.

56   For details of the tunnelling at Breadalbane, see *The Engineer*, Vol.206, pp.124-6, and *Water Power*, Vol.8, pp.8-16.

57   Each crew was made up of one shift boss, five drillers, one handyman, one compressor man, one loader operator, two loco drivers, two men on the rock tip, and one electrician. The services of a fitter, drill doctor and powder monkey were available on day shift only. *Water Power*, Vol.8, p.11. In 1954 a British and European record rate of advance had been achieved by three crews working on the Lednock-Almond tunnel, when 428ft was driven in seven consecutive days. *Ibid.*, p.10.

58   *The Engineer*, Vol.206, p.125.

59   *Water Power*, Vol.11 (1959), p.83.

60   NSHEB, *Annual Reports*, 1959-61.

61   Although the dates given for the component parts of the Sloy/Shira group of schemes include Sloy, the *basic* details for which are included in Table 12, no additional information on the Board's first Constructional Scheme will be provided here (for Sloy, see Chapter 5).

62   The most important source used for Shira was John Paton, 'The Glen Shira Hydro-Electric

Project', *Proceedings of the Institution of Civil Engineers*, Part I, Vol.5 (1956), pp.593-618, and the following 'Discussion', pp.619-32; see also *The Engineer*, Vol.201 (1956), pp.364-8, 396-9, *Water Power*, Vol.9 (1957), pp.4-12, 65-71; and the 'Discussion' of Charles Jaeger, 'Present Trends in the Design of Pressure Tunnels and Shafts for Underground Hydro-Electric Stations', *Proceedings of the Institution of Civil Engineers*, Part 1, Vol.4 (1955), pp.174-200.

63   A A Fulton in the 'Discussion' of the paper by John Paton, *loc.cit.*, p.619. It remained for an outsider, Dr Charles Jaeger, a consulting engineer to the English Electric Co., to emphasise that the complexity of the project 'required great versatility from the designer ... each of the [components of the scheme] required special knowledge and great skill ... backed by extensive investigations'. *Ibid.*, p.622. Jaeger cited examples from G F W Adler, 'Model Tests on Clachan Underground Power Station', *English Electric Journal*, Vol.11, No.4 (June 1950).

64   In fact, such a two-stage layout for Shira had originally been proposed by James Williamson, in his capacity as a member of the Board's panel of technical advisers. James Williamson died in August 1953. Paton, *op.cit.*, p.618. See also the 'Discussion' of Paton's paper, p.626.

65   The lower reservoir, which is fed by 38 per cent of the total catchment area, has a capacity of less than 7 per cent of the total storage of the scheme:

	Useful storage capacity (acre-feet)	Top Water Level (feet A.O.D.)	Catchment area supplying reservoir (sq. miles)		
			Direct	Indirect	Total
Upper reservoir	17,300	1,108	4.59	8.77	13.36
Lower reservoir	1,265	970	0.60	7.52	8.12

Source: *The Engineer* Vol.201 (1956), p.364.

66   This may be more fully explained. Although to pump water to the upper reservoir, only 100-130ft higher than the Sron Mor station, from the lower reservoir would require an input (or 'expenditure') of electrical energy greater than that produced by the water returning through the Sron Mor station *alone*, this water would continue on its way down to the Clachan station, where the gross head would be 1100ft. Moreover, because the energy used for pumping would be off peak power (since pumping would take place, say, at weekends), its economic value would be far less than that of the power generated to meet peak loads.

67   A point made by *Water Power*, Vol.9 (1957), pp.10-11. A small pumped storage scheme to serve a tweed mill existed on the Tweed at Walkerburn in the early 1920s. See *Engineering*, 17 February and 24 February 1922. I am indebted to Mr L H Dickerson for this reference.

68   Paton, *op.cit.*, pp.599-600.

69   One of the reasons for adopting this type of construction was that local supplies of fill suitable for forming an impervious core when compacted were both limited and too variable in quality to form a reliable watertight barrier.

70   An interesting issue was raised by J A Banks, a fellow partner of John Paton in Babtie, Shaw and Morton, concerning the economics of earthfill embankments situated in areas

of heavy precipitation. Although preliminary designs might often suggest that an earth dam would be cheaper than a concrete gravity structure (say, by some 20 per cent), delays in construction caused by torrential rainfall (as was the case at Sron Mor) were capable not only of adversely affecting the savings expected from earth dams, but of jeopardising the economic calculations underlying an entire scheme if progress *as a whole* was retarded by a failure to meet the expected timetable of the earth embankment. J A Banks in 'Discussion' of Paton, *loc.cit.*, p.620.

71   It should be mentioned that the entire tunnel was lined with 700 tons of steel pipes. These were backed by concrete and subsequently pressure grouted.

72   Paton, *op.cit.*, p.605.

73   The intensity of rainfall on the Shira site, giving rise to occasional flood spates, necessitated special measures to protect the stream intakes from the considerable qualities of debris carried downstream by the Highland burns. The solution to this problem is discussed by Paton, *op.cit.*, pp.613-16.

74   Angus Fulton in the 'Discussion' of the paper on the 'Allt-na-Lairige Prestressed Concrete Dam', presented to the Institution of Civil Engineers by J A Banks, senior partner in the firm of Babtie, Shaw and Morton, 20 November 1956. *Proceedings of the Institution of Civil Engineers*, Vol.6 (1957), p.430. This brief account of the Allt-na-Lairige scheme draws heavily on this source (pp.409-28).

75   It should be understood that 'first of its kind' means the first dam to be designed for construction in pre-stressed concrete. Other dams in various parts of the world had been 'stressed' after construction to give extra strength, either for safety or for the purposes of heightening. The principle involved is that 'concrete, which has great strength in compression but very little in tension, can be kept free from tension by subjecting it to a permanent compressive force. This force is supplied by stretched high-tensile steel wires or bars placed in the concrete. Either they are first stretched by jacks and the concrete cast round them, after which the ends are cut, leaving the wires embedded in the concrete; or else, more usually in this type of work, they are placed in holes left specially for the purpose in the concrete, and then stretched, the holes being filled or grouted afterwards with cement. The stretched wires or bars act like springs, keeping the concrete in compression and counteracting tensile stresses which would otherwise cause it to crack and fail'. Paton & Brown, *op.cit.*, pp.49,138.

76   Among the Agenda Papers for the Board Meeting of 15 July 1953, are letters explaining the advantages and possible disadvantages of a prestressed concrete dam at Allt-na-Lairige: James A Banks to A A Fulton, 6 July 1953; J Guthrie Brown to J A Banks, 24 June 1953. Fulton must have been highly gratified by the reception given to the dam by his fellow civil engineers who had in the past occasionally commented—as had Fulton himself—on a certain lack of novelty and originality in the designs of various Hydro schemes, though it was acknowledged that the topographical conditions confronting the Hydro Board precluded the adoption of more exciting designs. See, for example, A C Black's contribution to the 'Discussion' of Banks's paper, *loc.cit.*, p.435.

77   At the northern end of the dam was the spillway section, 252ft in width, which did not require prestressing, and a long spillway channel. This feature of the final design was apparently suggested by J Guthrie Brown, one of the Board's panel of technical advisers. See the 'Discussion' of the paper by Banks, *loc.cit.*, pp.431-2.

78   This point was made by F S Jackson, a director of Maples, Ridgway & Partners, the main contractors for the scheme. The total *number* of bars used was 4,440, grouped into 138 sets, the longest of which were 107ft. in length. 'Discussion', p.433.

79   Banks, *op.cit.*, pp.425-6; and see Fulton & Dickerson, *op.cit.*, p.739.

80 Banks, *op.cit.*, p.427. On a visit to Russia, Angus Fulton discovered that 'Russian engineers were familiar with the ... Allt-na-Lairige design and were devoting a good deal of attention to the use of the same techniques'. Fulton in 'Discussion' of the paper by Banks, p.430.

81 For a valuable technical survey, see Fulton and Dickerson, 'Design and constructional features of hydro electric dams built in Scotland since 1945', and the ensuing 'Discussion'. See also Angus Fulton's 'Presidential Address' to the Institution of Civil Engineers, *Proceedings of the Institution of Civil Engineers*, Vol.44 (1969), pp.311-21.

82 A A Fulton, 'Civil Engineering Aspects of Hydro-Electric Development in Scotland', p.253.

83 One of the Board's consultants, James A Banks, Senior Partner in Babtie, Shaw & Morton, of Glasgow, who was responsible for the design of the prestressed concrete dam at Allt-na-Lairige, commented in 1957 that, 'It was a great encouragement to have a client [like the Board] who was so willing to put his trust in the engineer and give him an opportunity which one might hope would bear fruit in future works'. (Banks, in 'Discussion' of his paper on the Allt-na-Lairige dam, p.348).

84 The acceleration in the speed with which many of the contractors completed their tasks was closely related to the alacrity with which they themselves adopted the latest developments in tunnelling and earth-moving plant, developments which were particularly striking in the twenty years following the second World War.

85 See above, p.45.

86 *Report* of the Cooper Committee, paras.34-43.

87 NSHEB: Minute 29, 20 December 1943. 'Notes of the meeting between the Board and the Scottish Council on Industry' are annexed as Appendix A.

88 'Notes of an informal meeting between Sir Steven Bilsland, A E MacColl and T Lawrie, Glasgow, 20 January 1944', Appendix B, NSHEB Minute 77, 31 January/1 February, 1944.

89 'Notes for meeting with Directors of the North of Scotland Hydro-Electric Board', 23 October 1944. The BOC memorandum estimated the cost of production of 280 million units at Tummel to be (at 1944 prices) 0.282*d*. per unit, compared with the 0.178*d*. per unit costs of the hypothetical 1936 Caledonian Power Scheme.

90 NSHEB: Minute 228, 23 October 1944.

91 NSHEB: Minutes 146(h), 11 July 1944; 178(b), 24 July 1944; 232, 23 October 1944; 361, 28 May 1945; 658, 11 September 1946.

92 NSHEB, 'Note of Meeting with the Scottish Council on Industry, 5 January, 1948', among the Agenda papers for the Board meeting of 14 January 1948. See also 'Note of a meeting of the Working Party on Aluminium Production held at the Ministy of Supply, 23 August 1948', among the Agenda Papers for the Board meeting of 8 September 1948.

93 NSHEB, 'Notes of Meeting held with the Scottish Council (Development and Industry), 2 April 1948'. Agenda paper for Board meeting of 14 April 1948. That 'the Board must give priority to the demands of the ordinary consumer' was constantly reiterated in the papers prepared for consideration by the members of the Board. See, for example, 'Supplies to Large Power Users', NSHEB, Agenda Paper for Board Meeting of 8 September 1948. This paper constituted the basis for a major speech by Tom Johnston at Tarbet three weeks later. It was widely reported in the Press and evoked considerable editorial comment. See, for example, *The Scotsman*, *Glasgow Herald* and *Daily Record* of 28 and 29 September 1948, and the powerful leader in the *Inverness Courier*, 1 October 1948.

94 NSHEB, C C Cunningham, Scottish Home Department, to T Lawrie, 30 January 1948. Among Agenda papers for Board Meeting of 14 February 1948.

95 *Ibid.*; NSHEB, 'Notes of a meeting with Mr Boex, Managing Director of the British

Aluminium Co., to discuss Power Supplies for Electro-Chemical Industry in the High-lands', 29 January 1948; NSHEB, D W Cameron of Lochiel to T Johnston, 14 December 1947; T Johnston to Cameron of Lochiel, 21 December 1947. Among Agenda papers for Board Meetings of 14 January 1948.

96   This is not to say that approaches by heavy current users for bulk supplies of cheap fuel were discontinued, simply that the Board would not entertain them on the terms requested. See, for example, 'Notes on a discussion between Messrs ICI and the ... Board held on 11 May 1951', NSHEB: Agenda Papers for Board Meeting of 14 June 1951; Board Minute 2391, 21 May 1952.

97   Later in the year, Sir Steven Bilsland sought the advice of Sir Andrew McCance, Deputy Chairman and Joint Managing Director of Colvilles Ltd., sending him a copy of a Memorandum prepared by The Scottish Council setting out the reasons why the prospect of hydro-electricity had failed to attract the large electrochemical and electrometallurgical industries to the Highlands. In the ensuing correspondence, Sir Steven observed: 'It is a tragedy that the Hydro-Electric scheme should have developed as it has. MacColl is apparently grid-minded and Johnston, who is much more interested in supplying electricity to outlying crofts on a hopelessly uneconomic basis ... has been preaching the dangerous doctrine that firms should apply for a subsidy to lower their power costs. I cannot imagine any firm being so foolish.' Bilsland to McCance, 6 October 1948 (McCance Papers, University of Glasgow Archives). I am indebted to Dr Martin Chick for drawing my attention to this source.

98   Johnston, *Memories*, p.182.

99   NSHEB, 'Notes of informal meeting with Sir Steven Bilsland', 20 January 1944, *loc.cit.*

100   No less than 72 per cent of the total recorded investment in the Highlands in the period 1951-1960 was accounted for by investment in hydro-electric power capacity and dis-tribution. See David Simpson, 'Investment, Employment, and Government Expenditure in the Highlands, 1951-1960', *Scottish Journal of Political Economy*, X (1963), pp.269-70.

101   See NSHEB, 'Notes of meeting held on 18 November 1953 to discuss the Allocation of Orders for Water Turbines', Agenda Papers for Board Meeting of 16 December 1953; NSHEB, Memorandum for the [Mackenzie] Committee on the Generation and Dis-tribution of Electricity in Scotland: 'Collaboration in Economic Development and Social Improvement in North Scotland', HEB.M.1, p.3 (hereinafter cited: 'Mackenzie Committee evidence: HEB.M.1.'); Select Committee on Nationalised Industries (Report and Accounts), 1957, *Minutes of Evidence*, paras 774-806 (hereinafter cited: 'Select Committee (N.I.), 1957'). As early as 1949 it was estimated that *in addition to* the Board's orders for nearly 900,000 horse power of water turbines and 368,400 Kilowatts of generators, export orders for similar equipment aggregated about 970,000 h.p. and 209,000kW, respectively. NSHEB, *Annual Report and Accounts*, 1949, p.12. For the Board's practical help to British manufacturers which resulted in export orders—in this case hydro-alternators for the McNeary Dam in the United States—see A R Blandford, English Electric Co. Ltd. Stafford, to J J Cargill, 17 December 1953. Agenda Papers for Board Meeting of 20 January 1954.

102   NSHEB, *Annual Report and Accounts, passim*. See also 'New Industrial Development in the Highlands', Agenda Papers for Board Meeting of 17 September 1957.

103   It is worth noting that the majority of the men employed were drawn from the Highland area, despite 'gossip [which] magnified the number of Irishmen employed out of all relation to the truth'. A survey made in mid-1954 showed the relative composition of the labour force to be as follows:

Scheme	Percentage of men who were			
	Scottish	Irish	English	Foreign
Affric (1950)	80	15	5	
Errochty★				
(Tummel Garry)	48	32	15	5
Glascarnoch, Luichart				
& Torr Achilty				
(Conon)	71	20	5	4
Killin, Lawers				
(Breadalbane)	n.d.	c30	n.d.	n.d.

★ 'It is usual for the proportion of Irish labour to be higher in Perthshire than in the North and they are accustomed also to work on the roads and on seasonal agricultural work in Perthshire'.

Source: NSHEB, 'Welfare Report for September 1954', among Board's Agenda Papers for meeting of 20 September 1954.

104   NSHEB, Mackenzie Committee evidence: HEB. M.1, p.5.
105   In *Sir Edward MacColl. A Maker of Modern Scotland*, Norrie Fraser (ed), pp.39-48. This is the source of the subsequent quotations.
106   NSHEB, *Report and Accounts*, 1950, p.13. See also NSHEB, *Board Minutes* No. 2376, 16 April 1952.
107   Mackenzie Committee evidence: HEB. M.1, p.5.
108   NSHEB *Report and Accounts*, 1951, p.17.
109   NSHEB, *Reports and Accounts*, 1948-56; MacColl, 'Hydro-Electric Development', p.454; T G N Haldane, 'Wind and Water', in N Fraser (ed), *op.cit.*, pp.37-8; Lawrie, 'Highland Water Power', p.219; *Engineering*, 7 July 1950, p.5; Mackenzie Committee evidence, HEB. M.1, pp.1-2, HEB. M.3(1), pp.1-4; NSHEB, Agenda Papers: Progress reports on Orkney Windmill Project, 1949-1956.
110   T G N Haldane, 'Wind and Water', *loc.cit.*, p.38.
111   NSHEB, *Reports and Accounts*, 1947-1961; NSHEB, 'Altnabreac Peat Scheme: Note for Agenda for Board Meeting', 17 February 1960; Norrie Fraser, 'The Man and the Mission', in N Fraser (ed), *op.cit.*, p.7; Sir Edward Appleton, 'Work on Peat', *ibid.*, pp.55-8; Mackenzie Committee evidence, HEB. M.1, pp.2-3, HEB. M.3(1), pp.5-8.
112   For the Mackenzie Committee, see below pp.213-19.
113   NSHEB, J E Stark, Secretary to the Mackenzie Committee, to H W Simpson, Secretary to the North of Scotland Hydro-Electric Board, 26 April 1961, in G/5, Part I.
114   Mackenzie Committee Evidence: HEB. M.1, (G/5, Part I).
115   Evidence that this view was not universally held is provided by a very sympathetic leading article in the *Scotsman*, 'Fishing and Power', 9 August 1956.
116   R M MacDonald to A A Fulton, 10 March 1961. In G/5, Part I.
117   Hamish MacKinven, *Highland Hydro-Electricity* (Inverness: An Comunn Gaidhealach, 1972) p.5. This useful and informative pamphlet, by the Assistant Information Officer of the Board, is number 28 in the An Comunn Gaidhealach series on *Highland Information*.
118   The quotations are from the resolution approved by Inverness County Council on 9 March 1961, and forwarded to John S Maclay, Secretary of State for Scotland on the following day. R Wallace, County Clerk of Inverness to John S Maclay, 10 March 1961, a copy of which is in NSHEB, G/5, Part I. Emphasis supplied.
119   NSHEB, Mackenzie Committee evidence, HEB M.1, p.8.

120   Sir A E MacColl, 'From Paraffin and Sod Peat to the All-Electric Age', *Electrical Age*,
      October 1946; reproduced in N Fraser (ed), *op.cit.*, pp.22-4.
121   *Ibid.*, p.23.
122   For example, a special survey carried out in connection with the supply of electricity to
      the Ardnamurchan and Morven districts in the County of Argyll in 1956 revealed that the
      number of potential consumers was 529 and that the estimated cost of connection was
      about £390,000, or £735 per consumer. The report is among the Agenda Papers for the
      Board meeting of 21 November 1956.
123   Indeed, in some cases, the expected (or actual) revenue was insufficient even to cover
      interest charges. An example cited in a letter dated 3 September 1958 from the Secretary
      of State to Mr J Grimond, MP, was South Walls, off the Island of Hoy, Orkney. See
      Agenda Papers for Board Meeting of 17 September 1958. In March 1959 Angus Fulton,
      in a speech to the Consultative Committee, emphasised that 'There are still far too many
      people who do not realise that interest and other changes on the cost of connections must
      be met by someone ... [the fact is that] over nearly all of the Highland area it is impossible
      to supply electricity to anyone except at a loss'. A copy of Fulton's speech is among the
      Agenda Papers for the Board's meeting of 15 April 1959.
124   For example, NSHEB, 'Memorandum to the Secretary of State on Rural Distribution
      Costs', 9 June 1959, Agenda Papers for Board Meeting of 17 June 1959. See also A A Fulton
      to A J Aglen, Scottish Home Department, 18 December 1959, and 'Note of Meeting at
      Scottish Home Department on 30 December 1959 on Uneconomic Rural Electrification',
      Agenda Papers for Board Meeting of 22 January, 1960.
125   G McCrone, *Scotland's Economic Progress 1951-60* (London: Allen & Unwin, 1965); and see
      Sir Kenneth Alexander, 'The Highlands and Islands Development Board', in J Saville (ed),
      The Economic Development of Modern Scotland, 1950-1980 (Edinburgh: John Donald, 1985),
      pp.214-21.
126   The following letter to a member of the Board, Mr G T McGlashan, is not untypical:

> Now that I have had some two years experience of the advantages of a supply of
> electricity from the Hydro-Electric Board, I think you may like to know what I feel
> about it.
>   The benefits in the house go without saying—no lamps to fill, no grates to clean
> and ashes to remove, no fires to lay and so on. To the farmer's wife, especially in
> these days of difficulty about domestic help, all this means a great relief, plus the
> comfort of having heat in any room when wanted.
>   But the advantages of electricity in the actual running of the farm have also proved
> to be far greater than I expected. You will remember that when as County Councillor
> for this District you addressed a meeting of farmers and others who might be
> interested in getting a supply of electricity in 1948, one of the statements you made
> was that you have been told by some other farmers that they had found electricity
> to be equal to an extra man about the steading.
>   At the time, I found this difficult to believe, but my experience has confirmed it
> ... Perhaps I should mention that I have 340 acres, all arable. I have a dairy herd of
> 103, including followers. There is a 10 H.P. motor for driving my threshing mill, a
> 4 h.p. for a hammer mill, and a 1/2 h.p. for a turnip cutter. Electricity is also used
> for milking and brine cooling. In the farmhouse, in addition to radiators there is an
> electric cooker, iron etc.

      John Murray, Burnside Farm, Greenloaning, Perthshire, to G T McGlashan, 26 March
      1951, Agenda Papers for meeting of 11 April 1951.

127   NSHEB, *Annual Reports*, particularly 1952-1956. See also T Lawrie, *op.cit.*, p.291, who reported that the greatly enhanced protein value of the dried grass or hay more than justified the cost of the treatment of 12 per ton: 'One of the crofters reported that he had a cow which had doubled its milk yield being fed exclusively on electrically dried hay. He would not concede that all this 100% increase could be due to dried hay; he preferred to leave it at a "phenomenon he cannot understand" '.

128   The annual growth rates computed from Tables 23 and 27, show that while the number of farm connections was growing at an annual rate of 15 per cent, electrically consumption on the farms was growing at the rate of 20 per cent.

129   Mackenzie Committee Evidence, HEB. M.7(9), p.2.

130   W D D Fenton, '*Pro Patria Mori*', in N Fraser (ed), *op.cit.*, p.33. The reluctance with which connection charges were at first imposed and subsequently increased is reflected in a series of detailed memoranda among the Board's Agenda Papers. For example, those for consideration at the meetings of 14 July 1948, 20 July 1949, 14 November 1951, and 18 November 1959.

131   NSHEB, (Draft) 'Evidence ... showing how the Board have discharged [their] obligations', undated, Mackenzie Committee Evidence, G/5, Part 6.
       The 108,000 'uneconomic rural consumers' were divided into connection term groups as follows:

Numbers	Terms for Supply
34,790	No payment or guarantee of use
20,483	Guarantee of use only
6,051	Guarantee of use plus a contribution
6,676	Line rental
40,000	Nominal service charge
108,000	

132   On connection charges, the full details are provided by the Board's *Annual Reports and Accounts*, 1948 onwards; the clearest summary, based on the Board's evidence (HEB. M.3(6)), is provided by the *Mackenzie Report*, paras 169-170 and Appendix IV, p.111.

133   Full details of the Board's tariffs are, of course, provided in the Board's *Annual Reports and Accounts*. They are not amenable to summary treatment. Suffice it to say they appear to have been roughly comparable with the average charged by other Electricity Boards in Great Britain—that at least was the intention— despite far greater distribution costs and, in diesel areas, generating costs. An example is provided in Table 28(b). Tom Johnston's response to government pleas to freeze prices in 1956 was discussed by the Select Committee on Nationalised Industries, *Report and Accounts*, 1957, paras. 189-95. See also L Hannah, 'Rought Draft', pp.54-5.

134   Lady Margaret MacColl, 'Last Word', in Norrie Fraser (ed.), *op.cit.*, p.64. For a careful analysis of 'Investment, Employment, and Government Expenditures in the Highlands, 1951-1960', see the article by David Simpson, *Scottish Journal of Political Economy* X (1963), pp.259-288; see also the words of Mr Joseph Grimond before the Scottish Grand Committee, 16 July 1963. *P D Commons*, Standing Committees, Official Report [of the Scottish Grand Committee], Session 1962-63, Vol.IV, cols. 24-5.

135   The foregoing paragraphs rest heavily on L Hannah, *Engineers, Managers and Politicians*, pp.161-2, and the *Mackenzie Report*, paras 6-8, p.10. A more detailed account is given by Hannah in his 'Rough Draft', pp.56-62, from which it is clear that Tom Johnston had successfully lobbied the Minister of Fuel and Power to keep the Hydro Board out of the

reorganisation plans. After the severence of the two Scottish Boards, the BEA was known as the Central Electricity Authority (CEA).

136 Select Committee on Nationalised Industries, *Minutes of Evidence*, 17 April 1957, Q.350, pp.44-5.

137 At every one of the 140 gauges set up by the Board, the rainfall recorded for the year 1955 was below average, and for the first eight months of the year was in many districts less than half the normal. In the areas of the main hydro schemes at Tummel-Garry, Affric, Fannich and Luichart, the rainfall on average was only 74 per cent of normal. At Rannoch Power Station the annual total of 29.58 inches of rain was the lowest recorded since the start of guaging by the Grampian Co. in 1931. NSHEB, *Annual Report*, 1955, pp.30-2.

138 The cost of the drought to the Board was considerable. The loss of sales to the south of Scotland, the additional imports of electricity from the South, and the expense of burning more coal at the Board's steam stations, added up to about £1,100,000, and the Board lost £782,000 on the year's operations. *Ibid*, p.7.

139 The relationship between the Hydro Board and the SSEB on the quantity and price of bulk supplies was explained and illustrated in a memorandum for the Mackenzie Committee by the NSHEB entitled 'Practical and Economic Effects of Sale of Power to the South Board'. HEB. M.3(3), G/5, Part 2.

140 Hannah, 'Rough Draft', p.69. Several officials interviewed by Hannah and his associates expressed the belief that Pickles could and should have insisted on more rigorous terms from the NSHEB.

141 NSHEB, *Annual Report*, 1956, pp.26-8.

142 The details are given in the Mackenzie Committee's Evidence, Sundry Papers: 'Arrangements for Consultation between the two Scottish Boards', significantly a 'joint submission by North and South Boards'. HEB, M.5(1), G/5 Part 2. The membership of the Joint Technical Committee comprised, from the North Board, the General Manager, the Chief Electrical and Mechanical Engineer and the Engineering Assistant, and from the South Board the Chief Engineer and his Personal Assistant, the Chief Commercial Officer and his Assistant, and the Deputy Chief Engineers (Generation and Distribution). For the Cruachan Scheme, see below, pp.230-9.

143 The new agreement is discussed and its effect on the bulk supply tariff shown in Evidence to the Mackenzie Committee, HEB. M.2 Appendix 2, and HEB M.3(3), G/5, Parts 1 and 2.

144 See, for example, the Minutes of Evidence, SCN1, 1957, *Report and Accounts*. 'Memorandum submitted by Sir David Robertson, MP', pp.99-100, and the evidence of a group of Scottish MPs, pp.100-109.

145 See above, as late as the early 1950s the Board's Annual Reports rarely failed to emphasise the coal-saving effected by hydro-electric production. For example: 'The rate of hydroelectric production is now equivalent to a saving of nearly 600,000 tons of coal per annum or about three-quarters of the year's export of cargo coal from Scotland; assuming that amount of coal to be released for export at a selling price of £4 5s. a ton, the benefit to the country as a whole is over £2,500,000 per annum of foreign exchange', NSHEB, *Annual Report*, 1952, p.7. Until 1959, the bar charts of generation published by the Board always gave the equivalent tonnage of coal saved by hydro power. See also T Lawrie to D B Frudd, Chief Scientist's Division, Ministry of Fuel and Power, 8 February 1955, among the Agenda Papers for the Board's meeting of 15 February 1955.

146 Gerald Nabarro, *Ten Steps to Power: A National Fuel and Power Policy* (London: St Catherines Press, 1952), p.19.

147 D L Munby, 'Electricity in the North of Scotland', *Scottish Journal of Political Economy*, Vol.III, No.1 (February 1956), pp.19-43.

148   Select Committee on Nationalised Industries, *Report and Accounts*, 1957, Appendix 6, pp.184-8.

149   Sir Murdoch MacDonald and J M Kay, 'Electricity in the North of Scotland', *Scottish Journal of Political Economy*', Vol.IV, No.1 (February 1957), an article to which Munby published 'A Rejoinder' in the same issue, pp.27-8.

150   A scathing attack on the rôle of Aims of Industry in the campaign against hydro-electric development in Scotland was made in the House of Commons by G M Thomson, the member for Dundee, East, in December 1960. *HC Deb*, 1960, 632, cols. 1315-21.

151   These criticisms are listed by Hannah, 'Rough Draft', p.88-9. See also *Capital Investment in the Coal, Gas and Electricity Industries*, Cmd. 132 (1957), para 20.

152   Personal interviews, Mr C L C Allan and Mr P L Aitken.

153   Evidence for Mackenzie Committee, HEB M7(8); Sir William Halcrow & Partners to Chief Hydraulic Engineer, NSHEB, 5 February 1962.

154   *HL Deb*, 1961, 229, cols. 301-305, and see NSHEB, *Annual Report and Accounts*, 1960, p.3, 1961, p.4; Hannah, 'Rough Draft', p.90.

CHAPTER 7

1   Scottish Development Department, *Electricity in Scotland: Report of the Committee on the Generation and Distribution of Electricity in Scotland*, 1962; Cmnd. 1859, p.5.

2   *Ibid*., and see, for example, *Scotsman*, 7 April 1961.

3   At least, so it seemed; but it would appear from a letter from Mr Hamish Mackinven, at that time the Board's Assistant Information Officer, published in *Scotsman*, 11 November 1987, that behind the scenes—and completely unofficially—he and Mr George Banks, the Board's Information Officer, 'fed background [information] to the Press [with whom they had 'close links'], inspired news stories, held off-the-record Press conferences in [Mackinven's] Edinburgh flat, [and generally] created a tremendous furore'.

4   Correspondence between R MacFarquhar, The Highland Fund, and various district councillors and officials in Sutherland and the outer isles, March 1961, and between P Hunter Gordon and A A Fulton, February 1961, NSHEB, Evidence for Mackenzie Committee, G/5, Part I.

5   NSHEB: Hamish Mackinven to G M Thomson, MP, 26 May, 1961. See also *H L Deb*., Vol.227, 16 March 1961, col.1026, and editorials and correspondence in *Scotsman*, *Scottish Daily Mail* and *Scottish Daily Express*, March 1961.

6   In addition to the formal memoranda submitted to the Committee by the Hydro Board (for example, 'Comparison of the South Board's Hypothetical Generation Costs in lieu of actual costs of the North Board's supplies, 1959-60', G/5, Part 3; SSEB, 'Cost of Supplying the Board's system requirements in 1960 if there had been no import of electricity from the North Board', G/5, Part 4; NSHEB, 'Comments on the SSEB paper', HEB M.10(2), G/5, Part 4, and HEB M.12, G/5, Part 5) and the 'Oral Evidence' given by the NSHEB on 4 July 1962 (SEC Oral Evidence 23), this account is based upon many letters in the G/5 files of the NSHEB (e.g. Sir Josiah Eccles to A A Fulton, August, 1962), Hannah's 'Rough Draft', pp.95-8, and the *Report* of the Mackenzie Committee itself.

7   'Oral Evidence', 4 July 1962, paragraphs 16,39.

8   J Henderson and E Maxwell, 'Scottish Electricity: More Hydro Development' 17 May 1960, in SSEB file 'Mackenzie Committee', cited Hannah, 'Rough Draft', p.92.

9   'Oral Evidence', 4 July 1962, paragraph 6.

10   Hannah, 'Rough Draft', p.95; based on the oral evidence given by the SSEB on 1 May 1962.

11 Eccles to Fulton, 7 August 1962 (NSHEB G/5, Part 5).

12 Mackenzie *Report*, para.178.

13 *Ibid.*, para. 180.

14 *Ibid.*, para. 187.

15 *Ibid.*, para. 182. Emphasis supplied.

16 *Ibid.*, paras.183-6.

17 *Ibid.*, para. 191.

18 *Ibid.*, paras. 194-9. To the last recommendation was added 'unless, or until, some other agency can take [these obligations] over in a stronger and wider form to bring to fulfilment the Cooper Committee's vision for the regeneration of the Highlands'.

19 E S Harrison to H W Simpson, 5 November 1962, 16 March 1962 (G/5, Part 5).

20 *HC Deb.*, 15 November 1962, col.35.

21 H G Tait, Town Clerk to the City and Royal Burgh of Elgin, to the NSHEB, 26 December 1962: Draft 'Observations by Elgin Town Council on the [Mackenzie] Report ...' (G/5, Part 5).

22 Stephen Macrae, 'Power for Scotland', *Scotland*, January 1963, p.62.

23 This issue figured prominently in the discussions of the Advisory Panel on the Highlands and Islands: 'Notes on a meeting held in Inverness on 14 December 1962 of the Advisory Panel' (G/5, Part 5).

24 The Highland Fund Ltd., ' "Electricity in Scotland" ... a statement of criticism approved by the Council of the Highland Fund', 12 February 1963 (G/5, Part 6); Advisory Panel on the Highlands and Islands: 'Draft Recommendations on the Mackenzie Committee's Report', undated, c March 1963. (G/5, Part 6).

25 Electricity Consultative Council for the North of Scotland District: 'Comment on the Report of the Departmental Committee on the Generation and Distribution of Electricity in Scotland', December 1962, Paras 1(a), (c), 5(d), (e) & (f).

26 E J K Chapman, 'Value of Water Power in a Mixed System', *Water Power*, Vol.15 (April 1963), pp.165-72.

27 The basic argument may perhaps be simplified. All discussions of the introduction and retirement of thermal plant assume that *new* plant, invariably larger, incorporating the most modern technology and hence more efficient than what has gone before, is initially used for base load generation. As this plant grows older and is superseded by even more efficient plant, it is partially retired, eventually to serve only as a generator of peak load requirements. That is, an *order of merit* exists with thermal plant being progressively moved from full-time to intermittent standby duties. In practical terms, plant newly-introduced into a system will be employed full-time in electrical generation, it will have a 100 per cent load factor, but this figure will decline as the plant grows older to, say, 10 per cent at the end of its life. In a rapidly expanding system with total demand *doubling* every 8-10 years, there will be every incentive for the industry to commission new generating sets—incorporating the latest technical advances—at frequent intervals. In such a situation, Chapman demonstrated that thermal plant spent a smaller proportion of its active life operating at full capacity, producing base load units, and a greater proportion of its life at progessively lower capacities than had hitherto been recognised. This, of course, increased the relative cost per unit of output of thermal plant and enhanced the competitive position of hydro plant which, as we have observed (see Appendix 1), was always characterised by a much higher level of efficiency than could be obtained by thermal units.

28 NSHEB; correspondence between A A Fulton and Sir Josiah Eccles, April 1963. (G/5, Part 6).

29 Hannah, 'Rough Draft', p.105, note 2.

30 Robert a Moore, National Coal Board, to Sir John C George, MP, 6 June 1963, contained in collection of correspondence between E J K Chapman and Sir John George and Bruce Millan, MP, June-July 1963, sent to A A Fulton, NSHEB, 22 July 1963 (G/5, Part 6).

31 *Ibid.*, E J K Chapman to Bruce Millan, MP, 14 June 1963. Sir Josiah remained unconvinced by Chapman's argument. He was 'satisfied that any error there may be in his calculations is sub-marginal and within the limits of accuracy of the other assumptions on which [his] whole exercise is founded. He therefore saw no reason to alter the calculations'.

32 *HC Deb.*, Vol.677, 15 May 1963, *Written answers*, cols.168-70. See particularly col. 169.

33 NSHEB: 'Comments on the Mackenzie Committee Report' prepared for the Secretary of State for Scotland, January 1963 (G/5, Part 6); NSHEB: Minute 6287, 2 November 1962. It was emphasised too that hydro schemes would become more economically attractive with each rise in the price of coal, an increase which it was anticipated would continue.

34 Hannah, 'Rough Draft', p.107; *Glasgow Herald*, 18 May 1963.

35 *Water Power*, Vol.15 (July 1963), p.270.

36 The interviews conducted by Hannah and his research team elicited that although Sir Douglas Haddow was probably in favour of the merger of the Boards, Sir Charles Cunningham and Sir John Anderson were not. Hannah, 'Rough Draft', p.108, note 3. This has been confirmed by Mr I A Duncan Millar.

37 Hannah, 'Rough Draft', pp.108-9.

38 *HC Deb.*, Vol.680, 10 July 1963, cols.1243-8.

39 Sir David Robertson had been a vigorous and persistent critic of the Board since the late 1940s. For over a decade, he had been expressing the belief that the Board's operations in Caithness were 'disgraceful'. Sir David never ceased to be dissatisfied with the speed with which his constituents were being connected to the grid and he bombarded the Board with specific cases of neglect, evasion and bloody-mindedness. See, for example, correspondence between Sir David Robertson and Tom Lawrie, December 1951 and June 1955, among the Board's Agenda Papers for meetings of 16 January 1951 and 19 July 1955. It is important to recognise that in the early 1950s the cost of connecting consumers in Caithness—a diesel area—was higher than that of any other area. NSHEB: Finance and General Purposes Committee, Minute 296, 7 March 1952. See Table 24. Sir David's annonyance was frequently given public expression in Parliamentary debates. In 1958, for example, he accused the Board of 'plunging on from one scheme to another in the most reckless fashion. It has followed a policy of squandermania ... [and yet] throughout the Highlands, from South Inverness right up to Caithness, any number of people are waiting for power and light which they will not get ...' *HC Deb.*, Vol.591, 14 July 1958, cols. 954-8. See also *PD Commons, Standing Committees*, Official Report [of the Scottish Grand Committee], Session 1962-63, Vol.IV, cols.74-6.

40 NSHEB, telegraph message from J E Whittaker, Area Manager, Aberdeen to A A Fulton, 11 July 1963 (G/5, Part 6).

41 One message was received from Lord Macdonald, the Chairman of the Electricity Consultative Council for the North of Scotland District, part of it read: 'I do not think I have ever seen such excitement as there was in Inverness on Wednesday afternoon and Thursday. There is no doubt that the St Andrew's House boys have taken the heaviest beating they have had for years, so I hope they will not do anything to make your negotiations with the South Board more tricky and difficult than I have no doubt they will be' Lord Macdonald to A A Fulton, 13 July 1963 (G/5, Part 6).

42 A A Fulton to E S Harrison, James Johnston & Co. of Elgin, Newmill, Elgin, 12 July 1963 (G/5, Part 6). This is typical of the replies sent by Fulton to well-wishers.

43 'The Power Problem', *Glasgow Herald*, 15 May 1963.

44 *Scottish Daily Mail*, 17 May 1963; NSHEB, Lord Strathclyde to A A Fulton, 17 May 1963 (G/5, Part 6).

45 'Notes from the record of a telephone call from Sir Norman Elliot to St Andrew's House, 27 February, 1963', in SO file E 11/1/4, cited by Hannah, 'Rough Draft', p.110, note 2.

46 *Mackenzie Report*, para 137, Appendix III, and Recommendation 10, p.99.

47 The Board had clearly been warned that this was likely to happen at the very beginning of the year, when the General Manager, together with C L C Allan and Peter Aitken had met officials of the Scottish Development Department on 7 January 1963. NSHEB, *Minute* 6359, 16 January, 1963. See also Hannah, 'Rough Draft', p.111, note 2. The figure of 8 per cent should be compared with the Government's required rate of return of 5 per cent (in real terms) adopted in 1978. See *The Nationalised Industries*, Cmnd. 7131, 1978, para 61 and Appendix 1.

48 NSHEB, *Minute* 6600, 20 December 1963; NSHEB, Finance and General Purposes Committee, *Minute* 2090, 6 December 1963, and annex 'Future Constructional Schemes: Comparative Costs', 3 December 1963. The Board's dismay at having to use the figure of 73 shillings per ton as the price of coal in their comparative cost estimates is understandable. The cost of 'electricity coal' in the South of Scotland in January 1963 was 108 shillings per ton. NSHEB, 'Comments on the Mackenzie Committee Report', 3 January 1963, annex to *Minute* 6358, 16 January 1963.

49 *Ibid.*, 'Future Constructional Schemes: Comparative Costs', p.2. Emphasis supplied.

50 Reference was made to the joint publication with the South Board of *Plans for the Future*.

51 See the report of the public inquiry into Fada-Fionn and Laidon, published by the Scottish Development Department as *Hydro-Electric Schemes* (Edinburgh: HMSO, 1965), 'Conclusions', para 48, p.97.

52 *Public Inquiry (Fada-Fionn), passim.* All objections to the Laidon scheme were withdrawn before the hearing began. A useful summary of the basis of the objections to Fada-Fionn is contained in NSHEB File CS/39 (P), Part I: Internal memorandum from A A Fulton to the Chairman (undated), c.January 1964. It is noteworthy that Col.Whitbread was a member of the Council of Aims of Industry.

53 The fishery questions relating to the Tummel-Garry scheme will be an adequate guide to the nature of the evidence and the arguments concerning similar aspects of Fada-Fionn. Those parts of the proceedings relating to the fishing occupy hundreds of pages. Attacks on the proposal centred upon the adequacy of the compensation water, the reliability of the rainfall statistics, the difficulties involved in operating the proposed barrage at Loch na Sealga, the loss of particular spawning grounds, the spinelessness of the Fisheries Committee, and the loss of employment in connection with the various private fishings.

54 Colin Clark, *Electricity Generation in Scotland: The Economic Factors* (London: Aims of Industry, May 1962), para 19, page 9.

55 This was subsequently explained in the report of the public inquiry into Fada-Fionn and Laidon. *Hydro-Electric Schemes*, 'Conclusions', paragraph 74, p.108. The price of coal for Longannet had been determined by a commercial agreement between the National Coal Board and the SSEB. Both parties to the agreement 'were opposed to [its] public disclosure ... on the ground that disclosure would adversely affect their commercial negotiations', and therefore the Reporters 'did not permit cross-examination ... on behalf of the [Hydro] Board, of the basis for the prices of fuel for the South Board's new thermal stations'. The report will subsequently be referred to as *Hydro-Electric Schemes*.

56 *HC Deb.*, Vol.721, 29 November 1965, cols.1002-7.

57 *Ibid.*, and Scottish Development Department to the Secretary of the North of Scotland Hydro-Electric Board, 29 November 1965. NSHEB, CS/39 (P), part 2.

58   This view was expressed in an interview conducted in the course of research for the book by Les Hannah, *Engineers, Managers and Politicians*, see Hannah, 'Rough Draft', p.111, note 3.

59   *Public Inquiry (Fada-Fionn)*, p.32, see also *Hydro-Electric Schemes*, para.80, p.110.

60   *Hydro-Electric Schemes*, paragraph 74, pp.53-4; 'Conclusions' paras 78-80, 134, pp.109-11, 127. The Reporters also acknowledged (paragraph 88) that 'There are substantial difficulties in calculating the rates of return on capital used to construct new generating stations because the annual return of an individual generating station does not depend on itself alone but also on the system and how the general load on the system affects different generating stations. It may be impossible to assess precisely and realistically the rate of return on a new power station in isolation'. The importance of establishing the *correct* discount rate for use in investment choice calculations is emphasised and discussed by M G Webb, 'Rate of Discount and Inflation with particular reference to the Electricity Supply Industry', *Oxford Economic Papers*, N.S. 18 (1966), pp.352-8. See particularly note 2, p.356.

61   *Ibid.*, para 94, p.64, and 'Conclusions', paras, 39, 49 and 84, pp.94-5, 97, 111, supplemented by Jones's evidence, *Public Inquiry (Fada-Fionn)* pp.1312, 1332, 1411, 1423, 1425. Jones's arguments should be compared with the Hydro Board's contentions and *Hydro-Electric Schemes*, para 95.

62   *Hydro-Electric Schemes*, 'Conclusions', paragraphs 24 and 25, pp.88-9.

63   *Ibid.*, 'Conclusions', para.29, p.90; cf *Mackenzie Report*, para.184.

64   *Hydro-Electric Schemes*, 'Conclusions', paras. 56, 84, p.99, 111-12.

65   *Ibid.*, 'Conclusions', para. 82, p.111. Later in their conclusions, the Reporters made a number of comments on 'the artificial economic division which exists between the Boards' (e.g. para.100, p.118).

66   *Ibid.*, 'Conclusions', para.104, p.120. The employment potentialities of Fada-Fionn were discussed and virtually dismissed, in para. 54, p.98 and, para.103(ii), p.119 ('We recognise that there would be temporary constructional employment for 400-500 men; but £6-7 million could be spent in other ways to provide such employment [which would not be so] temporary'). Nor could any significant weight be given to the matter of exports in connection with Fada-Fionn, para.53, p.98; and para.103(iii).

67   *Ibid.*, 'Recommendations', p.139.

68   *Ibid.*, 'Conclusions', para.31, p.91.

69   R D M Bell, Scottish Development Department, to the Secretary, NSHEB, 29 November, 1965. NSHEB, CS/39 (P), Part 2.

70   NSHEB, 'Pumped Storage', memorandum dated 12 April 1955 prepared for the Board Meeting of 19 April 1955.

71   NSHEB, *Annual Report*, 1958, p.5.

72   A A Fulton, 'The Cruachan Pumped-Storage Development', *Electronics and Power*, Vol.12 (July 1966), p.220.

73   This is basically because the less the horizontal distance between the dam and tailrace of the power station, the lower the expenditure on tunnels and pipes. For a clear discussion, see William Young and R H Falkiner, 'Some design and construction features of the Cruachan Pumped Storage Project', *Proceedings of the Institution of Civil Engineers*, Vol.35 (November 1966), p.408-9.

74   This paragraph is based on Fulton, 'The Cruachan ... Development', pp.221-2.

75   NSHEB, *Annual Report*, 1958, p.5.

76   Details of the Boving research programme and that of English Electric are given in *Water Power*, January 1966, pp.8,11. Further research was conducted at Sulzer Bros' laboratories in Winterhur. The final design for the reversible pump-turbine represented a compromise

328 Notes to pp. 234 to 247

between achieving the best turbine performance and the best pump performance. See
Fulton, 'The Cruachan ... Development', p.221.

77 Exactly where within the mountain the machine hall of the power station should be located
was the subject of further detailed investigation. The possible alternatives are discussed by
Young and Falkiner, *op.cit.*, pp.410-13. See also Fulton, 'The Cruachan ... Development',
p.222, for the influence of technical considerations relating to the positioning of the pump-
turbine runners.

78 For the design of the dam, see Fulton, 'Cruachan ...', p.222 and, in greater detail, Young
and Falkiner, p.413.

79 NSHEB, *Annual Report*, 1962, p.5.

80 *Water Power*, January 1966, pp.8-11.

81 One group of problems related to the dimensions of the surge shaft. The original design
had to be abandoned because the rock formation encountered proved to be rather different
from what had been expected. The new design required a mass of calculations to determine
the appropriateness of its configuration and its dimensions. These were originally checked
by hydraulic model experiments conducted by the Department of Fluid Mechanics of
Glasgow University, but before the construction of the surge shaft, fuller information
became available on the possible combinations of operating conditions which might set up
critical surges. These were studied using a computer at Aberdeen University. Only a
computer was capable of handling the complicated hydraulic conditions which might be
encountered. See Young and Falkiner, *op.cit.*, p.441.

82 *Water Power*, January 1966, p.12.

83 Young and Falkiner, *op.cit.*, p.450.

84 These are touched upon by Fulton, 'Cruachan', p.224, and outlined in NHSEB, *Annual
Report*, 1966-67, p.10.

85 The following account of the Foyers pumped storage scheme rests on an article in *Water
Power*, Vol.24, May and June 1972, pp.161-70, 201-205; two papers in the *Proceedings of the
Institution of Civil Engineers*, Part I, Vol.64 (1978), by J H Lander, F G Johnson, J R Crichton
and M W Baldwin, 'Foyers pumped storage project: planning and design', pp.103-117, and
D D Land and D C Hitchings, 'Foyers pumped storage project: construction; pp.119-136; a
paper in the *Proceedings of the Institution of Electrical Engineers*, Vol.122, No.11 (November
1975), pp.1222-34, by D J Miller, A J L Murray, C C Marshall and G G Argent, 'Foyers
pumped-storage project'; and the NSHEB, *Annual Reports*, 1968-1975. I am grateful to Mr
F G Johnson for clarifying certain matters discussed in these sources and to Mr. K R Vernon
for explaining the genesis of the scheme.

86 *Water Power*, Vol.24, May 1972, p.162, cf. the 1:4 head:distance ratio of Cruachan.

87 See particularly, Lander, Johnson, Crichton and Baldwin, *op.cit.*, p.106-108.

88 The first set was handed over for commercial service in October 1974, the second in March
1975. Miller *et al.*, *op.cit.*, p.1234.

89 NSHEB, 'Draft reply to the Highlands and Islands Development Board', *c.*1978, CS/40. It
should be emphasised that the Foyers project *was* built *within* the detailed revised estimates
formulated by the Board in 1969.

90 F G Johnson, 'Hydro-electric power in the UK: past performance and potential for future
development', *Proceedings of the Institution of Electrical Engineers*, Vol.133, Part C, Number
3 (April 1986), p.120.

CHAPTER 8

1   For example, an ecological study by the Institute of Terrestrial Ecology was carried out to investigate the possible impact of conventional hydro and pumped storage schemes on the biology, vegetation and wild life around Loch Lomond; a team from the Geography Department of the University of Glasgow led by Professor Joy Tivy surveyed the land use, vegetation, settlement and population, tourist and recreational facilities, and the archae-ological and historical features of the area; and a team of consultants (under the leadership of Prof. R E Nicoll of the University of Strathclyde) looked at the labour requirements, access problems, and the visual and economic impact of the scheme. Much of the information so gathered was shared with the public through meetings and exhibitions. It was all a far cry from the secrecy of which the Board were accused in the Inquiry into Tummel Garry, some thirty years earlier. Dr John Berry believes that the series of inquiries into the possible environmental impact of Craigroyston constitutes the most comprehensive investigation of its kind ever undertaken.

2   In September 1983, for example, after public meetings and detailed presentations to local residents and other interested parties, such as the Nature Conservancy Council, the Board submitted a Constructional Scheme to the Secretary of State for developing the Grudie and Talladale rivers in Wester Ross. Two small run-of-river projects with a combined average annual output of 40 million units were envisaged. Following the formal publication of the plans over 60 objections were received. The Secretary of State refused to approve the scheme, which had an estimated cost of £8.5m., 'in the present economic circumstances'. NSHEB, *Report and Accounts*, 1983/84, 1984/85; Frank G Johnson *op.cit.*, pp.117–18.

3   In the late 1940s, the Board was able to borrow at $2\frac{1}{2}$—3 per cent. Compare this figure with the *average* rate of interest on funded borrowing (a) outstanding at year end (percentage) and (b) borrowed during the year (percentage):

	1971	1972	1973	1974	1975	
(a)	5.7	5.8	6.1	6.7	6.9	
(b)	8.9	7.5	8.8	10.9	11.9	
	1976	1977	1978	1979	1980	1981
(a)	8.1	9.0	9.4	9.9	10.2	11.1
(b)	12.5	14.0	11.5	12.1	12.0	13.4
	1982	1983	1984	1985	1986	1987
(a)	11.5	11.3	11.2	11.3	11.3	11.2
(b)	13.5	11.7	10.6	11.0	none	9.7

Source: NSHEB, *Annual Reports and Accounts*, 1979/80—1986/87.

The rise in interest rates was of particular concern to the Board. In the late 1960s, 40 per cent of their costs were in respect of interest charges, whereas the average for the electricity supply industry in the United Kingdom as a whole was about 17 per cent. (NSHEB, *Report and Accounts*, 1969/70, p.3). Although the proportion of total expenditure represented by interest charges fell to below 30 per cent during the 1960s, this item was always burdensome.

4   This is not the place to discuss this issue, suffice it to say that in March 1970 the Board sought the consent of the Secretary of State to build a nuclear power station with an installed capacity of up to 1320MW at Stake Ness near Whitehills, Banffshire. It was expected to cost 'some £100 million', and was intended 'to meet the steadily increasing base load in the North which already absorbs the whole output of the 240MW Carolina Port "B" thermal station'. NSHEB, *Report and Accounts*, 1969/70, p.1.

5　Lea, 'Hydro-Electric Power Generation', p.164.

6　See above, p.135.

7　See Appendix Table 32. On 31 March 1970, the Board's gross capital investment stood at £329M. This figure may be disaggregated as follows:

Hydro–electric generation	£189.1 million	(58%)
Steam generation	15.0	(5%)
Diesel generation	3.5	(1%)
Transmission	32.8	(10%)
Distribution	83.6	(25%)
Other	4.6	(1%)

Source: NSHEB, Annual Report and Accounts, 1969/70, pp.54–6.

8　The underlying economics are fearsome. Masochists requiring enlightenment should consult Charles Jaeger, 'The Correlation of Nuclear, Thermal and Pumped Storage Capacity', Water Power, Vol.10 (1958), pp.206-11, 260-4, 292-8.

9　It has been estimated that the value of the Board's building and civil engineering works on their hydro schemes at March 1986 prices was £1,366m, and that the total value of the schemes, including plant, was £1,650m. Averaging the costs of operating (£3.227m) and maintaining (£2.485m., Building and Civil Works; £2.032m., plant) the hydro schemes over the five years 1981-86, and putting them on a 1986 base, reveals that they represent just under 0.5% of the capital value of the schemes. Another way of expressing these costs is to relate them to the number of units produced. The average output during the five year period was 3.137×10^9 units per year. Since the average annual total costs of operation and repair and maintenance over this period was £7.745m, the cost of operation and maintenance was 0.25p per kWh. I am indebted to Mr Frank Johnson for these valuable data.

10　Even in a year (1983/84) in which Peterhead, fuelled by low price flare gas, sent out 4,200 GWh, its unit cost of generation was 2.4 pence. This should be compared with the unit cost of conventional hydro power, 0.769 pence, and of diesel, 8.181 pence, in the same year. See Appendix 5.5(b), Monopolies and Mergers Commission, Report on the Efficiency and Costs of the [North of Scotland Hydro-Electric] Board, Cmnd.9628 (1985), pp.17, 215.

11　See above, p.122.

12　Monopolies and Mergers Commission, Report, p.5.

13　See NSHEB Annual Report and Accounts for 1965/66, p.2. 'After setting off against each Board's system requirements the production of their own hydro plants, for whose costs they are separately responsible, each Board obtain the balance of their requirements from a pool of all other generating plants (including pumped storage but not diesel) and other sources of supply. They pay for their requirements from the pool, having regard to their respective system maximum demands and the units of electricity which they take from the pool ... The collaboration includes joint examination and analysis of the most suitable and economical way in which new generation will be planned and developed in the Districts of each Board'.

14　Over the $2\frac{1}{2}$ years during which flare gas was available, the quantity burned at Peterhead power station was equivalent to 3.65m tonnes of coal valued at £150m.

15　The appropriate balance of thermal and hydro power (conventional and pumped storage) has not simply been ascertained empirically. By 1983 a mathematical model of the operation of the complete hydro generation network had been evolved at Edinburgh University and discussions were taking place to derive an integrated hydro/thermal optimisation programme. NSHEB, Report and Accounts, 1982/83, p.26.

16   For details of these special arrangements, see NSHEB, *Report and Accounts*, 1968/69, p.3; Monopolies and Mergers Commission, *Report*, p.210; and Board of Trade, *Industrial Investment: The Production of Primary Aluminium*, Cmnd.3819 (1968), paras. 10-13, pp.4-5. See also John S Smith, 'The Invergordon Aluminium Smelter—Growth Policy Gone Wrong? A Note', *Scottish Geographical Magazine*, Vol.98 (1982), pp.115-18.

17   See NSHEB, *Report and Accounts*, 1981-82, pp.3-4. Perhaps as a direct consequence of the Invergordon closure—which was partially blamed by some on the Board's refusal to offer discriminatory prices to the British Aluminium Co.—the Board acceded to Government pressure to give some relief to large industrial power users. In April 1982 a contracted load management scheme was introduced whereby large customers were offered a tariff reduction in return for reducing demand by a contracted amount at short notice. Five consumers with a maximum demand in excess of 6MW were offered the terms but only two found that they could meet the demand reduction requirements of the scheme and took up the offer. NSHEB, *Report and Accounts*, 1982/83, p.28. It is significant that in their submissions to the Monopolies and Mergers Commission, The Electricity Consultative Council for the North of Scotland District expressed strong doubts as to whether this scheme was fair to 'the general body of consumers'; whereas The Highland and Islands Development Board believed that there was even further 'scope for introducing special discount tariffs for certain carefully defined categories of bulk user ..."at a time of chronic electricity oversupply"' Monopolies and Mergers Commission, *Report*, pp.168,170.

18   NSHEB, *Annual Reports and Accounts*, 1980/81—1986/87.

19   See above, p.68.

20   The main features of the statutes governing the Secretary of State's relationship with the Board have remained largely unchanged since 1943. The provisions of the 1943 Act were essentially unaltered by the Electricity Act of 1947, which nationalised the electricity supply industry. Since 1979 much of the relevant legislation has been consolidated in the Electricity (Scotland) Act.

21   The clearest statement of these powers is that by James F Laing, Under Secretary in the Scottish Economic Planning Department, in an Acton Society Trust Paper, 'The Scottish Office and Nationalised Industries', undated, c.1982.

22   *Ibid.*, p.7.

23   See above, p.47 and Les Hannah, *Engineers, Managers and Politicians*, pp.272-3, 275.

24   I am greatly indebted to Mr I A Duncan Millar, a long-serving and sometime Deputy Chairman of the Board, for drawing my attention to this point.

25   See, for example, NSHEB, *Report and Accounts*, 1979/80, p.6; the subsequent publication of 'Performance Indicators' in the *Annual Reports*; the setting of 'financial targets and performance aims' in 1983 (*Report and Accounts*, 1983/84, p.8); and the findings and recommendations of the Monopolies and Mergers Commission, *Report*, pp.19-23.

26   See above, p.121.

27   See Industry Department for Scotland, *Privatisation of the Scottish Electricity Industry*, Cm 327, 1988.

APPENDIX 1

1   There were, for example, 'no records of rainfall for the Blackwater basin available when the Loch Leven Water Power Works were started' in 1904-5. See A H Roberts, 'The Loch Leven Water-Power Works', *Minutes of Proceedings of the Institute of Civil Engineers*,

CLXXXVII (1911-12), pp.32-3, 93-4, 140. See also W T Halcrow's observations on the paper by A S Valentine and E M Bergstrom, *op.cit.*, p.160.

2   Board of Trade: *Interim Report of the Water Power Resources* [*Snell*] *Committee*, 1919, Cmd.79, paragraph 21.

3   'Report on The Water Power Resources of Scotland with Special Reference to Potential Developments in the Scottish Highlands', typescript (signed by A E MacColl) in the NSH-EB archives, para.8. McColl was one of the panel of experts commissioned to produce the report by the Scottish Economic Committee, under the chairmanship of Major E L Hilleary, who subsequently published part of it as Chapter 13 of their *Highlands and Islands of Scotland* (1938), pp.128-38. The quotation is from p.130.

4   See the observations by James Williamson on the paper by William Hudson and John K Hunter, 'The Galloway Hydro-Electric Development, with special reference to the Constructional Works', *Journal of the Institution of Civil Engineers*, 8 (1937-38), p.433, and the authors' reply, p.448-9.

5   A E MacColl, *op.cit.*, pp.446-7. Knowledge of rainfall at higher altitudes was particularly inadequate. See also A A Fulton, 'Civil Engineering Aspects of Hydro-Electric Development in Scotland', *Proceedings of the Institution of Civil Engineers*, Part 1, Vol.1 (1952), p.267.

6   W T Halcrow was constantly lamenting the absence of such data. See, for example, his 'Water Power and its Application to the Production of Metals', *Journal of the Institute of Metals*, Vol.68 (1942), pp.158-60. See too Frederick Newhouse, in 'Discussion' of Fulton, *op.cit.*, p.285. A flow duration curve shows for what proportion of the total time the flow exceeds any given value.

7   A E MacColl, *op.cit.*, pp.446-7.

8   C M Roberts, 'Fundamental Economics in Hydro-Electric Design', *The Engineer*, Vol.191 (1951), p.262.

9   The article by Roberts, *ibid.*, provides a clear, if somewhat technical, explanation of why this is so.

10   See below, p.267.

11   T Lawrie, 'Highland Water Power—The Developments of the North of Scotland Hydro-Electric Board', *Proceedings of the Institution of Electrical Engineers*, Part A, Vol.103 (1956), p.216. It should be noted that the relationship between run-off and rainfall is too specialised for discussion in this study but the two have a fairly close resemblence.

12   C L C Allan, 'Hydro-Electric Power Station for Peak Loads', *Electrical Review*, 28 December 1956, p.1170. See also below, p.268.

13   For the layman, the clearest answer to this question and others discussed in the section is provided by T A L Paton & J Guthrie Brown, *Power from Water* (London: Leonard Hill), pp.24-30. The following treatment relies heavily on this invaluable source.

14   *Ibid.*, p.24. Emphasis supplied.

15   The load factor of a power station may be defined as the ratio of the amount of electricity actually produced during a given period (usually a year) to the amount that would have been produced if the installed plant had been kept running continuously throughout the same period. For example, *each* kW of generating capacity installed in a power station is capable of producing a kilowatt hour—commonly called a *unit*—of electricity every hour. As a year contains 8,760 hours, this means that each kilowatt of generating plant *working continuously* throughout the year would produce 8,760 units. But the demands made upon generating plant are *typically* much lower than this. As we will see, the demand for electricity varies from hour to hour, from day to day, from week to week and from month to month, so that far from producing 8,760 units (its maximum possible output), each kW of generating plant might be called upon to produce 2,190 units. The annual load factor of the plant in

this case would be, therefore,

$$\frac{2190}{8760} = \frac{1}{4} \quad \text{or 25 per cent.}$$

16 Paton and Brown, *op.cit.*, p.30.

17 *Report of the [Mackenzie] Committee on the Generation and Distribution of Electricity in Scotland*, Cmnd.1859 (1962), para 75, pp.29-30; see also MacColl, *op.cit.*, p.459, and above, p.231.

18 Of course, much additional plant is required for the conversion of water power into electrical energy. Interested readers should consult J Guthrie Brown (ed), *Hydro-Electric Engineering Practice* (London: Blackie, 1958), Vol.2.

19 For an excellent, non-technical general description of the basic engineering and economic principles involved in the production of hydro-electricity, see T A L Paton and J Guthrie Brown, *Power from Water* (London: Leonard Hill, 1961). The following discussion owes much to this source. Many civil and electrical engineers involved with hydro developments have touched upon economic factors in their papers; these have been useful, as have the ensuing 'Discussions'. Much relevant information was submitted to, and found some part in the *Report of the [Mackenzie] Committee on the Generation and Distribution of Electricity in Scotland*, Cmnd.1859 (1962): the written evidence of Graham R Bamber, editor of *Water Power*, was particularly valuable. For an example of the complexity of the economic issues involved in the supply of electricity, see Ralph Turvey, *Optimal pricing and Investment in Electricity Supply* (London: Allen & Unwin, 1968).

20 The demand for electricity is measured in kilowatts (kW) or megawatts (MW), one megawatt being 1,000 kilowatts. The quantity of electricity produced, or used, over a period is expressed in kilowatt-hours (kWh), commonly called units, the equivalent of one kilowatt of power over one hour.

21 For an analysis of the relationship between maximun simultaneous demand (the peak) and the necessary amount of generating plant to meet that demand, see R W Bates, 'Capital Costs and the Peak Problem in Electricity Supply', *The Manchester School of Economic and Social Studies*, Vol.XXX (1962), pp.149-67.

22 This need not necessarily be so if some generating plant, additional to the capacity actually in use, is kept rotating at full speed and ready to take load immediately on request by the control engineer. This plant is said to be 'spinning spare'. There may, in addition, be even further plant—called 'hot standby'—which is kept ready with steam up to pressure in the boilers to replace, as necessary, 'spinning spare' which is put on load. The 'price' of these arrangements to permit rapid response to sudden increases in demand is, of course, the cost of the fuel consumed.

23 The figure is from C L C Allan, *op.cit.*, who discusses the question, pp.1170-1, as does Roberts, 'Fundamental Economics of Hydro-Electric Design', p.263.

24 While this is a realistic representation of a mixed system, c.1950, a similar representation for the mid 1980s. would include a nuclear base load and a peak load provided by pumped storage generation.

25 In case the idea occurs to the reader that in a properly integrated British system, Scotland might concentrate on hydro and England and Wales on thermal, it has to be pointed out that even if every possible unit of hydro power was squeezed out of Scotland, a feasible total estimated at about 8,000 million units, it would supply only 3 per cent of total British consumption. This is just not enough to perform the ideal rôle suggested by the engineers.

26 Such thermal stations may, of course, employ various types of fuel; they may use coal, gas, oil or nuclear energy.

27   See Ralph Turvey, 'On Investment Choices in Electricity Generation', *Oxford Economic Papers*, N.S. Vol XV (1963), pp.278–88.

28   The sources of the illustrative data are: Hydro, NSHEB; Thermal, Paton & Brown, *op.cit.*, p.185; Nuclear, an average figure derived from Hannah, *Engineers, Managers and Politicians*, p.179. Three observations may be made on these data:
      (i) it should be borne in mind that in the case of both hydro and nuclear generation, fuel appears not as a variable cost but as a capital charge; the same is so in respect to the fuel needed *initially* to charge a nuclear reactor, although replacement fuel is included in the operating/fuel costs; (ii) the effect of the economies of scale may be seen in comparing the two coal-fired examples; (iii) in the late 1950s, when the use of nuclear energy was in its infancy, it was expected that improvements in technique would soon reduce the capital cost per kilowatt installed.

29   Paton & Brown, *op.cit.*, p.186

Select Bibliography

PRIMARY SOURCES

(i) *North of Scotland Hydro-Electric Board*
The author was given complete access to the archives of the North of Scotland Hydro-Electric Board. This meticulously arranged and preserved archive is extensive and comprehensive. This is partially because the Board, by its very nature, has throughout its existence been concerned with property rights, and because in order to exercise their functions, the part-time members of the Board have always required and demanded explanatory memoranda on the wide variety of complex technical and economic issues which they are called upon to discuss, assess and adjudicate. Although the archive is closed to the general public, it was, from the inception of this study, decided to provide full references to the sources employed, in the 'Notes'.

Of the many groups of papers consulted by the author, the more important were the Board's Minutes; the Agenda Papers relating to the meetings of the Board (these included the Minutes of the meetings of the Finance and General Purposes Committee, the monthly Progress Reports submitted by the consulting engineers, and the Reports of the Fisheries and Amenities Committees); the Construction Files relating to specific schemes; the verbatim accounts of evidence presented to the Public Inquiries into those Constructional Schemes which the Secretary of State for Scotland decided warranted such inquiry; and the files of evidence submitted by the Board to such Governmental Committees as that appointed to review the arrangements for generating and distributing electricity in Scotland (the Mackenzie Committee) in 1962.

Among such sources is a wealth of detailed statistical data on every aspect of the Board's activities, summaries of which are readily available in the Board's published *Annual Reports and Accounts*. Some files of newspaper cuttings have also survived.

(ii) *Scottish Record Office*
Certain files relating to the Scottish Committee on Post-War Problems (Scottish Home and Health Department: HM 50/166), the Cooper Committee, 1942 (Scottish Development Department: DD 11/18, 11/19, 11/20), and Electricity Supply in Scotland (Scottish Development Department: DD 11/15, 11/66) were consulted.

(iii) *Electricity Council*
I was permitted to consult the 'rough draft of the Scottish Section' of Professor Leslie Hannah's *Engineers, Managers and Politicians*, and the research notes and materials prepared for its compilation by Professor Hannah and Miss Stephanie Zarach.

(iv) *In the possession of Mr L H Dickerson*
Maps and papers relating to the Grampian Electricity Supply Co., 1928-1929, and the Caledonian Power Co. bills, 1936-37

OFFICIAL PUBLICATIONS

As a nationalised undertaking, the affairs of the North of Scotland Hydro-Electric Board
were periodically discussed in both Houses of Parliament. These debates were often vehement,
frequently witty, and invariably well-informed. The *Parliamentary Debates* (Hansard) have been
an important source of information in the compilation of this study. The following Reports
have been particularly valuable:

Board of Trade, *Interim Report of the Water Power Resources Committee* [Snell] Cmd.79, 1919
Board of Trade, *Second Interim Report of the Water Power Resources Committee*, Cmd.776, 1920
Industry Department for Scotland, Privitisation of the Scottish Electrical Industry, Cm 327, 1988
Ministry of Transport, *Report of the Committee to review the National Problems of the Supply of
    Electrical Energy* [the Weir Committee], 1926
Ministry of Transport, *Report of the Committee on Electricity Distribution* [the McGowan Commit-
    tee], 1936
Scottish Office, *Report of the Committee on Hydro-Electric Development in Scotland* [the Cooper
    Committee], Cmd.6406, 1942
Scottish Development Department, *Electricity in Scotland: Report of the Committee on the Generation
    and Distribution of Electricity in Scotland* [the Mackenzie Committee], Cmnd.1859, 1962
Scottish Development Department, *Hydro-Electric Schemes: Report of the public inquiry into the
    North of Scotland Hydro-Electric Board's Constructional Scheme No.39 (Fada/Fionn Project) and
    Constructional Scheme No.38 (Laidon Project)* (Edinburgh: HMSO, 1965)
Board of Trade, *Industrial Investment: The Production of Primary Aluminium*, Cmnd.3819, 1968
Monopolies and Mergers Commission, *North of Scotland Hydro-Electric Board: A Report on the
    Efficiency and Costs of the Board*, Cmnd.9628, 1985

PERIODICAL LITERATURE

The majority of the hydro schemes undertaken by the Board were discussed, often in considerable
detail, in the specialist journals. The following journals proved particularly valuable: *Electrical
Review, The Engineer, Engineering, Water Power.*

BOOKS, PAMPHLETS AND ARTICLES

Aims of Industry, *Electricity Generation in Scotland: A Memorandum* (London: Aims of Industry,
    1962)
Aitken, Peter L, L M Dickerson & W J M Menzies, 'Fish Passes and Screens at Water Power
    Works', *Proceedings of the Institution of Civil Engineers*, Vol.35 (1966) pp.29-57
Alexander, Sir Kenneth, 'The Highlands and Islands Development Board', in Richard Saville
    (ed), *The Economic Development of Modern Scotland, 1950-1980*(Edinburgh: John Donald, 1985)
    pp.214-232
Allen, Arthur C, 'Features of Lednock Dam, including the use of fly ash', *Proceedings of the
    Institution of Civil Engineers*, Vol.13 (June, 1959) pp.179-96
Allan, C L C, 'Hydro-Electric Power Stations for Peak Loads', *Electrical Review*, 28th December,
    1957 pp.1169-74
Anderson, R B, 'The Development of Electricity Supplies in the North of Scotland', *Proceedings
    of the Institution of Electrical Engineers*, Vol.108, Part A (1961) pp.30-32
Anonymous, 'Electric Lighting by water power at Fort William', *The Electrical Engineer*, Vol.19,
    5 March 1897 pp.294-5

Anonymous, 'Highlands Load Building: 1—A Very Sparsely Populated Area', *Electrical Review*, 7 November, 1947 pp.683-88

Anonymous, 'Power from the Conon Valley', *Journal of the Institute of Electrical Engineers*, N.S., Vol.2 (1956) pp.322-8

Balfour Beatty Ltd., *Balfour Beatty, 1909-1984: A 75th Anniversary Brochure*, (Thornton Heath, Surrey: privately published by Balfour Beatty, 1984)

Banks, James A, 'The Employment of prestressed technique on Allt-na-Lairige Dam', Paper R.68, *5th Congress on Large Dams*, Paris (1955)

——'Allt-na-Lairige Prestressed Concrete Dam', *Proceedings of the Institution of Civil Engineers*, Vol.6 (March 1957) pp.409-28

Bates, R W, 'Capital Costs and the Peak Problem in Electricity Supply', *The Manchester School of Economic and Social Studies*, Vol.XXXI (1963) pp.149-67

Bates, R W and M G Webb, 'Government Control over Investment Planning in Nationalised Electricity Supply Industry', *Bulletin of the Oxford University Institute of Economics and Statistics*, Vol.30 (1968) pp.37-53

Berry, John, 'Biological Problems and Possiblities: Electrification of the Scottish Highlands', *Biology and Human Affairs*, Vol.13 (1947) pp.3-6

——'Hydro-Electric Development and Nature Conservation in Scotland', *Proceedings of the Royal Philosophical Society of Glasgow*, Vol. LXXVII (1954-55) pp.23-36

——'Some recent studies of Ecological Effects of Montane Water Storage in the United Kingdom', *Papers and Proceedings of the 11th Technical Meeting of the International Union for Conservation of Nature and Natural Resources*, New Delhi, India, November 1969 Vol.1, pp.36-43

——'Do Power Schemes Desecrate the Environment?'. (Typescript). Address to the Royal Society of Edinburgh, 1 March 1976

Bowman, Waldo G., 'Hydro in the Highlands lifts Scotland's Economy', *Engineering News-Record*, Vol.173 (July 1964) pp.62-73

Brown, J. Guthrie (ed), *Hydro-Electric Engineering Practice* (London: Blackie, 1958) 3 volumes

Campbell, R H, 'The Committee of Ex-Secretaries of State for Scotland and Industrial Policy, 1941-1945' *Scottish Industrial History*, Vol.2 (1979) pp.3-10

Chapman, E J K, 'Value of Water Power in a Mixed System', *Water Power*, XV (1963) pp.165-172

Chapman, E J K and D F Campbell, 'The Design and Economics of Massive Buttress Dams', Paper R.61, *Fifth Congress on Large Dams*, Paris (1955) pp.277-300

Chester, Sir Norman, *The Nationalisation of British Industry* (London: HMSO, 1975)

Clark, Colin, *Electricity Generation in Scotland: Economic Factors* (London: Aims of Industry, 1962)

Coleman, Terry, *The Railway Navvies* (London: Hutchinson, 1965)

Collier, Adam, *The Crofting Problem* (Cambridge: CUP for Dept. of Econ. & Social Research, U.of Glasgow, 1953)

Dillon, Edmund Christopher, 'The Mullardoch-Fasnakyle-Affric Tunnels', The Institution of Civil Engineers, *Works Construction Engineering Division*, Paper No.16 (1950) pp.18-43

Donkin, Sydney Bryan, 'Presidential Address', *Journal of the Institute of Civil Engineers*, Vol.7, (1937-38)

Eastwood, W, G A Taylor and J Allen, 'Scale Model Experiments on High-Head Systems and Vortex Chambers connected thereto', *Proceedings of the Institution of Civil Engineers*, Part 1, Vol.2 (1953) pp.556-84

Fairthorne, Lt Comdr R B, 'Hydro-electric Development: Its Economic Limits in Comparison with Steam', *Electrical Review*, 17 March 1939 pp.382-4

Fraser, Norrie (ed), *Sir Edward MacColl: A Maker of Modern Scotland* (Edinburgh, The Stanley Press, 1956)

Fulton, Angus Anderson, 'Civil Engineering Aspects of Hydro-Electric Development in Scotland', *Proceedings of the Institution of Civil Engineers*, Part I, Vol.I, (1952) pp.248-77

—— 'The Cruachan Pumped-Storage Development', *Electronics and Power*, Vol.12 (July, 1966) pp.220-24

—— 'Presidential Address, 1969' *Proceedings of the Institution of Civil Engineers*, Vol.44 (1969) pp.311-21

Fulton, Angus Anderson and Leslie H Dickerson, 'Design and Constructional Features of Hydro-electric Dams Built in Scotland since 1945' *Proceedings of the Institution of Civil Engineers*, Vol.29 (December 1964) pp.713-42

Fulton, Angus Anderson, T G N Haldane and R W Mountain, 'The Practical Application and Economics of Pumped Storage in Great Britain', Paper 227 H/38, *5th World Power Conference*, Vienna (1956)

Fulton, Angus Anderson and W T Marshall, 'The Use of Fly Ash and Similar Materials in Concrete', *Proceedings of the Institute of Civil Engineers*, Part I, Vol.5 (November, 1956) pp.714-30

Gibson, John S, *The Thistle and the Crown: A History of the Scottish Office* (Edinburgh: HMSO, 1985)

Gowers, Alan G, 'Some Points of Interest in the Design and Construction of Orrin Dam, Ross-shire', *Proceedings of the Institution of Civil Engineers*, Vol.24 (April 1963) pp.449-72

Graeme, Alan, 'The Lochaber Power Scheme. Some details of its meaning and its magnitude', *The Scots Magazine*, New Series, XI, No.6 (September, 1929) pp.401-4

Grundy, Cecil Frederick, 'The Driving and Lining of the Clunie Tunnel on the Tummel-Garry Hydro-Electric Project', The Institution of Civil Engineers, *Works Construction Engineering Division*, Paper No.15 (1950) pp.3-17

Halcrow, William Thomson, 'The Lochaber Water-Power Scheme', *Minutes of Proceedings of the Institution of Civil Engineers*, Vol.231 (1930-31), Part I, pp.31-63

—— 'Scottish Hydro-Electric Stations' [Paper read before Section G. of the British Association at Aberdeen on 6 September 1934] *Engineering*, Vol.138, 14 September 1934 pp.288-90

—— 'Water Power and its Application to the Production of Metals', *Journal of the Institute of Metals*, Vol.68 (1942) pp.145-68

Haldane, T G N and P L Blackstone, 'Problems of Hydro-electric Design in Mixed Thermal-Hydro-Electric Systems', *Proceedings of the Institution of Electrical Engineers*, Vol. 102 A (1955) pp.311-22

Handley, James E, *The Navvy in Scotland* (Cork: Cork University Press, 1970)

Hannah, Leslie, *Electricity before Nationalisation: A Study of the Development of the Electricity Supply Industry in Britain to 1948* (London: Macmillan, 1979)

—— *Engineers, Managers and Politicians: The first Fifteen Years of Nationalised Electricity Supply in Britain* (London: Macmillan, 1982)

—— 'George Balfour', in David J Jeremy (ed), *Dictionary of Business Biography* (London: Butterworths, 1984) Vol.1, pp.125-128

Hardy, E, 'Salmon Ladders and Fish passes', *Water Power*, Vol.5 (1953) pp.180-4

Hawthorne, William and F H Williams, 'The Galloway Hydro-Electric Development, with special reference to the Mechanical and Electrical Plant', *Journal of the Institute of Civil Engineers*, Vol.8 (1937-38), pp.376-406

Henderson, J and C L C Allan, 'Economic Integration of Coal-fired, Nuclear and Hydraulic Generation of Electricity with special references to Scotland', *Transactions of the Canadian Sectional Meetings of the World Power Conference*, Montreal, 7-11 September, 1958. Vol.II, Section A, 33 A/4, pp.57-79

—— 'Energy Resources and Growth of Consumption in Scotland', *Proceedings of the World Power Conference*, Madrid, 1960. Paper 1A/4 Great Britain

—— 'A Survey of Electricity Supply in Scotland', *Papers of an Energy Symposium*, Edinburgh, 1960

Hill, George, *Tunnel and Dam: The Story of the Galloway Hydros* (South of Scotland Electricity Board, 1984)

Hinton, Sir Christopher, F H S Brown and L Rotherham, 'The Economics of Nuclear Power in Great Britain', *Proceedings of the World Power Conference*, Madrid 5-9th June, 1960. Paper IVB/8, pp.1-24

Hopkins, T G L, 'The Development and Location of the Aluminium Industry in the United Kingdom'. (Unpublished B.Litt thesis, University of Oxford, 1957)

Hudson, William and John Kenneth Hunter, 'The Galloway Hydro-Electric Development, with Special Reference to the Constructional Works', *Journal of the Institution of Civil Engineers*, Vol.8 (1937-38), pp.323-75

Hunter, John Kenneth and Richard William Mountain, 'Hydro-Electric Development: Some Economic Aspects', *Journal of the Institution of Civil Engineers*, Vol.19 (1942) pp.135-60

Jaeger, Charles, 'The Correlation of Nuclear, Thermal and Pumped-Storage Capacity', *Water Power*, Vol.10 (1958) pp.206-11, 260-4, 292-8

Johnson, F G, 'Hydro-electric power in the UK: past performance and potential for future development', *Proceedings of the Institution of Electrical Engineers*, Vol.133, Part C., No.3 (April 1986) pp.110-20

Johnston, Thomas, *Memories* (London: Collins, 1952)

Laing, James F, *The Scottish Office and Nationalised Industries* [The first of the series of Acton Society Trust Occasional Papers emanating from the Trust's Nationalised Industries Project], (London: Acton Society Trust: undated, *c*.1982)

Land, D D and D C Hitchings, 'Foyers pumped storage project: construction', *Proceeding of the Institution of Civil Engineers*, Part I, Vol.64 (1978) pp.119-36

Lander, J H, F G Johnson, J R Crichton and M W Baldwin, 'Foyers pumped storage project: planning and design', *Proceedings of the Institution of Civil Engineers*, Part I, Vol.64 (1978) pp.103-17

Lawrie, T, 'Electrical Aspects of Modern Hydro-Electric Development in Scotland' [Abridged version of Paper read before Section G of the British Association, Edinburgh, 13 August, 1951] *Engineering*, Vol.172 (1951) pp.313-15

—— 'Highland Water Power in the Development of the North of Scotland Hydro-Electric Board', *Proceedings of the Institution of Electrical Engineers*, Part A, Vol.103 (1956) pp.212-20

Lea, K J, 'Hydro-Electric Power Generation in the Highlands of Scotland', *Transactions and Papers of the Institute of British Geographers*, 1969 (Publication No.46), pp.155-65

MacColl, A E, 'Hydro-Electric Development in Scotland', *Transactions of the Institution of Engineers and Shipbuilders in Scotland*, Vol.89 (1946) pp.442-85

MacDonald, Sir Murdoch and J M Kay, 'Electricity in the North of Scotland', *Scottish Journal of Political Economy*, Vol.IV (1957)

MacGill, Patrick, *Children of the Dead End: The Autobiography of a Navvy* (London: Herbert Jenkins, 1914)

McGuire, Alistair, 'Excess Capacity and the Demand for Electricity in Scotland', *Scottish Journal of Political Economy*, Vol.29 (1982) pp.45-58

Meek, Ronald L, 'The Allocation of Expenditure in the Electricity Supply Industry: Some Methodological Problems', *Scottish Journal of Political Economy*, Vol.X (1963) pp.36-60

Miller, D J, A T L Murray, C C Marshall and G G R Argent, 'Foyers pumped-storage project', *Proceedings of the Institution of Electrical Engineers*, Vol.122, No.11 (November 1975) pp.1222-34

Moore, J T, *Electricity Generation in Scotland; the influences of Modern Developments on Future Policy* (London: Aims of Industry, 1962)

Morrison, W Murray, 'Aluminium and Highland Water Power', *Journal of the Institute of Metals*, Vol LXV (1939) pp.17-36

Mountain, R W, 'The Galloway Hydro-Electric Development, with special reference to its Interconnexion with the Grid', *Journal of the Institution of Civil Engineers*, Vol.8 (1937-38) pp.407-22

Mountain, R W and M V Ratcliffe, 'Electric Transmission from Hydro-Electric Generating Stations: Some Economic Aspects', *Journal of the Institution of Civil Engineers*, Vol.33 (1949-50) pp.253-57

Munby, D L, 'Electricity in the North of Scotland', *Scottish Journal of Political Economy*, Vol.III (1956) pp.19-43

—— 'Electricity in the North of Scotland: A Rejoinder', *Scottish Journal of Political Economy*, Vol.IV, No.1 (Feb.1957) pp.27-8

Nabarro, Gerard, *Ten Steps to Power: A National Fuel and Power Policy* (London: St Catherine Press, 1952)

Naylor, Arthur Holden, 'The Second Stage of the Lochaber Water-Power Scheme', *Journal of the Institution of Civil Engineers*, Vol.V (1936-37), pp.3-48

Page, A, 'Electricity Supply in Great Britain', *Journal of the Institution of Electrical Engineers*, Vol.66 (1927)

Paton, John, 'The Glen Shira Hydro-Electric Project', *Proceedings of the Institution of Civil Engineers*, Part I, Vol.5 (1956) pp.593-618

Paton, T A L and J Guthrie Brown, *Power From Water* (London: Leonard Hill, 1960)

Pottinger, George, *The Secretaries of State for Scotland, 1926-1976* (Edinburgh: Scottish Academic Press, 1979)

Richy, J E, 'Engineers and Geologists', *Water Power*, Vol.7 (1955) pp.29-34

Roberts, Alfred Henry, 'The Loch Leven Water-Power Works', *Minutes of Proceedings of the Institute of Civil Engineers*, CLXXXVI (1911-1912) pp.29-73

Roberts, C M, 'Fundamental Economics in Hydro-Electric Design', *The Engineer*, Vol.191 (1951) pp.262-3

—— 'Special Features of the Affric Hydro-Electric Schemes (Scotland)', *Proceedings of the Institution of Civil Engineers*, Vol.2, Part 1 (1953) pp.520-55

Roberts, C M, E B Wilson and J G Wiltshire, 'Design Aspects of the Strathfarrar and Kilmorack Hydro electric Scheme', *Proceedings of the Institution of Civil Engineers*, Vol.30 (1965) pp.449-87

Robertson, A J, *The Bleak Mid-Winter: 1947* (Manchester: Manchester University Press, 1987)

Rowland, John, *Progress in Power: the contribution of Charles Merz and his Associates to sixty years of Electrical Development, 1899-1959* (London: privately published by Newman Neame for Merz and McLellan, 1960)

Scottish Economic Committee (Hilleary Committee), *The Highlands and Islands of Scotland: A Review of the Economic Conditions with Recommendations for Improvement* (Edinburgh: Scottish Economic Committee Publication, 1938)

Simpson, David, 'Investment, Employment and Government Expenditures in the Highlands, 1951-1960' *Scottish Journal of Political Economy*, Vol.10 (1963) pp.259-88

Smith, John S, 'The Invergordon Aluminium Smelter—Growth policy gone wrong? A Note', *Scottish Geographical Magazine*, Vol.98, No.2 (1982) pp.115-118

Sonnenschein, Frederick Bolton, 'The Hydro-Electric Plant in the British Aluminium Company's Factory at Kinlochleven', *Minutes of Proceedings of the Institute of Civil Engineers*, CLXXXVII (1911-12), pp.74-84

Stevenson, James, 'The Construction of Loch Sloy Dam', *Proceedings of the Institution of Civil Engineers*, Vol.1, Part III (August, 1952) pp.169-205

Stott, Louis, *The Waterfalls of Scotland* (Aberdeen: Aberdeen University Press, 1987)

Tucker, D G, 'Hydro-Electricity for Public Supply in Britain, 1881–1894' *Industrial Archaeological Review*, Vol.1 (1977) pp.126-63

Turnock, David, *The New Scotland* (Newton Abbot: David & Charles, 1979)

Turvey, Ralph, 'On Investment Choices in Electrical Generation', *Oxford Economic Papers*, New Series, Vol XV (1963) pp.278-88

Webb, M G, 'Rate of Discount and Inflation with particular reference to the Electricity Supply Industry', *Oxford Economic Papers*, N.S., Vol.18 (1966) pp.352-8

Valentine, A S and E M Bergstrom, 'Hydro-Electric Development in Great Britain, with special reference to the works of the Grampian Electricity Supply Co.', *Journal of the Institute of Electrical Engineers*, Vol.76 (1935) pp.125-58

Young, William and R H Falkiner, 'Some design and construction features of the Cruachan pumped storage project', *Proceedings of the Institution of Civil Engineers*, Vol.35 (1966) pp.407-50

Index

Aberdeen, 22, 64, 117, 192, 202, 208, 224, 249, 309

Adler, G F W, 315

Aglen, A J, 44, 58, 300

agriculture, effect of hydro-electric development upon, 71-2, 144, 150, 190, 194, 206-7, 320, 321

Ailsa, Marquess of, 3

Aims of Industry, 212, 215, 227, 323, 326

Airlie, Earl of, 48, 50, 61, 62, 67-8, 70, 73, 75, 76, 77, 78, 81, 194, 298, 299, 302, 303, 304

Aitken, Peter, 309, 310, 323, 326

Albright & Wilson, 192

Alexander, Sir Kenneth, 320

Alexander, Brigadier-General Sir William, 32

Allan, C L C, 251, 299, 313, 323, 326, 332, 333

Allen, J, 311

Allen, A C, 314

Alliance Aluminium Co., 4

Alness, Lord, 38, 46, 48, 49, 296

Altnabreac, Caithness, 199-200

aluminium, 4-5, 6, 8, 13, 191, 290

Amalgamated Electrical Industries Ltd., 195

amenity and environmental issues, relating to hydro-electric schemes, 25, 26, 29, 34, 42-3, 48, 63, 65-72, 72-5, 110, 127, 137, 144, 146, 185, 212, 226-7, 229, 234, 245, 246, 247, 252, 329

Anderson, Alexander, 73, 74

Anderson, Sir John, 325

Anderson, R B, 289, 290, 292, 293

Appleton, Sir Edward, 199, 319

aqueducts, 99, 150, 161, 174, 176, 184, 242

Arbroath Electric Light and Power Co., 16, 293

Argent, G G, 328

Argyll, County Council of, 201

Armstrong, Whitworth & Co., 16-17

Arrochar, 99

Arrol, Sir William, & Co., 24, 94, 194, 293

Assheton, Ralph, 32

Association for the Preservation of Rural Scotland, 39, 70, 227

Atholl, Duke of, 4, 15

Auchterarder, 195

Ayrshire Joint Electricity Authority, 25, 26

Babcock & Wilcox, 17

Babtie, Shaw & Morton, 104, 175, 315, 316, 317

Baillie, J C N, 252

Baillie, Michael, 215

Baldwin, M W, 328

Balfour Beatty & Co., 8, 11, 14, 16-17, 20, 83, 88, 99, 124, 175, 299, 309

Balfour, D M, 292

Balfour, George, 16-17, 35, 299

Balloch, 82

Bamber, Graham R, 333

Banff, 202

Banks, George, 323

Banks, J A, 315-16, 317

Barbour, Dr George F, 69

Bates, R W, 333

Bayer, Dr K J, 4

Beard, J R, 54, 68, 121, 299

Beaton, Neil, 38, 52, 79

Beatty, Andrew, 16

Belper, Lord, 44

Ben Bhuidhe, 174

Ben Cruachan, 231, 234

Ben Nevis, 9, 11, 291

Ben Vane, 59, 82

Ben Vorlich, 59, 60, 81, 92-3, 99

Ben Wyvis, 3

Bergstrom, E M, 17, 289, 292, 293

Berry, Dr John, 54, 69, 300, 302, 329

Bilsland, Sir Steven, 191, 192, 318

Black, J, 305, 306

Blair Atholl, 4

Blair Castle, 4

Blairgowrie, 105

rivers and streams,   Affric, 135, 144, 146;
Allt-na-Lairige, 184; Beauly, 144, 146;
Blackwater, 127, 331; Bran, 127, 133, 261;
Brannie, 176; Brora, 158; Cannich, 135,
144, 146; Cassley, 158; Clachan Burn, 176;
Conon, 23, 76, 129; Dee (Aberdeenshire),
257; E, 242; Ericht, 293; Errochty Water,
64, 102; Falloch, 99; Farrar, 144, 146; Fechlin, 242, 246; Findhorn, 77, 303; Foyers,
246; Fyne, 174, 181, 184; Garry, 63-4, 72,
102, 149-50; Glascarnoch, 127; Glass, 135,
146; Grudie, 329; Grudie Burn, 161; Kerry,
301; Kilblaan, 176; Livishie, 150; Meig,
129; Moriston, 150; Nairn, 77, 303; Ness,
257; Nevis, 212; Orrin, 129; Shin, 161;
Shira, 174, 176; Spean, 14; Spey, 9, 14;
Talladale, 329; Tummel, 64, 75, 105, 107;
Vaich, 127
road construction,   81, 137, 161, 173, 176,
200, 245
Roberts, A H,   290, 331
Roberts, C M,   149, 311, 312, 313, 332, 333
Robertson, A J,   304
Robertson, David (later Sir David),   35, 224,
313, 325
Rosebery, Earl of,   75, 304
Ross, Sir Charles,   24
Ross, William,   228, 230, 247
Ross and Cromarty,   63, 123, 201
Ross-shire Electricity Supply Co.,   23
Rowland, John,   294, 299
run-off,   defined, 258; 267, 332
Rushcliffe, Lord,   76, 303

St Benedict Abbey,   3, 289
salmon,   3, 27, 29, 67, 69, 107, 110, 129, 131-
5, 150, 152, 161, 181, 185, 188, 201, 303,
307, 310, 313, 326
Saltire Society,   39
Samuel, Viscount,   48, 303
Scotsman,   317, 319, 323
Scottish Board for Industry,   215
Scottish Central Electric Power Co.,   15, 16,
17, 293
Scottish Council on Industry,   191, 192, 193
Scottish Council on Post-War Problems
(Tom Johnston's 'Council of State'),   38,
296

Scottish Daily Express,   323
Scottish Daily Mail,   225, 323, 326
Scottish Development Council,   39
Scottish Economic Committee (Hilleary
Committee),   39, 52, 55, 256, 294, 297,
332
Scottish Electricity Board, proposals for,
215, 219, 220
Scottish Office, The,   44, 46, 53, 57-8, 116-
17, 193, 209, 210, 215, 222, 223, 224, 228,
254 (*see also* Secretary of State for Scotland)
Scottish Peat Committee,   199
Scottish Power Investigation Committee,
212
Scottish Power Co. Ltd.,   17, 23, 34, 40, 41,
309
Scottish Co-operative Wholesale Society,
52-3
Secretary of State for Scotland, powers under
the Hydro-Electric Development (Scot-
land) Act, 45-6, 50, 54, 331; powers under
the Electricity Act (1947), 117-18; 25, 56,
61, 213, 226, 228, 235, 241, 242, 248, 254-
5, 297, 309, 329 (*see also* Scottish Office)
Select Committee on Nationalised Industries,
195, 211, 212, 228
Sempill, Lord,   303
Shearer, James,   54, 135
Shearer, William,   17, 195-6
Shinwell, Emmanuel,   114, 116, 309
Shrimpton, A P,   310
Simpson, David,   318, 321
Simpson, H W,   299
Simpson, T B, KC,   70
Sinclair, Sir Archibald,   36, 296
Slaven, A,   297
Smith, John S,   331
Snaddon, William,   72-3
Snell Committee, *see* Water Power Resources
Committee
Sonnenschein, Frederic B,   290
South of Scotland Electricity Board,   209-
11, 212, 214-24, 226, 229, 231, 241, 251-2,
326 (*see also* North of Scotland Hydro-
Electric Board: relations with the South of
Scotland Electricity Board)
South West Scotland Electricity Board,   209
Spill units,   218

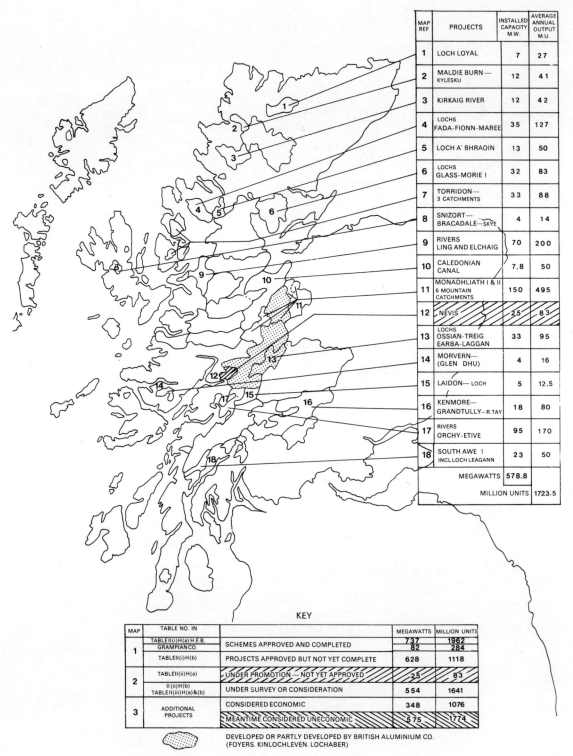

PROJECTS [UNDER PROMOTION] UNDER INVESTIGATION

MAP2

MAP REF	PROJECTS	INSTALLED CAPACITY M.W.	AVERAGE ANNUAL OUTPUT M.U.
1	LOCH LOYAL	7	27
2	MALDIE BURN — KYLESKU	12	41
3	KIRKAIG RIVER	12	42
4	LOCHS FADA-FIONN-MAREE	35	127
5	LOCH A' BHRAOIN	13	50
6	LOCHS GLASS-MORIE I	32	83
7	TORRIDON— 3 CATCHMENTS	33	88
8	SNIZORT— BRACADALE—SKYE	4	14
9	RIVERS LING AND ELCHAIG	70	200
10	CALEDONIAN CANAL	7.8	50
11	MONADHLIATH I & II 6 MOUNTAIN CATCHMENTS	150	495
12	NEVIS	25	83
13	LOCHS OSSIAN-TREIG EARBA-LAGGAN	33	95
14	MORVERN— (GLEN DHU)	4	16
15	LAIDON— LOCH	5	12.5
16	KENMORE— GRANDTULLY—R.TAY	18	80
17	RIVERS ORCHY-ETIVE	95	170
18	SOUTH AWE I INCL LOCH LEAGANN	23	50
	MEGAWATTS	578.8	
	MILLION UNITS		1723.5

KEY

MAP	TABLE NO. IN		MEGAWATTS	MILLION UNITS
1	TABLE II(i)H(a) H.E.B. GRAMPIAN CO.	SCHEMES APPROVED AND COMPLETED	737 / 82	1962 / 284
	TABLE II(i)H(b)	PROJECTS APPROVED BUT NOT YET COMPLETE	628	1118
2	TABLE II (ii)H(a)	UNDER PROMOTION — NOT YET APPROVED	25	83
	II (ii)H(b) TABLE II(iii)H(a)&(b)	UNDER SURVEY OR CONSIDERATION	554	1641
3	ADDITIONAL PROJECTS	CONSIDERED ECONOMIC	348	1076
		MEANTIME CONSIDERED UNECONOMIC	575	1774

DEVELOPED OR PARTLY DEVELOPED BY BRITISH ALUMINIUM CO. (FOYERS. KINLOCHLEVEN. LOCHABER)

NOTE: THERE ARE FACTORS OTHER THAN ECONOMICS TO BE CONSIDERED BEFORE A SCHEME IS PROMOTED

Source: NSHEB, Evidence for Mackenzie Committee, Sundry Paper 7, HEB M5 (dated August 1961)